Elementary Probability and Statistics

With Optional
Computer
Applications

Glencoe Press Mathematics Series

Series Editor
Eugene A. Maier

Professor
Mathematics Department
University of Oregon

Elementary Probability and Statistics

With Optional Computer Applications

A. William Gray and Otis M. Ulm

St. Petersburg Junior College
St. Petersburg, Florida

GLENCOE PRESS
A division of Benziger Bruce & Glencoe, Inc.
New York • Beverly Hills

Collier-Macmillan, Publishers
London

GLENCOE PRESS

A division of Benziger Bruce & Glencoe, Inc.
8701 Wilshire Boulevard
Beverly Hills, California 90211
Collier-Macmillan Canada, Ltd., Toronto, Canada

Library of Congress Catalog Card Number: 72-84883

First printing, 1973

Preface

This textbook is planned for use in a first course in elementary probability and statistics. A student who has completed two years of high school algebra is qualified to pursue a course of study in which it may be used.

For those who have access to a computer, we have included programming instructions in the BASIC language as well as elementary programs for use in statistical computation. Omission of computer programming is not detrimental to this course of study.

Our approach to the study of probability is based on the theory of sets. We have found that the teaching of probability is facilitated by a systematic application of set concepts.

Until recently, games of chance have been traditionally employed as models for studying probability. We believe that this approach tends to deflate the importance of the subject and does not adequately prepare the student for other applications of probability theory. In general, we have employed models from business, economics, industry, education, and science.

Contents

CHAPTER 4

Basic Statistical Concepts   83

CHAPTER 5

Random Variables and Distributions   113

CHAPTER 6

Sampling Distributions   142

CHAPTER 7

Estimation and Decision-Making   168

CHAPTER 8

Linear Regression and Correlation   213

Elementary Probability and Statistics

With Optional Computer Applications

CHAPTER I

Programming Statistical Computations

1.1 INTRODUCTION

Before the computer age the processing of statistical data was tedious and time-consuming. With the use of computers much of the tedium has disappeared, and complicated statistical studies not previously feasible can be accomplished readily. A modern statistical investigation of any magnitude would be rare, if not unthinkable, without the use of a computer. For this reason, we shall begin with an introduction to a computer language.

The language that we shall study is BASIC (*B*eginner's *A*ll-purpose *S*ymbolic *I*nstruction *C*ode). This language was developed at Dartmouth College by John G. Kemeny. Of the more than 200 computer languages, BASIC is one of the easiest to learn, and it is applicable to a variety of statistical problems.

The purpose of any computer language is to enable communication between man and computer. Man communicates with the computer by means of a series of statements written in a language the computer can "understand." The series of statements designed to instruct the computer to perform a specific task is known as a *program*. In this chapter we shall present several elementary programs leading towards the preparation and use of computer programs for statistical and probability computations. The operations that the computer is instructed to perform can be of three types: (1) arithmetic (numerical) computations; (2) logical or "decision-making" procedures; (3) input to or output from memory of data and instructions. We begin our study of BASIC with the numerical computation statement. As in English, the BASIC language is made up of words and symbols. All BASIC language words are shown in capitalized form.

1.2 ARITHMETIC STATEMENTS

LET. This word informs the computer that an arithmetic operation is to be performed. Consider the following instruction.

$$\text{LET} \quad X \ = \ A \ + \ 1$$

This statement tells the computer to add two numbers, A and 1, where A has a numeric value. The addition symbol in this statement has the same meaning as an addition symbol in ordinary arithmetic. However, the symbol for equality, $=$, has a new meaning. In BASIC this symbol instructs the computer to replace any current value of X which may be in the computer "memory" with the value of X found by adding two numbers. The last value calculated for X erases the previous value and places the last value in the memory location called "X."

   Arithmetic operations in a LET statement are symbolized as follows.

+	addition
−	subtraction
*	multiplication
/	division
↑	exponentiation

In the statement LET X = A + 1, X and A designate variable quantities and are called *variables*. A variable may be represented by a single letter or by a single letter followed by a single digit, 0 through 9. For example, X1 and A3 could be used in place of X and A. Ordinary numerals such as the 1 in the above LET statement are called *constants*.

   The rules for evaluating the LET statement are almost the same as those for regular arithmetic. Quantities in parentheses are evaluated first, followed by exponentiation, multiplication and division, and finally addition and subtraction. Consider the LET statement given below.

$$\text{LET} \quad A \ = \ P \ * \ (1 \ + \ R) \ \uparrow \ N$$

The computer calculates A in the following order:

(1) Adds 1 to R;
(2) Raises the sum of 1 and R to the Nth power;
(3) Multiplies P by (1 + R) to the Nth power.

Additional examples of LET statements follow.

BASIC *Statement*	Algebraic *Statement*
LET P = A/T * 100	$P = \dfrac{A}{T}(100)$
LET Y = .5 * (X + Z/X)	$y = .5\left(x + \dfrac{z}{x}\right)$
LET U = V + P * A	$U = v + pa$
LET D = A1 * B2 - B1 * A2	$D = a_1 b_2 - b_1 a_2$
LET Y = X ↑ 2 + 3 * X + 4	$y = x^2 + 3x + 4$
LET B = X/Y/Z	$b = \left(\dfrac{\frac{x}{y}}{z}\right) = \dfrac{x}{yz}$

1.3 READ AND DATA STATEMENTS

In order for the computer to perform the operations specified in a **LET** statement, any variable to the right of the equality sign must be given a numerical value before the evaluation. This is called *defining* the variable.

The names of the variables are supplied to the computer in a **READ** statement. The numerical values of the variables must then be furnished in a **DATA** statement. It is not important whether the **DATA** statement precedes or follows the **READ** statement.

When the computer encounters a **READ** statement, memory cells in the computer are earmarked for each variable. Multiple variables in the **READ** statement are separated by commas. Numerical values to be placed in the memory cells are obtained from the **DATA** statement. Numbers in the **DATA** statement must be written in decimal form. Common fractions are not allowed; for example, the quantity $3\frac{1}{2}$ must be written 3.5. If a decimal point is not included, the computer assumes the number is an integer. Numbers may be positive or negative and may contain as many as nine digits. Commas may *not* be used in numerals. If there are three variables in the **READ** statement, a minimum of three constants must be given in the **DATA** statement. The first constant is placed by the computer in the cell labeled for the first variable in the **READ** statement; the second constant is placed in the cell labeled for the second variable; and the third constant is placed in the cell labeled for the third variable. If additional constants appear in the **DATA** statement, they are placed in the variable memory cells in sequence as listed in the **READ** statement. If all constants in the **DATA** statement are used, the number of such constants must be an integral multiple of the number of variables. For three variables, there may be 3 constants, 6 constants, 9 constants, and so forth. As we shall soon see, the computer may be instructed to seek automatically the constants in the **DATA** statement to use in the **LET** statement until all entries in the **DATA** statement have been used.

1.4 PRINT STATEMENT

Each of the **BASIC** language statements discussed thus far either supplies information to the computer or informs the computer of the arithmetic operations to be performed. The primary purpose of the **PRINT** statement is to obtain the results of the operations performed by the computer. For the statement **LET A = P * (1 + R) ↑ N**, the **PRINT** instruction to obtain the computed numerical value of **A** could be written

PRINT A

When sufficient instructions have been given to the computer so that the desired calculations can be made, the computer is informed by the **BASIC** statement

END

The **END** statement must terminate every **BASIC** program.

1.5 THE COMPUTER PROGRAM

With the five **BASIC** words **READ, DATA, LET, PRINT,** and **END** we are ready to write a simple program for a computer. Each statement in the program is given a line number to inform the computer of the order in which instructions are to be translated into internal computer code, or *compiled*. Let us instruct the computer to compute how much $1,000 is worth if invested at 8% interest compounded annually for 10 years. If a principal P is invested at the rate of interest R for N investment periods, the worth A of the investment at the end of the N periods is given by the formula $A = P \times (1 + R)^N$.

Program 1.1

```
10 READ P,R,N
20 DATA 1000,.08,10
30 LET A = P * (1 + R) ↑ N
40 PRINT A
50 END
```

When instructed to do so, the computer will execute this program and print the result,

2158.92

1.6 LOOPING

If we wish to instruct the computer to find another value of **A** we must furnish another set of **DATA** and instruct the computer to again run the program. This may be accomplished with a **GO TO** statement.

This instruction, which takes the form **GO TO _____** , tells the computer to transfer control to a specified line in the program. The computer then performs its operations in sequence as before. Let us return to the program to compute **A**. In addition to the computation already indicated, we wish to know how much $5,000 is worth when invested at 5.5% compounded annually for 20 years. The program to accomplish this is program 1.2.

Program 1.2

```
10 READ P,R,N
20 DATA 1000,.08,10,5000,.055,20
30 LET A = P * (1 + R) ↑ N
40 PRINT A
50 GO TO 10
60 END
```

The computer performs the first calculation, prints the result, returns to line 10, finds the new data, and computes and prints the new value of **A**. This process will continue as long as unused **DATA** remains in the program. The program may contain as many **DATA** lines as required. The procedure of repeated sequences of execution resulting from the **GO TO** statement is known as *looping*.

1.7 ADDITIONAL PRINTING INSTRUCTIONS

Sometimes it is desirable to print more than the numerical values found by the computer. For program 1.3, let us assume that we wish to print the variables **P**, **R**, and **N** as well as the computed values of **A**. The computer can be instructed to do this by modifying line 40 in program 1.2 as follows.

```
40 PRINT P,R,N,A
```

The output would be printed on two lines, one line for each set of variables.

1000	.08	10	2158.92
5000	.055	20	14588.8

The commas in the **PRINT** statement determine the spacing between the entries in the printed line. Each comma reserves a "print zone" which consists of 15 columns. With this spacing a maximum of 5 variables and/or constants may be printed on each line which contains 75 columns. Anything over 5 variables and constants to be printed would be printed on a new line. As we shall see later in the chapter, more than 5 print zones can be established by modifying the instructions to the computer.

If only variables and constants could be printed, it would often be difficult to interpret the printout, particularly for a long program with several printouts. This difficulty may be remedied by instructing the computer to print column headings, or *labels*. Again referring to program 1.2, it would be helpful for the printed columns to be labeled as follows.

PRINCIPAL	INTEREST	YEARS	AMOUNT
1000	.08	10	2158.92
5000	.055	20	14588.8

The computer may be instructed to print the column headings by placing a **PRINT** statement in the program as shown in line **5**, program 1.3.

Program 1.3

```
 5 PRINT "PRINCIPAL", "INTEREST",
   "YEARS", "AMOUNT"
10 READ P,R,N
20 DATA 1000,.08,10,5000,.055,20
30 LET A = P * (1 + R) ↑ N
40 PRINT P,R,N,A
50 GO TO 10
60 END
```

The computer will now print the following.

PRINCIPAL	INTEREST	YEARS	AMOUNT
1000	.08	10	2158.92
5000	.055	20	14588.8

Notice that the labels in line **5**, program 1.3, are enclosed in quotation marks. A minimum of 15 columns is reserved for each label, as is the case for variables and constants. If a label requires more than 15 but fewer than 31 columns, a total of 30 columns is reserved, etc.

The positioning of the **PRINT** statement for the labels is significant. For example, if the labels are to be printed on only one line for program 1.3, the instructions in line **5** must not be included in the loop; otherwise, the labels would be printed for each computation of **A**. It is a good idea to place label printing instructions at the beginning of the program when labels are to be printed only one time.

The **PRINT** statement has some other important properties. If the word **PRINT** alone is shown on a line in the program, the computer skips a line in the printout. If two successive lines are to be skipped, the instruction **PRINT** would appear on two successive lines in the program. Let us rewrite program 1.3 to make our printout easier to read. The revision is shown in program 1.4.

Program 1.4

```
 5 PRINT "PRINCIPAL", "INTEREST",
   "YEARS", "AMOUNT"
 6 PRINT
 7 PRINT
10 READ P,R,N
20 DATA 1000,.08,10,5000,.055,20
```

```
30 LET A = P * (1 + R) ↑ N
40 PRINT P,R,N,A
50 GO TO 10
60 END
```

The printout now appears as follows.

PRINCIPAL	INTEREST	YEARS	AMOUNT
1000	.08	10	2158.92
5000	.055	20	14588.8

A separate **LET** statement is not always necessary, but may be incorporated in a **PRINT** statement. For example, in program 1.4, line 30 could be omitted and line 40 could be changed to:

```
40 PRINT P,R,N,P * (1 + R) ↑ N
```

EXERCISE 1.1

1. Which of the following programs are correct? If a program is not correct, revise it so that it will run.

    (a)
```
1 READ A,B
2 DATA 3,5,7,9,11,13
3 LET X = A + B
4 PRINT X, "IS THE SUM OF", A, AND, B
5 GO TO 1
6 END
```

    (b)
```
10 DATA X,Y
20 READ 2,4,6,8
30 LET Z = X2 + Y2
40 PRINT
50 END
```

    (c)
```
5 DATA 1,2,3,4,5,6,7,8,9,10
6 READ X
7 LET X = X ↑ 3
8 PRINT "THE CUBE", OF X, "IS", Y
9 GO TO 5
10 END
```

2. What is the printout for 1(a) as written or as you corrected it? For 1(b) and 1(c)?

3. Find the error in the following **LET** statements.
    (a) **LET A = B(C + D)**
    (b) **LET B2 = X1 + X2 + 3X**
    (c) **LET X + Y = 2 * Z**

(*d*) **LET Z5 = 2 * (5 + .03X)**
(*e*) **LET W7 = X2 * 7X**

4. Which of the following constants are permitted in a **BASIC** program?
   (*a*) **22.925**   (*d*) **−3027.5**   (*g*) **√15**
   (*b*) **7,421**   (*e*) **0.02**   (*h*) **164324683222**
   (*c*) **007**   (*f*) **5/7**

5. Write a **BASIC** program to compute and print how much each person owes based on the following tabulation.

Purchaser	Units Purchased	Unit Cost	Owed
John	3,000	.035	
Mary	5,150	.022	
Jim	10,310	.018	

1.8 SPACING THE PRINTOUT

Sometimes column labels are not needed for all columns. The computer can be instructed to skip column labels in the following manner.

$$\text{PRINT} \quad " \quad "$$

For each pair of quotation marks, the computer omits a label for 15 spaces. Consider the following statement.

$$\text{PRINT} \quad " \quad ", \quad "\text{RATE}", \quad " \quad ", \quad "\text{AMOUNT}"$$

In this instance, the computer omits a label for the first print zone (15 spaces), prints **RATE** in the second zone of 15 spaces, omits a label in the next 15 spaces, and prints the label **AMOUNT** in the fourth print zone.

After a **PRINT** statement has been executed, the next **PRINT** statement spaces to a new line if the program instructions are in the form already specified. However, it is possible to use one line for several **PRINT** statements until all print zones are used. The computer can be so instructed by the use of commas at the ends of **PRINT** statements. For example,

$$\text{PRINT P,}$$
$$\text{PRINT R,N,}$$
$$\text{PRINT A}$$

The printout would now appear on one line, unless more than 5 print zones (75 spaces) were needed. In that case printing would continue on the next line after using up the 75 spaces.

EXERCISE 1.2

1. What is the printout for the following program?
```
10 PRINT "QUANTITY", "UNIT COST",
   "TOTAL COST"
20 READ Q,U
```

```
30 DATA 10000,.01,12000,.012,16000,.025
40 LET C1 = Q * U
50 PRINT Q,U,C1
60 GO TO 20
70 END
```

2. What is the printout of the following program?

```
10 READ Q1,U1,Q2,U2,Q3,U3
20 DATA 10000,.01,12000,.012,16000,.025
30 LET C1 = Q1 * U1
40 LET C2 = Q2 * U2
50 LET C3 = Q3 * U3
60 PRINT "THE COST OF C1 IS" C1
70 PRINT "THE COST OF C2 IS" C2
80 PRINT "THE COST OF C3 IS" C3
90 PRINT "THE TOTAL COST IS" C1 + C2 + C3
100 END
```

3. A company employs 5 people. The owner decides to perform his payroll calculations by computer. Assume a tax deduction rate of 10% and a Social Security deduction of 5%. Write the program and show the complete printout in the following format.

Emp	Gross	Tax	SS	Net
1	500			
2	1000			
3	700			
4	900			
5	400			

4. Write the program for finding the value of $Y = X^2 + 2X^{1/2} + 3$ when X has the following values: 4, 9, 16, 25, 36.

5. You work for the SIPJAC Supermarket; the manager instructs you to work up a model computer program for finding the present value of the store stock. He suggests the following format.

Item	Quan	Unit Cost	Total Cost
A			
B			
o			
o			
o			

Write a program to produce the desired format.

1.9 COMPUTER DECISIONS BY COMPARING NUMBERS

We have seen that useful programs are possible utilizing only six BASIC statements: DATA, READ, LET, GO TO, PRINT, and END. Two additional types of statements greatly increase the usefulness of the computer. The first that we shall discuss is the **IF/THEN** statement, which takes the general form **IF____ THEN____**. The basic purpose of this statement is to instruct the computer to proceed to a specified line in the program **IF** certain conditions are met. Consider the statement

$$\text{IF } X = 6 \text{ THEN } 10$$

If the computed value of **X** is equal to 6, then the computer switches to line 10. If **X** is not equal to 6, then the computer proceeds to the next line in sequence. In addition to equality, the computer is able to make five other comparisons.

Comparison	**BASIC** *Symbol*
Not equal to	$< >$
Greater than	$>$
Greater than or equal to	$> =$
Less than	$<$
Less than or equal to	$< =$

Illustrations of the first three follow.

$$\text{IF } X < > 2 * Y \text{ THEN } 20$$

If the variable **X** is not equal to $2Y$, then the computer transfers control to line 20. Otherwise, the next instruction in sequence is executed.

$$\text{IF } A2 > 2 \uparrow X \text{ THEN } 80$$

If the variable **A2** is greater than 2^X, then the computer goes to line 80; otherwise, to the next line in sequence.

$$\text{IF } (X \uparrow 2 + 3 * X + 2) > = 0 \text{ THEN } 60$$

If the sum $X^2 + 3X + 2 > = 0$, then the computer switches to line 60; otherwise, the next line is executed.

The two expressions that are to be compared can be simple, as illustrated above, or complicated, as in the following example.

$$\text{IF } (X * 2)/(X/2 + 1) + 1/2 > (X + 2)/(X - 5) \text{ THEN } 180$$

No matter how complicated the compared expressions may be, the computer calculates each expression and compares the two numbers.

Program 1.5 illustrates the use of an **IF/THEN** statement.

Program 1.5

```
10 LET N = 0
20 READ A
30 DATA 9,7,5,1,6,11,12,24,3,2
40 LET N = N + 1
50 PRINT A
60 IF N < 10 THEN 20
70 END
```

Program 1.5 instructs the computer to PRINT the numbers 9, 7, 5, etc., in one column. The IF/THEN statement causes the computer to loop until N = 10. Program 1.5 illustrates another use of a LET statement. In line 10 we assign an initial value to N, a process called *initializing the variable*. The number 0 is stored in the memory cell reserved for N until another value of N is computed in step 40. The new N then replaces the value 0.

1.10 ANOTHER METHOD OF LOOPING

The eighth and ninth BASIC statements that we shall consider are the FOR and NEXT statements. The use of these instructions sets up a loop, just as does the use of the IF/THEN and GO TO statements. Let us first examine the BASIC word FOR. Consider the statement

$$20 \text{ FOR } N = 1 \text{ TO } 50$$

Line 20 instructs the computer to assign an initial value of 1 to the variable N for the first computation. The FOR statement initiates an automatic loop in which the value of N is increased in each pass, taking on the integer values from 2 through 50. Consider program 1.6, in which line 20 above appears.

Program 1.6

```
10 PRINT "N", "N SQUARED"
20 FOR N = 1 TO 50
30 LET X = N ↑ 2
40 PRINT
50 PRINT N,X
60 NEXT N
70 END
```

The output of this program is as follows.

N	N SQUARED
1	1
2	4
3	9
.	.
.	.
.	.
50	2500

Line 60 in program 1.6 accomplishes the loop in this program. The first computation is made for N = 1, the number 1 is printed under the label N and the number 1^2 is printed under the label N SQUARED.

Line 60 then instructs the computer to return to line 20 for the **NEXT** value of **N** which, of course, is 2. Steps 30, 40 and 50 are then performed for **N** = 2. This procedure is repeated through **N** = 50.

In program 1.6, **N** was increased by 1 in each step. This change in the variable in a **FOR** statement is called the *increment*. The increment of 1 in program 1.6 can be changed by modifying the **FOR** statement in the following manner.

20 FOR N = 1 TO 50 STEP .5

N now changes by .5 in each step. The first **N** would be 1, the second 1.5, etc. Consider another example of a **FOR** statement with an increment other than 1.

FOR I = 0 TO 1 STEP .001

The first **I** is 0, the second .001, the third .002, etc.

Another procedure known as *nesting* can be accomplished with the **FOR** and **NEXT** statements. Nesting is the process of placing one loop inside another loop. Consider the following nest.

FOR I = 1 TO 10
FOR J = 1 TO 5
.
.
.
NEXT J
NEXT I
.
.
.

For **I** = 1, the inside or **J** loop repeats 5 times; for **I** = 2, the inside loop repeats 5 times. In other words, the **J** loop is performed a total of 50 times. This procedure is illustrated in program 1.7.

Program 1.7

```
 10 FOR I = 1 TO 5
 20 FOR J = 1 TO 3
 30 IF I = J THEN 60
 40 PRINT "0"
 50 GO TO 70
 60 PRINT "1"
 70 NEXT J
 80 PRINT
 90 NEXT I
100 END
```

The printout is as follows.

1	0	0
0	1	0
0	0	1
0	0	0
0	0	0

1.11 SUBSCRIPTED VARIABLES

From our discussion of variables, you will recall that A0, A1, A2, A3, and up to A9 are permissible variables. There is another method of defining a variable which removes the restriction that a specific letter can be used for only ten variables. This method is called *subscripting*. If we wish to use A for more than 10 variables, say for 50, we denote the first variable by A(1)—note the parentheses around . 1—and continue to A(50). If more than 10 subscripts are to be used on a variable, the number of that variable is to be subscripted must be specified by a dimension statement written as DIM in the BASIC language.

This statement is normally placed in the program preceding the variable, or variables, to which it applies. Usually it is the beginning statement in the program. One DIM statement may be used to specify the dimensions of several variables. For example,

10 DIM A(50), B(50), C(50)

This statement tells the computer to reserve 50 storage locations for A, 50 for B, and 50 for C. When a DIM statement is not used, 10 storage locations are automatically reserved for each of the subscripted variables. Consider program 1.8, which includes a DIM statement.

Program 1.8

```
 10 DIM A(20)
 20 LET S = 0
 30 FOR I = 1 TO 20
 40 READ A(I)
 50 LET S = S + A(I)
 60 NEXT I
 70 PRINT "SUM =", S
 80 DATA 5,10,15,20,25,30,35
 90 DATA 40,45,50,55,60,65,70,75
100 DATA 80,85,90,95,100
110 END
```

Program 1.8 will cause the twenty numbers in DATA to be added with the sum shown in the following printout.

SUM = 1050

Variables may also be defined with two subscripts. The general form is $A(I,J)$ where I and J are nonnegative integers. In this case a DIM statement with the dimension of both I and J must be included in the program if either I or J is ever larger than 10.

1.12 ADDITIONAL BASIC WORDS

Three additional BASIC statements can often be used to advantage. They are the INPUT, STOP, and REMARK statements.

The INPUT statement can be used instead of READ and DATA statements. Program 1.9 could replace program 1.1.

Program 1.9

```
10 INPUT P,R,N
20 LET A = P * (1 + R) ↑ N
30 PRINT A
40 END
```

When the computer is instructed to run this program, a question mark will be printed. The programmer then furnishes the data:

1000, .08,10

When A is printed, the computer again prints a question mark, and additional data may be supplied.

If there is no more data to be supplied, the programmer can inform the computer by the statement STOP. This statement can be used at any point in the program to cause execution of the program to cease.

The BASIC language word REM is an abbreviation for "remark." A REM statement can be inserted at any point in a program before the END statement. The REM statement is never executed, but is used for program documentation. Programmers can use this statement to explain steps in the program. Several examples of REM statements follow.

```
10 REM PROGRAM FOR FINDING COMPOUND INTEREST
50 REM BE SURE TO PUT INTEREST IN DECIMAL
   FORM
15 REM IS THE FIRST OF FIVE PRACTICE PROGRAMS
```

EXERCISE 1.3

1. What is the printout for the following program?

```
 5 INPUT X
10 PRINT "TABLE OF POWERS OF", X
15 PRINT
16 PRINT "EXPONENT", "2 ↑ E"
20 FOR E = 0 TO 10
25 LET A = X ↑ E
30 PRINT E,A
```

```
35 NEXT E
40 END
RUN
? 2
```

2. What is the printout for the following program?

```
 5 PRINT   "AMOUNT",  "PERCENTAGE"
10 DIM A(10)
12 LET T = O
15 FOR I = 1 TO 10
20 READ A(I)
25 DATA 6,8,10,12,14,16,18,20,22,24
30 LET T = T + A(I)
40 NEXT I
45 FOR I = 1 TO 10
50 LET P = A(I)/T * 100
55 PRINT A(I),P
60 NEXT I
65 END
```

3. Write a program to find the sum of the first 100 integers.

4. Write a program to compute the squares of the integers from 1 through 100.

5. Write a program to compute the square root of the integers from 1 through 10.

6. Write a program to compute the square roots of numbers between 2 and 3 in intervals of .01.

1.13 CORRECTING PROGRAM ERRORS

Computer programs often contain errors. The process of correcting errors in a program is known as *editing* or *debugging*. Program errors are of three types: typing errors, **BASIC** language (including punctuation) errors, and logical errors.

Typing errors and language errors are detected by the computer when it is instructed to **RUN** a program. The computer prints a brief description of each error and gives the line number in which the error appears. For instance, a line in a program might be

$$10 \ \text{LAT} = A + B$$

This is not a **BASIC** language statement. The computer will so inform the programmer by printing

ILLEGAL INSTRUCTION IN 10

The programmer may then correct line **10** by rewriting the entire line, again using 10 for the line number. The computer always uses the last statement when a line number is repeated. For the illegal line 10 the program should probably be:

10 LET X = A + B

A partial listing of **BASIC** error messages is given below.

Error Message	*Error*
ILLEGAL FORMULA IN ---	Missing ( ), illegal operation or illegal variable.
ILLEGAL INSTRUCTION IN ---	Misspelled words, or words not in **BASIC**.
NO DATA	Programmer forgot to include a **DATA** statement following a **READ** statement.
ILLEGAL VARIABLE IN ---	Form of the variable is wrong.
NEXT WITHOUT FOR or **FOR WITHOUT NEXT**	A **FOR** or **NEXT** statement is missing.
INCORRECT FORMAT IN ---	Incorrect punctuation or spelling.
NO END INSTRUCTION	Program has no **END** statement.

After studying the error messages and making corrections in the indicated lines, the computer is again instructed to **RUN** the program.

The computer is able to find only the errors in typing or language —not in the program logic. If the programmer has instructed the computer to multiply when he meant to divide, no error message will be received. The program may **RUN** and give an incorrect answer. It is always desirable to check a program with data which will yield a known answer. It is possible to write additional steps into a program to enable the programmer to find errors in logic. A discussion of such procedures is left for a more sophisticated treatment.

1.14 PROGRAM INPUT TO THE COMPUTER

A completed program may be given to the computer in several ways, depending upon the computer facilities available. A teletypewriter resembling an ordinary typewriter may be used. When this type of input device is available, the program may be fed directly to the computer as it is typed. Programs are often input to the computer by the familiar punched card. The cards may be punched by hand with a keypunch machine or by machine from electrographic pencil markings. Punched paper tapes also may be used. Other methods for entering the program include magnetic tape, printed magnetic characters (such as those on a bank check), magnetic discs, and visual display consoles. Because of the great computational speed of most computers, researchers are continually seeking faster methods of furnishing programs to computers.

The same input devices are used to provide the computer with the data required for program execution.

CHAPTER 2

Sets, Permutations, Combinations, and the Binomial Theorem

2.1 INTRODUCTION TO SETS

One of the fundamental notions of mathematics is the concept of the *set*. While much of mathematics may be studied without a formal understanding of sets, the set concept is vital to the study of modern probability theory.

A set is a collection of objects such as dishes, pencils, numbers, or people. Mathematically, a set must consist of a *well-defined* collection of objects. A set is said to be well defined when there is no doubt that any given object *belongs to* or *does not belong to* the set. The objects which belong to a set are called the *elements* of the set. The elements of a set are distinct; i.e., each element differs from all other elements in the set.

Sets are classified as *finite* or *infinite*. A finite set contains a limited number of elements. An infinite set contains an unlimited number of elements. A set with no elements is called the *empty* or *null* set and is denoted by $\emptyset$ or { }.

Sets may be denoted in several ways. One method is to list the elements and enclose them with braces. For example, $\{1, 2, 3\}$. The order in which the elements are listed makes no difference; e.g., the set $\{1, 2, 3\}$ is the same as the set $\{3, 1, 2\}$.

Another method is to state a rule that defines the elements of the set. The set $\{1, 2, 3\}$ could be denoted as

$$\{x \mid x \text{ is a natural number } < 4\}$$

This statement is read, "the set of all x such that x is a natural number less than 4."

Capital letters are used to designate sets and small letters to denote elements; e.g., $A = \{x, y, z, w\}$. When we wish to indicate that an object x is an element of the set A (or "belongs to" the set A), we may do so by writing $x \in A$ (read: "x is an element of A"). Consider the following examples of set notation.

Example 1. Let A be the set of counting numbers.

$$A = \{1, 2, 3, \ldots\}$$
$$A = \{x \mid x \text{ is a counting number}\}$$
$$1 \in A, \ 2 \in A, \ 3 \in A, \text{ etc.}$$

Example 2. Let B be the set of integers.

$$B = \{x \mid x \text{ is an integer}\}$$
$$B = \{\ldots, -3, -2, -1, 0, 1, 2, 3, \ldots\}$$

Example 3. Let C be the set of divisors of 80.

$$C = \{x \mid x \text{ is a positive divisor of } 80\}$$
$$C = \{1, 2, 4, 5, 8, 10, 16, 20, 40\}$$

In these examples of set notation, the elements have been numbers. There is no limitation on the composition of an element. For example, the following set consists of ordered pairs.

Example 4. Let $A = \{(s, s), (s, f), (f, s), (f, f)\}$

$$(s, s) \in A, \ (s, f) \in A, \text{ etc.}$$

Each element of the above set A consists of two *components*. Notice that *the order of the components of the elements in set A is significant.* The ordered pair (s, f) with first component s and second component f is distinct from the ordered pair (f, s). The component concept will be explored in more detail when we study permutations and combinations.

In the study of probability, each element of a set may consist of many components. For example, the following set contains four elements, each of which has four components.

$$A = \{(b, b, b, b), (b, b, b, g), (b, b, g, g), (b, g, g, g)\}$$

Two sets, A and B, are said to be *equivalent* when A and B contain the same number of elements. Two equivalent sets A and B are said to be *equal* when they contain the same elements.

2.2 SUBSETS

In mathematics we often study objects that belong to a large set of objects.

We are familiar with the set of real numbers and the sets of integers and fractions that are a part of the real numbers. Any set that includes all of the elements under consideration in an investigation is called the *universal set* and is denoted by U. Any collection of elements in U is called a *subset* of U. Consider the following examples.

Example 1. Let U be the set of all families.

Subsets of U: $\begin{cases} \text{Let } A \text{ be the set of families with two children.} \\ \text{Let } B \text{ be the set of families with incomes above} \\ \$10,000. \end{cases}$

Example 2. Let U be the set of all automobile tires.

Subsets of U: $\begin{cases} \text{Let } A \text{ be the set of automobile tires that fail after} \\ 30,000 \text{ miles.} \\ \text{Let } B \text{ be the set of automobile tires that cost over} \\ \$30.00. \end{cases}$

Example 3. Let U be the set of all TV viewers.

Subsets of U: $\begin{cases} \text{Let } A \text{ be the set of viewers who watch sports.} \\ \text{Let } B \text{ be the set of viewers who watch comedy.} \\ \text{Let } C \text{ be the set of viewers who watch wrestling.} \end{cases}$

The subsets in the examples above could become the universal set if the totality of the objects under consideration were changed.

We formalize the subset concept in the following definition.

DEFINITION 2.1

Set A is said to be a *subset* of B, denoted by $A \subseteq B$, if and only if each element of A is an element of B.

Examples of sets and subsets follow.

Example 1. Let $A = \{(s,f,), (f,s), (f,f)\}$
and $B = \{(s,f,), (f,s)\}$
then $B = \subseteq A$

Example 2. Let A be the set of freshmen
and let B be the set of freshmen women
then $B \subseteq A$

Example 3. Let A be the set of U.S. voters
and let B be the set of Republican voters
then $B \subseteq A$

By Definition 2.1, each set is a subset of itself, i.e., $A \subseteq A$. All other subsets of A are called proper subsets. Each subset in the three examples is a proper subset.

DEFINITION 2.2

Set A is a *proper subset* of B, denoted by $A \subset B$, if and only if each element of A is an element of B, and there is at least one element of B that is not an element of A.

Each of the subsets of the above examples satisfies Definition 2.2.

The universal set and its subsets may be geometrically represented by means of a Venn* diagram (figure 2.1). The rectangle U in the diagram represents the universal set. The subsets of U are represented by circles or other closed geometric figures contained in the rectangle representing U.

Let $U = \{1, 2, 3, \ldots, 10\}$, $A = \{1, 2, 3, 4\}$, $B = \{1, 2\}$, and $C = \{6, 7\}$. Since $B \subset A$, the circle representing B must lie within the circle representing A.

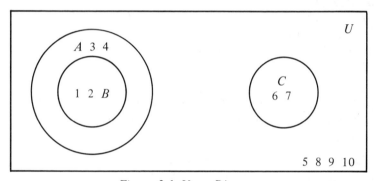

Figure 2.1 Venn Diagram

$$A \subset U, \quad B \subset U, \quad B \subset A, \quad C \subset U$$

The sets A and C in figure 2.1 have no elements in common; likewise the sets B and C have no points in common. This relationship between sets is defined as follows.

DEFINITION 2.3

Two sets A and B are said to be *disjoint*, or *mutually exclusive*, if they have no elements in common.

In probability theory it is important that we determine the number of subsets that can be formed from a given set. We shall examine this problem in some detail in subsequent sections of this chapter. For now, let it be said that if a set consists of n elements, then it has 2^n subsets. Try this rule for a set of three elements.

---

* After its inventor John Venn, the nineteenth century English logician.

EXERCISE 2.1

1. List the elements of the following sets.
   (*a*) Integers from 5 through 10
   (*b*) Vowels including y
   (*c*) Talking catfish
   (*d*) The set of ordered pairs using the components 1, 2, and 3 (Repetition of components is permitted; i.e., (1, 1) is in the set.)

2. Which of these sets are equal to the first set listed?
   (*a*) $\{1, 2, 3\}$ (*b*) $\{2, 1, 3\}$ (*c*) $\{3, 2, 1\}$ (*d*) $\{3, 1, 2\}$

3. Which of these sets are equal to the first set listed?
   (*a*) $\{(s, r), (r, s)\}$ (*b*) $\{(r, s), (s, r)\}$ (*c*) $\{s, r, r, s\}$ (*d*) $\{(s, r, r, s)\}$

4. List all subsets of each of the following sets.
   (*a*) $\{1, 2, 3\}$
   (*b*) $\{(1, 2), (2, 1)\}$
   (*c*) $\{(B, B, B), (G, G, G)\}$
   (*d*) $\{(S, S), (S, F), (F, S), (F, F)\}$
   (*e*) $\{(A, U, R), (U, A, R), (R, U, A)\}$

5. List the subsets of the following sets.
   (*a*) Football teams in the 1972 Super Bowl
   (*b*) Presidents of the United States since 1960
   (*c*) The set of positive odd integers less than or equal to 9

6. Which of the following sets are infinite?
   (*a*) Real numbers (*b*) atoms in the ocean (*c*) counting numbers

7. How many subsets can be formed from each indicated set?
   (*a*) $\{F, H, T\}$
   (*b*) $\{(F, H), (H, F)\}$
   (*c*) $\{(B, B), (B, G), (G, B), (G, G)\}$
   (*d*) $\{(S, F, U), (S, U, F), (F, U, S)\}$

8. Represent the following sets with a Venn diagram.
   $U = \{2, 4, 6, \ldots, 24\}$
   $A = \{2, 8, 16\}$
   $B = \{4, 16\}$
   $C = \{2, 4, 6, 8, 16\}$

9. Represent the following sets with a Venn diagram.
   Let U be the set of students at S.P. College.
   Let A be the set of students at S.P. studying English.
   Let B be the set of students at S.P. studying English and math.
   Let C be the set of students at S.P. studying English and history.
   Let D be the set of students at S.P. studying history and math.
   Let E be the set of students at S.P. studying history, English, and math.
   (Assume that no set is empty.)

10. Write the following in set notation.
    (*a*) *A* is a subset of *B*
    (*b*) *x* is a member of *Z*
    (*c*) (x_1, y_1) is an element of *F*
    (*d*) $\{(B, B), (G, G)\}$ is a subset of $\{(B, B), (G, G), (B, G)\}$

2.3 SET OPERATIONS

Given a universal set *U*, it is possible to *operate* on the subsets of *U* to form new sets. We shall study three set operations in this section and consider a fourth in a subsequent section.

   In two of the definitions that follow, the words "or" and "and" appear. In our study of probability, it is vital that the meaning of these words be understood. When "or" is used in defining a set operation, it is always used in the inclusive sense. To say that an element *x* is in set *A or* set *B* means that *x* may be in *A* only, in *B* only, or in both *A* and *B*. To say that an element *x* is in *A and B* means that *x* is in both sets *A* and *B* simultaneously.

   The first operation we shall consider is called *intersection*.

DEFINITION 2.4

The *intersection* of sets *A* and *B* is the set of all elements of *U* that belong to both *A* and *B*. The intersection of *A* and *B* is symbolized by $A \cap B$ (read: "*A* intersect *B*"). Symbolically,

$$A \cap B = \{x \mid x \in A \text{ and } x \in B\}$$

   The reason for selecting the term "intersection" for this operation is apparent in the following diagram.

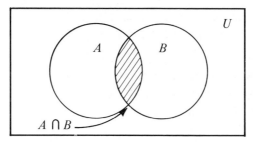

Figure 2.2 Intersection of A and B: $A \cap B$

   The second set operation that we shall define is called *union*.

DEFINITION 2.5

The *union* of sets *A* and *B* is the set of all elements of *U* that belong either to *A* or to *B* or to both *A* and *B*. The union of *A* and *B* is symbolized by $A \cup B$ (read: "*A* union *B*"). Symbolically,

$$A \cup B = \{x \mid x \in A \text{ or } x \in B \text{ or } x \in \text{both } A \text{ and } B\}$$

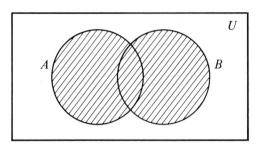

Figure 2.3 Union of A and B: $A \cup B$

The last operation to be considered at this time is called *complementation*.

DEFINITION 2.6

The *complement* of the set A is the set of all elements in U that are not in A. The complement of A is symbolized by A' (read: "A complement"). Symbolically,

$$A' = \{x \mid x \in U \text{ and } x \notin A\}$$

(Note: $\notin$ means "not an element of.")

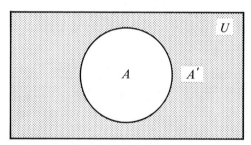

Figure 2.4 Complement of A : A'

The operations of intersection, union, and complementation are illustrated in the following examples.

Example 1. Let $U = \{1, 2, 3, \ldots, 10\}$
$$A = \{1, 2, 3\}$$
$$B = \{3, 4, 5\}$$

Find: (*a*) $A \cap B$, (*b*) $A \cup B$, (*c*) A'

Solution: (*a*) $A \cap B = \{x \mid x \in A \text{ and } x \in B\}$
$$A \cap B = \{3\}$$
(*b*) $A \cup B = \{x \mid x \in A \text{ or } x \in B \text{ or both}\}$
$$A \cup B = \{1, 2, 3, 4, 5\}$$
(*c*) $A' = \{x \mid x \in U \text{ and } x \notin A\}$
$$A' = \{4, 5, 6, \ldots, 10\}$$

Example 2. Let $U = \{(s, s,), (s, f,), (f, s,), (f, f)\}$
$$A = \{(s, s,), (s, f)\}$$
$$B = \{(s, f,), (f, s)\}$$

Find: (a) $A \cap B$, (b) $A \cup B$, (c) A'

Solution: (a) $A \cap B = \{(s, f)\}$

(b) $A \cup B = \{(s, s), (s, f), (f, s)\}$

(c) $A' = \{(f, s,), (f, f)\}$

Example 3. Let $U =$ the set of United States presidents

Let A be the set of United States presidents from 1932 to 1972

Let B be the set of United States presidents who were assassinated

Find: (a) $A \cap B$ and (b) $A \cup B$

Solution: (a) $A \cap B = \{\text{Kennedy}\}$

(b) $A \cup B = \{\text{Roosevelt, Truman, Eisenhower, Kennedy, Johnson, Nixon}\}$

2.4 THE ALGEBRA OF SETS

In a thorough study of the algebra of sets, each of the several properties of set operations would be proved. Since our purpose in introducing sets is solely to develop the theory of probability, we present without proof the properties of set operations listed below.

Let A, B, and C be any subsets of U.

1. Closure of union, intersection, and complementation.
   (a) $A \cup B$ is a set
   (b) $A \cap B$ is a set
   (c) A' is a set

2. Associative laws of union and intersection.
   (a) $A \cup (B \cup C) = (A \cup B) \cup C$
   (b) $A \cap (B \cap C) = (A \cap B) \cap C$

3. Commutative laws of union and intersection.
   (a) $A \cup B = B \cup A$
   (b) $A \cap B = B \cap A$

4. Distributive laws.
   (a) $A \cup (B \cap C) = (A \cup B) \cap (A \cup C)$
   (b) $A \cap (B \cup C) = (A \cap B) \cup (A \cap C)$

EXERCISE 2.2

1. Given: $U = \{1, 2, 3, \ldots, 14\}$
$A = \{1, 2, 3, \ldots, 10\}$
$B = \{2, 4, 6, 8, 10, 12, 14\}$
$C = \{1, 3, 5, 7, 9\}$

Find: (a) $A \cup B$ (f) $A \cup (B \cap C)$
(b) $B \cup C$ (g) A'
(c) $A \cup C$ (h) B'
(d) $(A \cup B) \cup C$ (i) C'
(e) $A \cup (B \cup C)$ (j) $A' \cap (B' \cup C')$

2. Given: $U = \{(s, s, s), (s; s, f), (s, f, s), (f, s, s), (s, f, f), (f, s, f), (f, f, s),$
$(f, f, f)\}$
$A = \{(s, s, s), (s, s, f)\}$
$B = \{(s, s, s), (s, f, s)\}$
$C = \{(s, f, f), (f, s, s), (s, s, f)\}$

Find: (a) $A \cup B$ (f) $A \cup (B \cap C)$
(b) $B \cup C$ (g) A'
(c) $A \cup C$ (h) B'
(d) $(A \cup B) \cup C$ (i) C'
(e) $A \cup (B \cup C)$ (j) $A' \cup (B' \cup C')$

3. If set A has 5 elements and set B has 5 elements, what is the maximum number of elements in (a) $A \cup B$? (b) $A \cap B$?

4. If set A has 10 elements, set B has 5 elements, and set C has 3 elements, determine:
(a) the maximum number of elements in $A \cup B \cup C$
(b) the minimum number of elements in $(A \cup B) \cup C$
(c) the maximum number of elements in $(B \cap C) \cup A$
(d) the minimum number of elements in $A \cap B \cap C$

5. Given: $U = \{(x, y) \mid x = s \text{ or } x = f, y = s \text{ or } y = f\}$
$A = \{(s, x) \mid x = f \text{ or } x = s\}$
$B = \{(x, f) \mid x = f \text{ or } x = s\}$

Find: (a) $A \cup B$
(b) $A \cap B$
(c) A'
(d) B'

6. Given: $U = \{(b, b), (b, g), (g, b), (g, g)\}$
A is the set of elements with first component b
C is the set of elements with first component b or g
D is the set of elements with first component b and second component b or g

Find: (*a*) the elements in A
(*b*) the elements in C
(*c*) the elements in D
(*d*) the elements in $A \cup C$
(*e*) the elements in $A \cap C$
(*f*) the elements in $A \cup C \cup D$

7. Given: $U = \{x \mid x$ is a human being$\}$
$A = \{y \mid y$ is a human being 21 years of age or older$\}$
$B = \{z \mid z$ is Caucasian$\}$
$C = \{w \mid w$ is Negroid$\}$

Describe each of the following in words.
(*a*) $A \cap B$ (*d*) $A \cup C$
(*b*) $A \cup B$ (*e*) $B \cap C$
(*c*) $B \cup C$

8. Using diagrams similar to that given below, shade those portions indicated by the sets specified in (*a*) through (*h*).

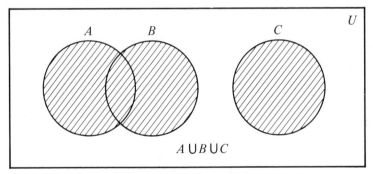

$A \cup B \cup C$

(*a*) $A \cup (B \cap C)$ (*e*) $(A \cap B) \cup C$
(*b*) $A \cap B$ (*f*) $(A \cup B) \cap C$
(*c*) $A \cap C$ (*g*) $C \cap (A \cup B)$
(*d*) $B \cap C$ (*h*) $A \cap (B \cup C)$

9. Referring to your answers to problem 8,
(*a*) Which diagrams illustrate the commutative property of union or intersection?
(*b*) Which diagrams illustrate the associative property of union or intersection?
(*c*) Which diagrams indicate closure of union or intersection?
(*d*) Which diagrams illustrate the distributive property?

2.5 THE CARTESIAN PRODUCT SET

The fourth set operation that we shall consider is called *the Cartesian product.* This operation differs from the others because it is based on the idea of *ordered pairs.*

DEFINITION 2.7

The *Cartesian product* of two sets A and B is the set of all ordered pairs (a, b) such that $a \in A$ and $b \in B$. The Cartesian product is denoted by $A \times B$ (read: "A cross B"). Symbolically,

$$A \times B = \{(a, b) \mid a \in A \text{ and } b \in B\}$$

Example 1. If $A = \{1, 2, 3\}$ and $B = \{a, b, c\}$, find $A \times B$ and $B \times A$.

Solution: $A \times B = \{(1, a), (1, b), (1, c), (2, a), (2, b), (2, c),$
$\qquad\qquad\qquad (3, a), (3, b), (3, c)\}$

$\qquad\quad\;\; B \times A = \{(a, 1), (a, 2), (a, 3), (b, 1), (b, 2), (b, 3),$
$\qquad\qquad\qquad (c, 1), (c, 2), (c, 3)\}$

Each element of A is matched with each element of B to yield $3 \times 3 = 9$ elements in $A \times B$. Similarly, each element of B is matched with each element of A to yield $3 \times 3 = 9$ elements of $B \times A$. For both $A \times B$ and $B \times A$, each element consists of two components.

Example 2. If $A = \{(s, s), (s, f)\}$ and $B = \{(f, s), (f, f)\}$, find $A \times B$ and $B \times A$.

Solution: Each element of A is matched with each element of B to yield $2 \times 2 = 4$ elements in $A \times B$ and vice versa.

$\qquad A \times B = \{((s, s), (f, s)), ((s, s), (f, f)), ((s, f), (f, s)),$
$\qquad\qquad\qquad ((s, f), (f, f))\}$

$\qquad B \times A = \{((f, s), (s, s)), ((f, s), (s, f)), ((f, f), (s, s)),$
$\qquad\qquad\qquad ((f, f), (s, f))\}$

The Cartesian product is named for the inventor of the coordinate system, René Descartes. If we let $A = \{1, 2, 3, \ldots, n\}$, $A \times A$ is the set

$\{(1, 1), (1, 2), (1, 3), \ldots, (1, n), (2, 1), (2, 2), (2, 3), \ldots, (2, n), (n, 1), (n, 2),$
$(n, 3), \ldots, (n, n)\}$

The entire set of coordinates, integral, rational, and irrational may be found in this manner; hence, the name "Cartesian product." In the study of probability we shall make extensive use of the Cartesian product concept.

The Cartesian product can be extended to any finite number of sets. The product $A \times B \times C$ is the set of ordered triples, each triple consisting of three components,

$$A \times B \times C = \{(a, b, c) \mid a \in A, b \in B, \text{ and } c \in C\}$$

The number of elements in a product set $A \times B$ may be found by finding the arithmetic product of the number of elements in A and the number of elements in B. For example, if A has m elements and B has n elements, then $A \times B$ has $m \cdot n$ elements.

EXERCISE 2.3

1. Given: $A = \{1, 2, 3\}$
        $B = \{x, y, z\}$
   Find: (a) $A \times B$ (c) $A \times A$
          (b) $B \times A$ (d) $B \times B$

2. See if you can relate the cross product of sets to ordinary multiplication.

3. Given: $A = \{a, b, c, d\}$
        $B = \{1, 5, 7, 9\}$
        $C = \{a, 2, b, 3\}$
   Find: (a) $A \times B$ (c) $B \times C$
          (b) $A \times C$ (d) $A \times B \times C$ (list 4 elements)

4. Set A has 3 elements, set B has 5 elements, and set C has 7 elements. How many elements are in each of the following sets?
   (a) $A \times B \times C$
   (b) $B \times A \times C$
   (c) $C \times A \times B$

5. Based on your answers to problem 4, what conjecture can be made regarding the Cartesian product?

2.6 THE FUNDAMENTAL PRINCIPLE OF COUNTING

In the study of probability often it is not feasible to count directly all of the elements in a set. We shall make extensive use of the principle of counting stated in the following definition.

DEFINITION 2.8

The Fundamental Principle of Counting. If there are n_1 ways of performing one procedure, and after this procedure has been performed there are n_2 ways of performing a second procedure, a third procedure can be performed in n_3 ways, and so forth, then the number of ways the sequence of procedures can be performed in the indicated order is the product $n_1 \cdot n_2 \cdot n_3 \ldots$.

Example 1. In how many ways can three prizes be won if there are fifteen people competing and no person is permitted to win more than one prize?

Solution: Applying the fundamental principle of counting, there are 15 choices for the winner of the first prize. After the first prize winner has been selected there are 14 choices for the winner of the second prize, and after both first and second prize winners are selected, there are 13 choices for the winner of the third prize. Hence, the number of ways in which the prizes may be distributed is the product 15(14)(13).

Example 2. How many license plates can be made using two letters followed by four digits? Repetitions are allowed.

Solution: Applying the fundamental principle, the first position can be filled in 26 ways, the second in 26 ways, and the third, fourth, fifth, and sixth positions in 10 ways each; hence, the number of distinct plates is the product

$$26 \cdot 26 \cdot 10 \cdot 10 \cdot 10 \cdot 10 = 6{,}760{,}000$$

Example 3. A given model automobile may be equipped with three types of engine, two types of transmission, five body styles, and thirty different colors. If a firm stocks one of each, how many automobiles must be in stock?

Solution: Applying the fundamental principle, the number of autos is the product

$$3 \cdot 2 \cdot 5 \cdot 30 = 900$$

The fundamental principle of counting, which is also called the *multiplication principle*, leads directly to a method of counting the number of possible ordered arrangements to a given number of objects. This method is discussed in the next section.

2.7 PERMUTATIONS

In applications of probability theory, we have indicated that it is often necessary to determine the number of elements in sets and subsets. When the number of elements is small, it is feasible to list and count the elements. When the number of elements in a set is large, this procedure is impractical and sometimes virtually impossible. Fortunately, techniques have been developed to find the number of elements in sets without direct enumeration. Such techniques are collectively referred to as *combinatorial analysis*. All counting techniques are based on the fundamental principle that we stated in the previous section. The first technique that we shall study enables us to find the number of different arrangements of a given number of things.

Suppose that ten people are to be arranged in linear order for a picture. How many different linear arrangements of the ten people are possible? This problem can be solved by application of the fundamental principle. The first position can be filled in 10 ways, the second in 9 ways, the third in 8 ways, and so forth. The number of different linear arrangements is the product $10 \cdot 9 \cdot 8 \cdot \ldots \cdot 1$. Each of the different arrangements is called a *permutation* of the ten people.

DEFINITION 2.9

A *permutation* of a number of things is any arrangement of these things in a definite order.

It is awkward to write (in the usual way) a product such as that for the number of arrangements of 10 people. A simplified method for denoting such products is known as *factorial notation*.

DEFINITION 2.10

Let n be a positive integer. The product $n \cdot (n - 1) \cdot (n - 2) \cdot \ldots \cdot 3 \cdot 2 \cdot 1$ is called *n-factorial* and it is denoted by the symbol $n!$.

With this notation, the number of permutations of the 30 mathematics students is 30!. The number 0! is defined to be 1. We shall consider $n!$ to be meaningless unless n is 0 or a positive integer. Examples of factorial notation follow.

$$3! = 3 \cdot 2 \cdot 1$$
$$50! = 50 \cdot 49 \cdot 48 \cdot \ldots \cdot 1$$
$$(7 - 3)! = 4 \cdot 3 \cdot 2 \cdot 1$$
$$\frac{(4 - 2)!}{2!} = \frac{2!}{2!} = 1$$

Recall that we have introduced the concept of permutations to enable us to find the number of elements in a set. Suppose that we define A as the set of all possible linear arrangements of ten people for a photograph. Set A then has 10! elements, each element of which consists of 10 components; obviously, listing and counting the elements is impractical.

Sometimes we wish to consider the number of possible arrangements of n different objects in which some, but not necessarily all, of the objects appear. Suppose that we define set B as the set of all possible linear arrangements of 3 books chosen from 6 books. We have a choice of 6 books for the first position. After the first position is filled, 5 books remain, so that the second position can be filled in 5 ways. The third position can be filled 4 or $(6 - 2)$ ways. Hence, there are $6 \cdot 5 \cdot 4$ elements in set B, each element consisting of 3 components. In general, this procedure enables us to find the arrangements of r things selected from a total of n things. This procedure is stated in theorem 2.1.

THEOREM 2.1

Suppose r objects are selected from a group of n distinguishable objects and placed in order. The number of possible permutations of those n things, taken r at a time, denoted by the symbol $P(n,r)$ or $P\binom{n}{r}$, is

$$P(n,r) = \frac{n!}{(n - r)!}$$

Discussion of the theorem: From the fundamental principle,

$$P(n, r) = n \cdot (n - 1) \cdot (n - 2) \cdot \ldots (n - r + 1)$$

The right side of this formula consists of r factors. If we multiply the right side by $(n - r)!/(n - r)!$ we get

$$P(n, r) = \frac{n(n - 1)(n - 2)\ldots(n - r + 1)(n - r)!}{(n - r)!}$$

The numerator of this expression is $n!$; hence, we may write

$$P(n, r) = \frac{n!}{(n - r)!}$$

Examples of the application of theorem 2.1 follow.

Example 1. How many six-letter "words" can be formed from the letters of the alphabet, if letters cannot be repeated?

Solution: $P(26, 6) = \dfrac{26!}{20!} = 26 \cdot 25 \cdot 24 \cdot 23 \cdot 22 \cdot 21 = 173{,}300{,}400$

Example 2. A code consists of ten different symbols. How many "words" may be written in the code if letters in a word are not repeated and a word may consist of from 1 to 10 symbols?

Solution: $P(10, 1) + P(10, 2) + P(10, 3) \ldots P(10, 10)$

$$= \frac{10!}{9!} + \frac{10!}{8!} + \frac{10!}{7!} + \frac{10!}{0!}$$

$$= 10 + 90 + 720 + 4320 + \ldots + 10!$$

Example 3. A store stocks 4,000 different items. The management decides to advertise a different item for 10 successive days. How many ways may the 10 items be scheduled for advertising?

Solution: $P(4000, 10) = \dfrac{4000!}{3990!}$

Sometimes it is necessary to find the number of distinguishable arrangements of n objects when all of the objects are not distinguishable. Suppose that we wish to know the number of ways that eight colored tiles, three of which are red and the remaining five of which are other distinct colors, may be arranged in a line. The number of distinguishable arrangements of the eight tiles depends only on the arrangement of the five nonred distinct colors; hence, the number of distinct arrangements is given by

$$\frac{8!}{(8 - 5)!} = \frac{8!}{3!}$$

We can find the number of different arrangements of n objects when k of them are alike by use of the formula

$$\frac{n!}{\left(n - (n - k)\right)!} = \frac{n!}{k!}$$

By repeatedly applying this formula the following theorem can be derived.

THEOREM 2.2

If in n objects there are k_1 objects of one type alike, k_2 objects of another type alike, and so forth, the number of distinct permutations of the n objects taken n at a time is given by

$$P\left(\begin{matrix} n \\ k_1,k_2,\ldots \end{matrix}\right) = \frac{n!}{k_1!\cdot k_2!\ldots}$$

Example 1. In how many ways can ten chairs be arranged in a row if four of the chairs are black, three are brown, and three are red?

Solution: $P\left(\begin{matrix} 10 \\ 4,3,3 \end{matrix}\right) = \dfrac{10!}{4!3!3!}$

Example 2. In a given period, a traveling salesman must make 18 visits to his customers. He makes four calls on one customer, three calls on another customer, and two calls on a third customer; the others are visited once. In how many ways can the salesman plan his itinerary? (Note: disregard geography.)

Solution: $P\left(\begin{matrix} 18 \\ 4,3,2 \end{matrix}\right) = \dfrac{18!}{4!3!2!}$

EXERCISE 2.4

1. Compute $3!$, $6!$, $11!$.

2. Compute $\dfrac{4!}{10!}$, $\dfrac{6!}{12!}$.

3. In how many ways can five people seat themselves (a) in a row? (b) in a circle? (Be careful!)

4. Evaluate: (a) $P(5,5)$ (c) $P(n, n-1)$
   (b) $P(9,4)$ (d) $P(n,0)$

5. A student has a choice of four languages and five sciences. In how many ways can he choose one language and one science?

6. In how many ways can five letters be mailed if three mailboxes are available?

7. In how many ways can eight people be seated around a table? (Hint: start with three people and develop a formula for n people.)

8. A football stadium has six entrances and twelve exits. In how many ways can two men enter together but leave by different exits?

9. There are six main roads between Largo and Clearwater and four roads between Clearwater and Tarpon Springs. In how many ways can a

person drive from Largo to Tarpon Springs and return, going through Clearwater on both trips, without driving on the same road twice?

10. How many license plates can be made if each is to have two letters of the alphabet followed by a four-digit number? (Repetitions are allowed.)

11. In how many ways can four men and four women be seated on a bench that seats eight people if:
    (a) they may be seated in any position?
    (b) the men and women are seated alternately, beginning with a man?
    (c) the men sit together and the women sit together?

12. Seven chairs are placed in a row. In how many ways can seven people be seated if persons A and B must always be seated together?

13. In how many distinct ways can the following be arranged?
    (a) aaabb
    (b) ssssf
    (c) AHNT
    (d) sssfffrr

14. A dial, or combination, lock has numbers 0 through 12 on its face. The lock is opened by starting at zero and turning the dial clockwise one revolution to one of the digits, then counterclockwise one revolution to a second digit and finally clockwise one revolution to a third digit. How many different "combinations" are possible?

15. A football pool consists of ten games. For each game a participant must select one of the teams to win or indicate that he expects a tie. In how many ways may the participant designate the outcomes of the ten games? (Hint: how many choices does he have for each of the ten games?)

16. Refer to problem 15. Of the total number of possible outcomes of the ten games, how many of the outcomes would include five wins, three losses, and two ties? How many of the outcomes would include seven wins, two losses, and one tie? (Hint: use theorem 2.2.)

2.8 COMBINATIONS

In the study of probability, we often need to find the number of elements in a set when the order of the components of an element is not significant. Consider the problem of finding the number of committees that can be formed from a group of people. Our interest is in finding the number of different ways the committee members may be chosen without regard to the order in which the members are chosen. Suppose a city commission consists of five members. How many different committees of two members each can be selected? To find the ways the two members may be chosen, we first find the number of permutations of five members selected two at a time.

$$P(5, 2) = \frac{5!}{3!} = 20$$

Each of the pairs of members may be selected in two ways; e.g., (Jones, Smith) or (Smith, Jones). Hence, if the order of the components Jones and Smith is disregarded, the number of committees is reduced to ten. A selection of objects made without regard to order is called a *combination*.

DEFINITION 2.11

A selection of r objects made without regard to their order from n different objects is called a *combination* of n objects taken r at a time. The total number of such combinations is denoted by $C(n,r)$ or $\binom{n}{r}$ or $C\binom{n}{r}$.

In general, consider the problem of selecting r objects from n different objects. Each selection contains r objects which may be arranged in $r!$ ways; hence, we are able to find $C\binom{n}{r}$ by applying the following theorem.

THEOREM 2.3

The number of combinations of a set of n different objects taken r at a time is

$$C\binom{n}{r} = \frac{n!}{r!(n-r)!}$$

Example 1. Three transistors are to be selected for test from ten transistors. In how many ways can the selection be made?

Solution: $C\binom{10}{3} = \frac{10!}{3!7!}$

Example 2. 100 students are to be contacted in a survey of 1,000 students. In how many ways can this be done if no student can be contacted twice?

Solution: $C\binom{1000}{100} = \frac{1000!}{900!100!}$

Example 3. A factory receives ten orders and selects five of the orders for immediate shipment. In how many ways can this be done?

Solution: $C\binom{10}{5} = \frac{10!}{5!5!}$

2.9 COMPUTER PROGRAMS TO COUNT THE NUMBER OF SETS

By now, you have observed that the computation required to count the number of elements in relatively simple sets is voluminous. If you have mastered the programs in chapter 1 it is likely that you will have no difficulty in understanding the computer programs in this section. Each is planned to assist you in finding the number of elements in a set, in a subset of a given set, or the number of subsets of a set.

Program 2.1

The Number of Subsets of a Set of **N** Elements

```
10 READ N
20 DATA (enter N)
30 LET S = 2 ↑ N
40 PRINT S
50 END
```

Program 2.2

The Computation of **N**!

```
10 PRINT "N", "N FACTORIAL"
20 INPUT N
30 LET F = 1
40 FOR X = 1 TO N
50 LET F = F * X
60 NEXT X
70 PRINT N,F
80 END
```

Program 2.3

Permutations

```
10 PRINT "PERMUTATIONS OF N THINGS TAKEN
   R AT A TIME"
20 INPUT N,R
30 LET W = 1
40 FOR X = (N - R + 1) TO N
50 LET W = W * X
60 NEXT X
70 PRINT W
80 END
```

Program 2.4

Combinations

```
 1 PRINT "COMBINATIONS OF N THINGS TAKEN
   R AT A TIME"
 5 INPUT N,R
10 LET W = 1
20 FOR X = 1 TO R
30 LET W = W * X
```

```
 40 NEXT X
 50 LET P = 1
 60 FOR Y = (N - R + 1) TO N
 70 LET P = P * Y
 80 NEXT Y
 90 LET C = P/W
100 PRINT C
9999 END
```

EXERCISE 2.5

1. Evaluate:

   (a) $C\binom{8}{4}$ (c) $C\binom{12}{0}$

   (b) $C\binom{n}{n-2}$ (d) $C\binom{18}{2}$

2. How many subsets can be formed from the set $\{a, b, c, d\}$?

3. Evaluate:

$$C\binom{4}{0} + C\binom{4}{1} + C\binom{4}{2} + C\binom{4}{3} + C\binom{4}{4}$$

   Is there a relationship between your answers to problem 2 and this problem?

4. On a test, a student is given the choice of answering eight of the twelve questions asked, with the stipulation that he must answer five of the first six. In how many ways can he select the questions to answer?

5. An arbitration committee in a labor dispute is to be chosen from ten people not connected to either labor or management, twenty-five employees, and six from management. The committee must contain two outside arbitrators, three employees, and two members from management. In how many ways can the committee be formed?

6. In how many ways can a person get a bridge hand of 13 cards consisting of only aces, kings, queens, or jacks?

7. A group of six is to be chosen from a group of eight. If A is chosen, then B must be chosen. In how many ways can this be done?

8. Show that $C\binom{n}{r} = C\binom{n}{n-r}$

9. From a deck of 52 playing cards, how many distinct 5-card hands may be dealt?

10. In how many ways may twelve people be assigned to four rooms if each room must have at least two people in it?

11. From a group of six Democrats and nine Republicans, how many committees of four may be selected with the indicated composition?

(*a*) All Democrats.
(*b*) Two Democrats and two Republicans.
(*c*) At least two Republicans.
(*d*) Not more than two Democrats.

12. See if you can establish a relationship between

$$C\binom{n}{r} \quad \text{and} \quad P\binom{n}{n-r, r}$$

2.10 THE BINOMIAL THEOREM

You will recall from your study of algebra that a binomial is an algebraic expression of the form

$$(a + b)$$

In our work in probability and statistics, we shall often require that such an expression be multiplied by itself n times; i.e., we shall require the expanded form of

$$(a + b)^n$$

One way of obtaining this expansion is to find the product $(a + b) \cdot (a + b) \cdot (a + b) \ldots n$ times. For even relatively small values of n, this process soon becomes tiresome. For large values of n, we would go to the computer, if at all possible. The purpose of this section is to develop a procedure for expanding $(a + b)^n$ without direct multiplication. The procedure to accomplish this is known as the *Binomial Theorem*.

The last four of the following expansions may be obtained by direct multiplication.

Binomial	*Expansion*
$(a + b)^0 =$	1
$(a \mp b)^1 =$	$1a + 1b$
$(a + b)^2 =$	$1a^2 + 2ab + 1b^2$
$(a + b)^3 =$	$1a^3 + 3a^2b + 3ab^2 + 1b^3$
$(a + b)^4 =$	$1a^4 + 4a^3b + 6a^2b^2 + 4ab^3 + 1b^4$
$(a + b)^5 =$	$1a^5 + 5a^4b + 10a^3b^2 + 10a^2b^3 + 5ab^4 + 1b^5$

If we continue to expand $(a + b)^n$, where n is any natural number, the following properties of the expansion become apparent.

(1) The first term is a^n.
(2) The second term is $na^{n-1}b$.
(3) The exponent of a decreases by one and the exponent of b increases by one from left to right.
(4) Each expansion contains $n + 1$ terms.
(5) When the coefficient of a term is multiplied by the exponent of a in the term and this product is divided by the number of the term in the expansion, the coefficient of the next term is obtained.

(6) The sum of the exponents of all terms is always n.

Based on these observations the expansion of $(a + b)^n$ is stated in theorem 2.4. This theorem, called the Binomial Theorem, is of fundamental importance in applications of probability theory.

THEOREM 2.4

The Binomial Theorem

$$(a + b)^n = a^n + na^{n-1}b + \frac{n(n-1)}{2} a^{n-2}b^2$$

$$+ \frac{n(n-1)(n-2)}{2 \cdot 3} a^{n-3}b^3 + \dots + nab^{n-1} + b^n$$

Example 1. $(a + b)^5 = a^5 + 5a^4b + \dfrac{5 \cdot 4}{2} a^3b^2 + \dfrac{5 \cdot 4 \cdot 3}{2 \cdot 3} a^2b^3$

$$+ \frac{5 \cdot 4 \cdot 3 \cdot 2}{2 \cdot 3 \cdot 4} ab^4 + b^5$$

$$= a^5 + 5a^4b + 10a^3b^2 + 10a^2b^3 + 5ab^4 + b^5$$

Example 2. $\left(\dfrac{1}{2} + \dfrac{1}{2}\right)^4 = \left(\dfrac{1}{2}\right)^4 + 4\left(\dfrac{1}{2}\right)^3\left(\dfrac{1}{2}\right) + \dfrac{4 \cdot 3}{2}\left(\dfrac{1}{2}\right)^2\left(\dfrac{1}{2}\right)^2$

$$+ \frac{4 \cdot 3 \cdot 2}{2 \cdot 3}\left(\frac{1}{2}\right)\left(\frac{1}{2}\right)^3 + \left(\frac{1}{2}\right)^4$$

$$= \frac{1}{16} + \frac{1}{4} + \frac{3}{8} + \frac{1}{4} + \frac{1}{16}$$

Example 3. $\left(\dfrac{1}{10} + \dfrac{9}{10}\right)^5 = \left(\dfrac{1}{10}\right)^5 + 5\left(\dfrac{1}{10}\right)^4\left(\dfrac{9}{10}\right)$

$$+ 10\left(\frac{1}{10}\right)^3\left(\frac{9}{10}\right)^2 + 10\left(\frac{1}{10}\right)^2\left(\frac{9}{10}\right)^3$$

$$+ 5\left(\frac{1}{10}\right)\left(\frac{9}{10}\right)^4 + \left(\frac{9}{10}\right)^5$$

$$= \frac{1}{10^5} + \frac{5 \cdot 9}{10^5} + \frac{10 \cdot 9^2}{10^5} + \frac{10 \cdot 9^3}{10^5} + \frac{5 \cdot 9^4}{10^5} + \frac{9^5}{10^5}$$

$$= \frac{1}{10^5} + \frac{45}{10^5} + \frac{810}{10^5} + \frac{7290}{10^5} + \frac{32805}{10^5} + \frac{59049}{10^5}$$

$$= 1$$

Note: Examples 2 and 3 are typical of applications of binomial expansions in probability theory.

It is interesting to note that the coefficients of successive terms of the binomial expansion beginning with $(a + b)^0$ may be arranged in a triangular array known as *Pascal's triangle*.

Binomial *Coefficients (Pascal's Triangle)*

Binomial														
$(a + b)^0$							1							
$(a + b)^1$						1		1						
$(a + b)^2$					1		2		1					
$(a + b)^3$				1		3		3		1				
$(a + b)^4$			1		4		6		4		1			
$(a + b)^5$		1		5		10		10		5		1		
$(a + b)^6$	1		6		15		20		15		6		1	
$(a + b)^7$	1	7		21		35		35		21		7		1

The coefficients of the expansion of $(a + b)^n$ may also be determined by counting the number of distinguishable arrangements (permutations) of the components of each term of the expansion. Consider the following table showing the expansion of $(a + b)^4$.

Table 2.1 Table of Expansion of $(a + b)^4$

$(a + b)^4 =$	a^4	$+ 4a^3b$	$+ 6a^2b^2$	$+ 4ab^3$	$+ b^4$
$(a + b)^4 =$	*aaaa*	+*aaab* *aaba* *abaa* *baaa*	+*aabb* *abab* *abba* *baba* *bbaa* *baab*	+*abbb* *babb* *bbab* *bbba*	+*bbbb*
	Permutations of 4 things, all alike	Permutations of 4 things, 3 of 1 kind and 1 of another	Permutations of 4 things, 2 of 1 kind, 2 of another	Permutations of 4 things, 3 of 1 kind and 1 of another	Permutations of 4 things, all alike
	$\dfrac{4!}{4!}a^4$	$\dfrac{4!}{3!}a^3b$	$\dfrac{4!}{2!2!}a^2b^2$	$\dfrac{4!}{1!3!}ab^3$	$\dfrac{4!}{4!}b^4$
$(a + b)^4 =$	$P\binom{4}{4}a^4$	$P\binom{4}{3,1}a^3b$	$P\binom{4}{2,2}a^2b^2$	$P\binom{4}{1,3}ab^3$	$P\binom{4}{4}b^4$

As shown in table 2.1, the coefficients in the binomial expansion are permutations with repeated elements. Mathematically, it is simpler to write the Binomial Theorem in combination form. The basis for using combinations instead of permutations is shown below.

$$\left(\begin{array}{c}\text{Permutations of } n \\ \text{things, all alike}\end{array}\right) = \frac{n!}{n!} = C\binom{n}{0}$$

$$\left(\begin{array}{c}\text{Permutations of } n \\ \text{things, } (n - 1) \text{ alike}\end{array}\right) = \frac{n!}{(n - 1)!} = C\binom{n}{1}$$

$$\begin{pmatrix} \text{Permutations of } n \\ \text{things, } (n - 2) \text{ of } 1 \\ \text{kind and 2 of} \\ \text{another} \end{pmatrix} = \frac{n!}{(n - 2)!\,2!} = C\binom{n}{2}$$

$$\vdots$$

$$\begin{pmatrix} \text{Permutations of } n \\ \text{things, } (n - r) \text{ of } 1 \\ \text{kind and } r \text{ of} \\ \text{another kind} \end{pmatrix} = \frac{n!}{(n - r)!\,r!} = C\binom{n}{r}$$

$$\vdots$$

$$\begin{pmatrix} \text{Permutations of } n \\ \text{things, all alike} \end{pmatrix} = \frac{n!}{n!} = C\binom{n}{n}$$

With the substitutions indicated above, we restate the Binomial Theorem in combination form.

$$(a + b)^n = C\binom{n}{0}a^n + C\binom{n}{1}a^{n-1}b + C\binom{n}{2}a^{n-2}b^2 + \ldots + C\binom{n}{n}b^n,$$

the $(k + 1)$st term of the expansion being $C\binom{n}{k}a^{n-k}b^k$.

This latter form of the Binomial Theorem shall be employed throughout the remainder of this textbook to count the elements of sets when some of the components of an element are repeated and ordering of the distinct components is significant.

By continuing the reasoning that enabled us to arrive at the combination form of the Binomial Theorem, we are able to develop a method for counting the elements in sets generated by expanding expressions with three or more terms. Consider the following expansion.

$$(a + b + c)^2 = a^2 + ab + ac + ba + b^2 + bc + ca + cb + c^2$$
$$= a^2 + 2ab + 2ac + b^2 + 2bc + c^2$$

We may write the above expression in permutation form as follows.

$$(a + b + c)^2 = P\binom{2}{2_a, 0_b, 0_c}a^2 + P\binom{2}{1_a, 1_b, 0_c}ab$$

$$+ P\binom{2}{1_a, 0_b, 1_c}ac + P\binom{2}{0_a, 2_b, 0_c}b^2$$

$$+ P\binom{2}{0_a, 1_b, 1_c}bc + P\binom{2}{0_a, 0_b, 2_c}c^2$$

$$= \frac{2!}{2!\,0!\,0!}a^2 + \frac{2!}{1!\,1!\,0!}ab + \frac{2!}{1!\,0!\,1!}ac + \frac{2!}{0!\,2!\,0!}b^2$$

$$+ \frac{2!}{0!\,1!\,1!}bc + \frac{2!}{0!\,0!\,2!}c^2$$

In general, an expression with three terms, called a trinomial, may be expanded by applying theorem 2.5.

THEOREM 2.5

$$(a + b + c)^n = P\left(\begin{matrix} n \\ n_a, 0_b, 0_c \end{matrix}\right)a^n + P\left(\begin{matrix} n \\ (n-1)_a, 1_b, 0_c \end{matrix}\right)a^{n-1}b$$

$$+ P\left(\begin{matrix} n \\ (n-1)_a, 0_b, 1_c \end{matrix}\right)a^{n-1}c + P\left(\begin{matrix} n \\ (n-2)_a, 2_b, 0_c \end{matrix}\right)a^{n-2}b^2 + \text{etc.}$$

That is, the coefficient of the term $a^{n_1}b^{n_2}c^{n_3}$ is $P\left(\begin{matrix} n \\ n_1, n_2, n_3 \end{matrix}\right)$, where $n_1 + n_2 + n_3 = n$.

The use of theorem 2.5 is illustrated in the following examples.

Example 1. $\left(\dfrac{1}{2} + \dfrac{1}{4} + \dfrac{1}{4}\right)^2 = P\left(\begin{matrix} 2 \\ 2,0,0 \end{matrix}\right)\left(\dfrac{1}{2}\right)^2 + P\left(\begin{matrix} 2 \\ 1,1,0 \end{matrix}\right)\left(\dfrac{1}{2}\right)\left(\dfrac{1}{4}\right)$

$$+ P\left(\begin{matrix} 2 \\ 1,0,1 \end{matrix}\right)\left(\dfrac{1}{2}\right)\left(\dfrac{1}{4}\right) + P\left(\begin{matrix} 2 \\ 0,2,0 \end{matrix}\right)\left(\dfrac{1}{4}\right)^2$$

$$+ P\left(\begin{matrix} 2 \\ 0,1,1 \end{matrix}\right)\left(\dfrac{1}{4}\right)\left(\dfrac{1}{4}\right) + P\left(\begin{matrix} 2 \\ 0,0,2 \end{matrix}\right)\left(\dfrac{1}{4}\right)^2$$

$$= \dfrac{2!}{2!}\dfrac{1}{4} + \dfrac{2!}{1!1!}\dfrac{1}{8} + \dfrac{2!}{1!1!}\dfrac{1}{8} + \dfrac{2!}{2!}\dfrac{1}{16}$$

$$+ \dfrac{2!}{1!1!}\dfrac{1}{16} + \dfrac{2!}{2!}\dfrac{1}{16}$$

$$= \dfrac{1}{4} + \dfrac{1}{4} + \dfrac{1}{4} + \dfrac{1}{16} + \dfrac{1}{8} + \dfrac{1}{16}$$

$$= 1$$

Example 2. Find the coefficient of the term involving a^2bc in the expansion of $(a + b + c)^4$.

Solution: $P\left(\begin{matrix} 4 \\ 2,1,1 \end{matrix}\right)a^2bc = \dfrac{4!}{2!}a^2bc$

$$= 12a^2bc$$

In the expansion of $(x_1 + x_2 + \ldots + x_r)^n$, the coefficient of the term $x_1^{n_1}x_2^{n_2}\ldots x_r^{n_r}$ is $P\left(\begin{matrix} n \\ n_1, n_2, \ldots, n_r \end{matrix}\right)$, when $n_1 + n_2 + \ldots + n_r = n$.

Example 3. Find the coefficient of the term involving a^3b^2cd in the expansion of $(a + b + c + d)^7$.

Solution: $P\left(\begin{smallmatrix}7\\3,2,1,1\end{smallmatrix}\right)a^3b^2cd = \dfrac{7!}{3!2!1!1!}\,a^3b^2cd$

$$= \frac{7\cdot6\cdot5\cdot4}{2!}a^3b^2cd$$

$$= 420a^3b^2cd$$

EXERCISE 2.6

1. Expand and simplify.
   (a) $(x + y)^5$ (c) $(S + F)^9$
   (b) $\left(\dfrac{x}{2} + \dfrac{y}{3}\right)^7$ (d) $(2a - 7)^4$

2. Find the coefficient of the indicated term.
   (a) The term involving x^3y^4 in the expansion of $(x + y)^7$
   (b) The term involving S^7F^{12} in the expansion of $(S + F)^{19}$
   (c) The term involving A^5R^6 in the expansion of $\left(\dfrac{A}{2} + \dfrac{R}{3}\right)^{11}$

3. Expand and simplify.
   (a) $\left(\dfrac{1}{2} + \dfrac{1}{2}\right)^5$
   (b) $\left(\dfrac{1}{4} + \dfrac{3}{4}\right)^7$
   (c) $(.1 + .9)^9$

4. Expand and simplify.
   (a) $(A + R + D)^5$
   (b) $(H + O + D + I)^6$

5. Find the coefficient of the indicated term.
   (a) The term involving $A^4R^3D^2$ in expansion of $(A + R + D)^9$
   (b) The term involving $a^{10}b^{10}c^5d^5$ in expansion of $(a + b + c + d)^{30}$

6. Show that $2^n = C\left(\begin{smallmatrix}n\\0\end{smallmatrix}\right) + C\left(\begin{smallmatrix}n\\1\end{smallmatrix}\right) + C\left(\begin{smallmatrix}n\\2\end{smallmatrix}\right) + \ldots + C\left(\begin{smallmatrix}n\\n\end{smallmatrix}\right)$
   (Hint: expand $(1 + 1)^n$ using the Binomial Theorem.)

7. Show that $3^n = P\left(\begin{smallmatrix}n\\n,0,0\end{smallmatrix}\right) + P\left(\begin{smallmatrix}n\\n-1,1,0\end{smallmatrix}\right) + P\left(\begin{smallmatrix}n\\n-2,2,0\end{smallmatrix}\right) + \ldots +$
   $P\left(\begin{smallmatrix}n\\0,0,n\end{smallmatrix}\right)$
   (Hint: expand $(1 + 1 + 1)^n$.)

CHAPTER 3

Basic Probability Concepts

3.1 INTRODUCTION

You, the reader of this textbook, are probably a student. Further, you are probably a senior in high school or a freshman in college. It is also probable that you are a business major or an education major. In this context, the words "probably" and "probable" mean "most likely." The statement about you, the individual reader, is not of much value to anyone. To be useful, specific information is needed about all the users of this book. The facts that 90% of the users of the book are students, 80% are college students, and 70% are business majors provide valuable information to the publisher, to the authors, and to the reader. The publisher can plan where to sell the book, the authors can plan for its revision, and the reader can decide whether the book might be of use to him. In other words, all concerned are able to make better decisions. The main reason for studying probability and its close relative, statistics, is to aid man in making decisions about his future courses of action.

The first known study of the mathematics of probability appeared in Italy about 1525. The mathematician and physician Geronimo Cardano (1501–1576) wrote a treatise entitled *Book on Games of Chance.* Galileo

(1564–1642) also studied games of chance and published a complete probability table for throws of three dice. Perhaps the most important early contributions were made by a Frenchman, Blaise Pascal (1623–1662). He is usually considered to be the father of probability. In 1812 another Frenchman, Pierre Simon de LaPlace (1749–1827), formalized probability theory in his book *Analytic Theory of Probability*. Despite this early interest, the study of probability declined until the twentieth century, when two Russians, P. L. Chebyshev and A. A. Markov, revived interest in the subject. In 1933 another Russian, A. Kolmogorov, established the relationship between the theory of sets and probability. Since the work of Kolmogorov, probability has reached the level of a major mathematical discipline. We shall use the set approach in our study of the subject.

3.2 EXPERIMENT, SAMPLE SPACE, AND SAMPLE POINT

Suppose we test three light bulbs from a factory production line and record the results. When a tested bulb burns we record s for success; otherwise we record f for failure. If all bulbs burn we record (s,s,s); if all bulbs fail to burn we record (f,f,f), etc. A list of all possible outcomes of the test follows.

Test Outcome	*Record*
(1) All bulbs burn	(s,s,s)
(2) Two bulbs burn	
(*a*) first and second bulbs burn; third fails	(s,s,f)
(*b*) first and third bulbs burn; second fails	(s,f,s)
(*c*) first bulb fails; second and third burn	(f,s,s)
(3) One bulb burns	
(*a*) first bulb burns; second and third fail	(s,f,f)
(*b*) second bulb burns; first and third fail	(f,s,f)
(*c*) third bulb burns; first and second fail	(f,f,s)
(4) No bulbs burn	(f,f,f)

In the study of probability, a process such as the light bulb test we have described is called an *experiment*.

DEFINITION 3.1

An *experiment* is a well-defined course of action with more than one possible outcome.

For the experiment of testing three bulbs, we recorded a total of eight possible distinct outcomes. These outcomes form a sample space for the bulb experiment.

DEFINITION 3.2

A *sample space* for an experiment is the set of all possible outcomes of the experiment.

We shall denote the set that forms a sample space with the symbol S, subscripted when necessary to identify different experiments. An element of S is defined as follows.

DEFINITION 3.3

A *sample point* is an element of a sample space.

At first thought, it appears that "outcome" and "sample point" are synonymous. It should be kept in mind, however, that a sample point is a *possible* outcome and is not necessarily one that is known to have occurred. For example, it is possible that all of the children in a family of 30 children may be boys, but this is not necessarily a known outcome of the experiment.

A sample point, an element of a set, can have any number of *components*. The nature of the experiment determines the components of each point and whether or not arrangement of the components is important. In the bulb experiment, each sample point consists of three components. If four bulbs were tested, each sample point would contain four components. If one bulb were tested, the sample space would be the set $S = \{s, f\}$, and each sample point would consist of one component. In the examples that follow, experiments 1, 2, and 4 require ordering of components; experiment 3 does not require ordering of components.

Experiment 1. Observe and record the sex of children *in order of arrival* in families of three children.

$$S_1 = \{(b,b,b), (b,b,g), (b,g,b), (g,b,b), (b,g,g), (g,b,g), (g,g,b), (g,g,g)\}$$

Experiment 2. A salesman selling one product calls on one customer and records the result (s = sale, f = no sale).

$$S_2 = \{s, f\}$$

Experiment 3. Select a committee of two people from a group of three people and record the committee membership. The number of sample points which satisfy this experiment is given by $C\left(\frac{3}{1}\right) = \frac{3!}{2!1!} = 3$. Why? Using P_1, P_2, and P_3 to symbolize people, the committees are:

$$S_3 = \{(p_1,p_2), (p_1,p_3), (p_2,p_3)\}$$

Note that (p_1,p_2), (p_3,p_1), and (p_3,p_2) are not in S_3.

Experiment 4. Call on four customers for the purpose of selling encyclopedias and record the results in order of occurrence (s = sale, f = no sale).

$$S_4 = \{(s,s,s,s), (s,s,s,f), (s,s,f,s), (s,f,s,s),$$
$$(f,s,s,s), (s,s,f,f), (f,f,s,s), (s,f,f,s),$$
$$(s,f,s,f), (f,s,f,s), (f,s,s,f), (s,f,f,f),$$
$$(f,s,f,f), (f,f,s,f), (f,f,f,s), (f,f,f,f)\}$$

EXERCISE 3.1

1. Construct a sample space for the testing of two radios. Consider that each radio either passes or fails the test.

2. Two people seat themselves in any two of four chairs. Construct the sample space.

3. From a group of five people a committee of two is selected. Using P_1, P_2, etc., as components, list the points in the sample space.

4. Two electric motors are tested. A motor is either discarded, returned to the factory, or accepted. Using the notation d for discard, r for return, and a for accepted, construct a sample space for the experiment. Compare your space with the terms in the expansion of $(d + r + a)^2$.

5. A salesman calls on two customers hoping to sell two different products to each. Construct the sample space. How does this experiment differ from calling on four customers to sell one product?

6. Four people line up in random order for a picture. How many sample points are in this space? If all possible different pictures were made, in how many pictures would a given person appear on the extreme left of the photo?

7. Ten orders were received by a warehouse on a certain day. Only four orders were shipped. If a sample space of the orders shipped were constructed, how many sample points would be in the space? In how many sample points would a given order appear?

8. In a telephone survey, six people were called to determine which, if any, of two television programs, A and B, was being observed. If no program was being observed a zero was recorded; otherwise A or B was recorded. How many sample points are in the sample space? How many sample points would show that only three are watching a program?

9. Ten patients visit a medical clinic. The following dispositions are made:
   (1) The patient is pronounced medically fit (denote by F).
   (2) The patient is asked to return for further treatment (denote by T).
   (3) The patient is hospitalized (denote by H).
   How many points are contained in the sample space for the disposition

of the ten patients? How many points show that five of the patients were hospitalized?

10. A survey was made of the number of people who read classified ads in a newspaper. One hundred people were contacted and asked to indicate which one of the following statements applies to them.
    (1) Read no ads (denote by N).
    (2) Read "articles for sale" ads (denote by S).
    (3) Read "help wanted" ads (denote by H).
    (4) Read all ads (denote by A).
    How many points are in this sample space? How many points would include people who read the "articles for sale" ads? How many of the points would include people who read "articles for sale" and "help wanted" ads?

3.3 EVENTS

Let us again consider the experiment of testing three bulbs. The sample space for this experiment is as follows:

$$S = \{(s,s,s), (s,s,f), (s,f,s), (f,s,s), (f,f,s), (f,s,f), (s,f,f), (f,f,f)\}$$

One's interest in the results of this experiment depends on his point of view. A housewife shopping for bulbs would insist that all bulbs burn. If she is discarding three bulbs she wants to know that all bulbs fail to burn. The bulb manufacturer in controlling the quality of his product is interested in all outcomes of the experiment. The retailer may be satisfied if at least two bulbs burn 99% of the time. In each instance the individual interests involve subsets of the points in the sample space. Such subsets are known as *events*.

DEFINITION 3.4

An *event* is a subset of a sample space.

We shall denote an event with the symbol E. When several events are under consideration, E will be subscripted.

Recall from our study of sets that 2^n subsets may be formed from a set of n elements. The three-bulb experiment has a sample space of 8 elements; hence, 2^8 events are possible. We describe and list the sample points in a few of the events.

Description of Events	*Sample Points in the Event*
(1) All bulbs burn	$E_1 = \{(s,s,s)\}$
(2) No bulbs burn	$E_2 = \{(f,f,f)\}$
(3) Exactly two bulbs burn	$E_3 = \{(s,s,f), (s,f,s), (f,s,s)\}$
(4) The first bulb tested burns	$E_4 = \{(s,s,s), (s,s,f), (s,f,s), (s,f,f)\}$
(5) At least two bulbs burn	$E_5 = \{(s,s,s), (s,s,f), (s,f,s), (f,s,s)\}$

An event of an experiment is said to occur if the outcome of the experiment is described by one of the sample points in the event. Event E_3 for the bulb experiment occurs if the result of the experiment is described by any one of the three sample points in the event. An event is called a *simple event* if exactly one sample point of S describes the event. *One* performance of an experiment *always* results in the occurrence of *one and only one* simple event. A compound event consists of two or more simple events. Events E_1 and E_2 in the bulb experiment are examples of simple events. Events E_3, E_4, and E_5 are examples of compound events.

3.4 COMBINING EVENTS

We can combine the events of an experiment to form new events. Consider the experiment of testing two radios.

$$S = \{(s,s), (s,f), (f,s), (f,f)\}$$

The sample space has $2^4 = 16$ subsets, each of which is an event of this experiment. Eleven of the events can be obtained by combining the four simple events of the experiment, as illustrated by events E_5, E_6, and E_7 below.

$E_1 = \{(s,s)\}$ $E_2 = \{(s,f)\}$ $E_3 = \{(f,s)\}$ $E_4 = \{(f,f)\}$

$E_5 = $ the first radio is acceptable

$\quad = E_1 \cup E_2 = \{(s,s), (s,f)\}$

$E_6 = $ at least one radio is acceptable

$\quad = E_3 \cup E_5 = \{(s,s), (s,f), (f,s)\}$

$E_7 = $ the second radio is acceptable

$\quad = E_1 \cup E_3 = \{(s,s), (f,s)\}$

Sets E_5, E_6, and E_7 were obtained by finding the union of other events. In general, the union of two events is an event described by all sample points contained in either or both of the two events. We say that the union of two events occurs if and only if at least one of the two events occurs.

Another event which can be found by combining two events is the event described by the sample points in the intersection of the two events. The intersection of two events occurs if and only if both of the two events occur. Consider the intersection of events E_5 and E_6.

$$E_5 = \{(s,s), (s,f)\}$$
$$E_6 = \{(s,s), (s,f), (f,s)\}$$
$$E_5 \cap E_6 = \{(s,s), (s,f)\} = E_5$$

Now consider the intersection of E_5 and E_7.

$$E_5 \cap E_7 = \{(s,s)\} = E_1$$

Associated with each event E is another event called the *comple-ment of E* denoted by E'. The event E' occurs if and only if the event E does *not* occur. The union of E and E' is the sample space S, and the intersection of E and E' is the empty set. That is,

$$E \cup E' = S \quad \text{and} \quad E \cap E' = \emptyset$$

Again referring to the radio testing experiment,

$$E'_5 = \{(f,s), (f,f)\}$$
$$E_5 \cup E'_5 = S \quad \text{and} \quad E_5 \cap E'_5 = \emptyset$$

It is often helpful to represent events with Venn diagrams, as illustrated in figure 3.1.

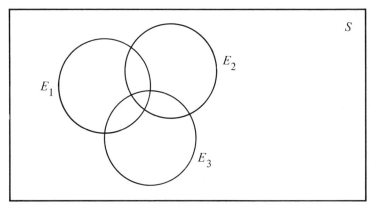

Figure 3.1

EXERCISE 3.2

1. List the sample points in the events indicated below for the experiment:
   "A salesman calls on four customers."
   E_1: Exactly two sales are made.
   E_2: Two or more sales are made.
   E_3: No sale is made.
   E_4: The first two customers buy but the second two do not buy.
   $E_1 \cup E_2$
   $E_2 \cap E_4$
   E'_1

2. List the sample points in the indicated event for the experiment: "Test four ball bearings for acceptance or rejection."
   E_1: All four bearings are accepted, or all four bearings are rejected.
   E_2: All bearings are accepted, or only one bearing is rejected.
   E_3: The first three bearings are rejected.
   E_5: The first bearing is rejected and the last is rejected.
   $E_2 \cap E_5$
   $E_3 \cup E_5$
   E'_5

3. A telephone survey is made to determine how many of ten people called are watching a given program. How many points are in the sample space? How many points are in the event, "half of the people called are watching"? How many points are in the event, "at least half of the people are watching"?

3.5 PROBABILITY OF AN EVENT

We are now ready to discuss the mathematical meaning of the word *probability*. We begin our discussion with the experiment of selecting at random one of two books, *a* or *b*. The sample space consists of two points.

$$S = \{a,b\}$$

The four events for S are shown below.

$E_1 = \{\ \}$: No book is selected.
$E_2 = \{a\}$: Book a is selected.
$E_3 = \{b\}$: Book b is selected.
$E_4 = \{a, b\}$: Book a or book b is selected.

Since the selection of one of two books is to be performed at random, it is reasonable to assume that each of the two books is equally likely to be chosen; hence, the probability of event E_2, as well as that of event E_3, is 1/2. Denoting the probability of event E by the symbol $P(E)$, the probability of each of the four events for the book experiment is as follows.

Probability of Event	Discussion
$P(E_1) = 0$	One book *must* be selected; hence this event is impossible.
$P(E_2) = \frac{1}{2}$	*One* of *two* books is randomly selected.
$P(E_3) = \frac{1}{2}$	*One* of *two* books is randomly selected.
$P(E_4) = 1$	One book *must* be selected; hence, E_4 is certain to occur.

Before we state a definition for the probability of an event, let us consider the somewhat more complicated experiment of testing two bulbs. Again denoting a burning bulb with s and one that fails to burn with f,

$$S = \{(s, s), (s, f), (s, f), (f, f)\}$$

The 16 events for the two bulb test are:

$E_1 = \{\ \}$,
$E_2 = \{(s,s)\}$, $\quad E_3 = \{(s,f)\}$, $\quad E_4 = \{(f,s)\}$, $\quad E_5 = \{(f,f)\}$,
$E_6 = \{(s,s), (s,f)\}$, $\quad E_7 = \{(s,s), (f,s)\}$, $\quad E_8 = \{(s,s), (f,f)\}$,
$E_9 = \{(s,f), (f,s)\}$, $\quad E_{10} = \{(s,f), (f,f)\}$, $\quad E_{11} = \{(f,s), (f,f)\}$,
$E_{12} = \{(s,s), (s,f), (f,s)\}$, $\quad E_{13} = \{(s,s), (s,f), (f,f)\}$,
$E_{14} = \{(s,s), (f,s), (f,f)\}$, $\quad E_{15} = \{(s,f), (f,s), (f,f)\}$,
$E_{16} = \{(s,s), (s,f), (f,s), (f,f)\}$.

As we assumed for the book experiment, we shall again assume that each of the points of S is equally likely to occur. If an experiment has four equally likely outcomes, our intuition leads us to conclude that the probability of occurrence of any one outcome is $1/4$. Thus each event E_6 through E_{11} of the bulb test experiment is twice as likely to occur as events E_2 through E_5. Each event E_6 through E_{16} contains two sample points. Hence, the probability of each event is $1/2$. Similarly, each of events E_{12} through E_{15} with three equally likely sample points has a probability of $3/4$.

3.6 EQUALLY PROBABLE SIMPLE EVENTS

For many experiments, all of the simple events are equally probable. We assumed that the simple events of both the book selection experiment and the bulb testing experiment were equally probable. Other examples of equally probable simple events were those involving the births of children, selection of committees, and seating arrangements. In assigning probability values for events that are made up of equally probable simple events we shall use the following definition.

DEFINITION 3.5

If the simple events of a finite sample space S are *equally probable* and if $E \subseteq S$ then

$$P(E) = \frac{n(E)}{n(S)}$$

where $n(E)$ denotes the number of sample points in event E and $n(S)$ denotes the number of sample points in S.

Example 1. For the experiment: "Record the birth of two children," what is the probability that both children are of the same sex? What is the probability that at least one child is a boy?

Solution: The sample space is:

$$S = \{(b,b), (b,g), (g,b), (g,g)\}$$

We assume that each of the simple events is equally probable. The simple events are:

$$E_1 = \{(b,b)\}, \qquad E_2 = \{(b,g)\}, \qquad E_3 = \{(g,b)\}, \qquad E_4 = \{(g,g)\}$$

Since each of the four simple events is equally probable, the probability of events E_1 through E_4 is $1/4$. Now, let E_5 be the event "both children are the same sex," $E_5 = \{(b,b), (g,g)\}$.

$$P(E_5) = \frac{n(E_5)}{n(S)} = \frac{2}{4} = \frac{1}{2}$$

Again, let E_6 be the event, "a family has at least one boy," $E_6 = \{(b,b), (b,g), (g,b)\}$; then,

$$P(E_6) = \frac{n(E_6)}{n(S)} = \frac{3}{6} = \frac{1}{2}$$

Example 2. For the experiment: "Randomly select and record the members of a committee of three from a group of five people," what is the probability of each of the following events?

E_1: Persons P_1 and P_2 are both selected.
E_2: Persons P_1 and P_2 are selected and P_3 is not selected.
E_3: Person P_1 is selected and neither person P_3 nor P_4 is selected.

Solution: The sample space consists of $C\binom{5}{3}$ distinct committees. Each point in the sample space is equally probable. Why? The sample space is

$$S = \{(P_1, P_2, P_3), (P_1, P_2, P_4), (P_1, P_2, P_5), (P_1, P_3, P_4), (P_1, P_3, P_5),$$
$$(P_1, P_4, P_5), (P_2, P_3, P_4), (P_2, P_3, P_5), (P_2, P_4, P_5), (P_3, P_4, P_5)\}$$

(Why is the point (P_2, P_1, P_3) not included in this space?)

Since each sample point in S is equally probable, the probability of each of the 10 simple events is $1/10$. Let E_1 be the event P_1 and P_2 are both selected; let E_2 be the event P_1 and P_5 are selected and P_3 is not selected; and let E_3 be the event P_1 is selected and neither P_3 nor P_4 are selected.

$$E_1 = \{(P_1, P_2, P_3), (P_1, P_2, P_4), (P_1, P_2, P_5)\}$$

$$P(E_1) = \frac{n(E_1)}{n(S)} = \frac{3}{10}$$

$$E_2 = \{(P_1, P_2, P_4), (P_1, P_2, P_5)\}$$

$$P(E_2) = \frac{n(E_2)}{n(S)} = \frac{2}{10} = \frac{1}{5}$$

$$E_3 = (P_1, P_2, P_5)$$

$$P(E_3) = \frac{n(E_3)}{n(3)} = \frac{1}{10}$$

Example 3. For the experiment: "Four people are randomly seated at a circular table," find the probability of events E_1 and E_2 as specified below.

Solution: The number of points in the sample space is given by $P\binom{3}{3} = 6$. The sample space is

$$S = (P_1, P_2, P_3, P_4), (P_1, P_3, P_2, P_4), (P_2, P_1, P_3, P_4),$$
$$(P_2, P_3, P_1, P_4), (P_3, P_1, P_2, P_4), (P_3, P_2, P_1, P_4)$$

Each of the six points is equally probable since the seating is random. We apply definition 3.5 to find the probability of events E_1 and E_2 as follows.

Let E_1 be the event person P_3 is seated next to person P_4. (Be careful! Remember the circle.)

$$P(E_1) = \frac{n(E_1)}{n(S)} = \frac{4}{6} = \frac{2}{3}$$

Let E_2 be the event person P_1 is seated next to person P_4.

$$P(E_2) = \frac{n(E_2)}{n(S)} = \frac{4}{6} = \frac{2}{3}$$

EXERCISE 3.3

1. Five people randomly seat themselves about a circular table. In how many distinct ways may the five people seat themselves? What is the probability that persons P_1 and P_2 are seated side by side? What is the probability that person P_1 is seated next to person P_2 or person P_3?

2. Two houses in a block of ten houses are randomly selected in a survey. What is the probability that houses H_1 and H_2 are both selected in the survey? What is the probability that house H_2 is selected but H_1 is not selected?

3. Of a class of 30 students, two are randomly selected for testing in a national survey. How many points are in the sample space for the class survey? What is the probability that students A_1 and A_2 are both selected? What is the probability that if A_1 is selected A_{15} will not be selected?

4. In a national political poll, one of every 100 voters is queried as to whether he voted in an election. In a town of 1,000 voters how many would be queried? If each voter questioned is randomly selected, how many points are in the sample space for the survey of voters in the town of 1,000 voters? What is the probability that a husband and wife, both of whom are voters, are questioned?

5. In a manufacturing plant, 10 of every 100 items produced are randomly selected for inspection. How many points are in this sample space? What is the probability that the first and last element of the 100 items are tested? What is the probability that the 49th item is selected? Is it desirable that the items for testing be randomly selected?

3.7 ASSIGNMENT OF EMPIRICAL PROBABILITY TO EVENTS

In our discussions of probability to this point, we have often arbitrarily assigned a probability value to simple events. While this concept is useful, there are important applications of probability theory in business, economics, and industry that require the assignment of probabilities *based on experience*. Consider the experiment: "Record the number of real estate sales made each day by a sales staff for a period of 100 days."

Sales Rate per Day	Number of Days Sales Rate Occurred
0	10
1	25
2	40
3	15
4	10
	$\overline{100}$ days

The sample space S for this experiment is

$$S = \{0, 1, 2, 3, 4\}$$

We shall let f denote the number of days that each of the five simple events of this experiment occurred, and n shall denote the total number of days the experiment was conducted.

E_1 is the event *one of the 100 days is selected at random and for that day no sale was made.* From the sales record, we find

$$P(E_1) = \frac{f}{n} = \frac{10}{100} = \frac{1}{10}$$

If E_2 is the event *one sale is made*, then

$$P(E_2) = \frac{f}{n} = \frac{25}{100} = \frac{1}{4}$$

If E_3 is the event *two sales are made*, then

$$P(E_3) = \frac{40}{100} = \frac{2}{5}$$

If E_4 is the event *three sales are made*, then

$$P(E_4) = \frac{15}{100} = \frac{3}{20}$$

If E_5 is the event *four sales are made*, then

$$P(E_5) = \frac{10}{100} = \frac{1}{10}$$

$$P(S) = P(E_1) + P(E_2) + P(E_3) + P(E_4) + P(E_5)$$

$$P(S) = \frac{2}{20} + \frac{5}{20} + \frac{8}{20} + \frac{3}{20} + \frac{2}{20} = 1$$

If we repeated this experiment many times, the ratio of f/n for an event would vary greatly. However, as n becomes large, the ratio f/n tends to stabilize around some number a (we say f/n converges to a). The number a is the "true" probability of the event. Hence, if the number of repetitions of the experiment is large, for any given event E, the ratio f/n for the event E may be used as an estimate of $P(E)$. The ratio f/n is called the *empirical probability* of the event E.

DEFINITION 3.6

The *empirical probablity* of an event *E* of an experiment is the ratio f/n where f is the number of times *E* occurs and *n* is the number of times the experiment is performed. Symbolically,

$$P(E) = \frac{f}{n}$$

Two examples of empirical probability follow. In each example, the events are simple and consist of one component.

Example 1. A tabulation of the type of injury sustained in each of the last 1,000 automobile accidents reported to an insurance company is given below. Use the table to find the empirical probability of the occurrence of each type of injury.

E_1: No injury   700
E_2: Minor injury—no hospitalization   200
E_3: Minor injury—hospitalization—15 days or less   78
E_4: Major injury—hospitalization in excess of 15 days   20
E_5: Fatal injury—(not included in other events)   2

Solution: The sample space for this experiment contains five simple events, as listed above. The empirical probability of each may be determined by using definition 3.6.

$$\frac{f}{n} = \frac{700}{1000} = \frac{7}{10}$$

$$\frac{f}{n} = \frac{200}{1000} = \frac{1}{5}$$

$$\frac{f}{n} = \frac{78}{1000} = \frac{39}{500}$$

$$\frac{f}{n} = \frac{20}{1000} = \frac{1}{50}$$

$$\frac{f}{n} = \frac{2}{1000} = \frac{1}{500}$$

Example 2. A factory produces 10,000 transistors daily. Five percent of the daily production was inspected for 30 days, with the results indicated below. What is the empirical probability that a transistor produced by the factory is defective?

Defective Transistors	Number of Days
5	5
7	3
9	2
4	10
2	8
0	1
18	1
	$\overline{30}$ days

Solution: $f = 25 + 21 + 18 + 40 + 16 + 18$
$\qquad = 138$ defective transistors
$\qquad n = .05(10,000) \times 30$
$\qquad = 15,000$ total transistors inspected

Let E be the event *a defective transistor is produced.*

$$\frac{f}{n} = \frac{138}{15000}$$

EXERCISE 3.4

1. The personnel records of SIPJAC Manufacturing Co. indicate the following relationship between education and type of position.

Highest Education Level	Number of Persons Employed		
	Administrative	Supervisor	Production
8th Grade	2	5	200
High School Graduate	5	10	100
College Graduate	10	20	50

If an employee is selected at random, what is the probability that he is:
(*a*) a high school graduate?
(*b*) an administrator?
(*c*) a college graduate in a supervisory position?

2. Present enrollment at St. Petersburg Junior College is 9,000. The following is a listing of some of the courses pursued, with the number of students enrolled in each.

Subject	Number in Course
English	3,000
Math	2,000
Social Sciences	3,000
Engineering	300

(*a*) What is the empirical probability that a student who attends SPJC studies: (1) English? (2) Mathematics?
(*b*) Can you determine the probability that a student will study math or English? Justify your answer.

3. In a study of 1,000 women shoppers at the Trojan Department Store, 100 women were observed to purchase shoes, 50 to purchase hats, and 200 to purchase dresses. Among these, 10 purchased a hat and shoes, 50 purchased shoes and a dress, 20 purchased a hat and a dress, and 5 purchased all three items. Based on this data, what is the empirical probability that a woman shopper at Trojan's will purchase (1) hats, (2) dresses, (3) shoes and hats, (4) shoes, hats, and dresses, (5) no shoes, hats, or dresses?

4. (a) Use a Venn diagram to illustrate the record of the effect of various types of training on the job performance of 1,000 college graduates.

Job Performance Improved by	Frequency
College education	700
On-the-job training	400
Previous job experience	300
College and on-the-job training	150
College and previous job	200
On-the-job and previous job	150
All three	100

(b) Based on this data what is the empirical probability that:
    (1) college education improves job performance;
    (2) both previous job experience and on-the-job training are helpful;
    (3) a person's performance is not helped by any of the three?

3.8 ASSIGNMENT OF PROBABILITIES TO COMPONENTS

In the previous experiments it has not been necessary to *compute* the probability of an event. The nature of the experiments was such that the probabilities could be assigned either empirically or through equally probable simple events. However, many, and in fact most, experiments do not result in equally probable simple events, nor can an empirical probability be readily assigned. In such cases, the probability of a simple event must be *computed*, based on the components of the event.

In each of the examples regarding empirical probability, the sample space consisted of simple events of one component (sometimes called *singleton events*). For events with one component, probabilities may be assigned based on one or more of the following:
    (1) The nature of the experiment;
    (2) The properties of the objects involved in the experiment;
    (3) The experience gained in previous performances of the experiment;
    (4) The anticipated use of the probability determinations;
    (5) The assignment of probabilities so that the sum of the probabilities of the simple events in S is equal to 1.

Whenever the sample point for a simple event contains more than one component, each of the components is assigned a probability value as if the component were an event of one component. Each of the components must occur before the simple event can occur. Let us illustrate this concept by considering the experiment: *Select two transistors from a box of ten transistors, four of which are defective and six of which are satisfactory; record s if the transistor selected is satisfactory, otherwise record f.* The sample space is

$$S = \{(s, s), (s, f), (f, s), (f, f)\}$$

If each of the ten transistors has an equal chance of being the first selected and each of the remaining nine transistors has an equal chance of being the second selected, we say that the selection of the two transistors is made *at random.* On the criteria of this experiment, we can assign a probability value of 6/10 when the first component of a sample point is s and a probability value of 4/10 when the first component is f. Having selected the first component, we are then willing to assign probability values to the second component based on the nine transistors remaining. For the point (s, s), we assign 5/9 to the second component; for the point (s, f) we assign 4/9 to the second component; for the point (f, s) we assign 6/9 to the second component; for the point (f, f) we assign 3/9 to the second component. Each assignment is based on the nature of the experiment, the properties of the transistors, and the assumption of randomness.

When probability values have been assigned to the components of simple events we are able to determine *mathematically* all probabilities associated with the experiment. The remainder of this chapter is devoted to mathematical determinations of probabilities.

EXERCISE 3.5

1. Three bulbs are randomly selected from twelve bulbs, four of which are defective. If a bulb is acceptable, s is recorded; otherwise f is recorded. Construct the sample space. Assign probabilities to the components of the following sample points: (s,s,s), (s,f,s), (f,f,s).

2. Four cards are randomly selected from 52 cards, 26 of which are red and 26 of which are black. If a card is red, record r; otherwise record b. Construct the sample space. Assign probabilities to the components of the following sample points: {(r,b,r,b), (r,r,r,r), (b,b,b,r)}.

3. A freshman class is composed of 1,800 men and 1,200 women. If three freshmen are randomly selected, construct the sample space for the experiment. Assign probabilities to the components of the following points: {(m, w, m), (w, w, w), (m, m, w)}. Can a student be selected twice?

4. Records of a real estate firm indicate that the probability that a visitor to the firm will make a purchase is $1/10$. Construct a sample space for expected sales to the next three visitors. Assign probabilities to the components of the following points: $\{(s, s, f), (s, f, s), (f, f, f)\}$.

5. Records of an insurance company show that $1/5$ of all persons insured have made claims against the company. Construct a sample space for random selection of three insured persons. Record c if a claim is made; otherwise record n. Assign probabilities to the following points: $\{(c, n, c), (n, n, n), (n, c, n)\}$.

6. Two motors are tested. The probability that a motor is defective is $1/10$. Construct a sample space for the testing of the motors. Record s if satisfactory; otherwise record f. Assign probabilities to the following points: $\{(s, s), (s, f), (f, s), (f, f)\}$.

7. A deck of 52 cards consists of 13 spades, 13 hearts, 13 diamonds, and 13 clubs. Five cards are randomly selected. How many points are in the sample space if order of selection is disregarded? Assign probabilities to the following points: $\{(As, Ks, Qs, Js, 10s), (H, H, H, H, H), (As, Ah, Ad, Ac, 2c)\}$.

3.9 ASSIGNMENT OF PROBABILITY TO MULTIPLE COMPONENT SIMPLE EVENTS

Again we consider the experiment of testing two light bulbs from a continuous production line. However, based on prior observations (or empirical probabilities), we shall assume now that the probability (empirical) of an acceptable bulb is $3/4$ and the probability of an unacceptable bulb is $1/4$. The sample space for this experiment is the set

$$S = \{(s, s), (s, f), (f, s), (f, f)\}$$

Each sample point consists of two components. It seems reasonable to doubt that the simple events are equally probable since the components are not equally probable. The purpose of this section is to develop a method for finding the probability of the simple events of an experiment that may not be equally probable. The method is based on the Cartesian product discussed in chapter 2. For the bulb test experiment that we are considering, the assumed probability of $3/4$ for an acceptable bulb may be represented by the equally probable space

$$S_1 = \{s_1, s_2, s_3, f\}$$

where each s denotes an acceptable bulb and f represents an unacceptable bulb.

Similarly, the probability of $3/4$ for the second bulb may be represented by the equally probable space

$$S_2 = \{s_1, s_2, s_3, f\}$$

We now find the Cartesian product $S_1 \times S_2$.

$$S_1 \times S_2 = \{(s_1, s_1), (s_1, s_2), (s_1, s_3), (s_1, f), (s_2, s_1), (s_2, s_2), (s_2, s_3), (s_2, f),$$
$$(s_3, s_1), (s_3, s_2), (s_3, s_3), (s_3, f), (f_1, s_1), (f_1, s_2), (f, s_3), (f, f)\}$$

Of the sixteen equally probable points in $S_1 \times S_2$, both bulbs are acceptable in nine of the points (count them); one bulb is acceptable in six points, and both bulbs are unacceptable in one point.

Returning to the sample space S for the two-bulb test, we are now able to assign probabilities to each of the four simple events as follows.

$$P(E_1) = P\{(s, s)\} = \frac{9}{16}$$

$$P(E_2) = P\{(s, f)\} = \frac{3}{16}$$

$$P(E_3) = P\{(f, s)\} = \frac{3}{16}$$

$$P(E_4) = P\{(f, f)\} = \frac{1}{16}$$

The above values for the probability of each of the four simple events of S are directly obtainable from the equally probable Cartesian product space $S_1 \times S_2$ by use of definition 3.5, $P(E) = \dfrac{n(E)}{n(S_1 \times S_2)}$.

$$P(E_1) = \frac{n\{\{s_1, s_2, s_3\} \times \{s_1, s_2, s_3\}\}}{n\{S_1 \times S_2\}} = \frac{3 \times 3}{4 \times 4}$$

$$P(E_2) = \frac{n\{\{s_1, s_2, s_3\} \times \{f\}\}}{n\{S_1 \times S_2\}} = \frac{3 \times 1}{4 \times 4}$$

$$P(E_3) = \frac{n\{\{f\} \times \{s_1, s_2, s_3\}\}}{n\{S_1 \times S_2\}} = \frac{1 \times 3}{4 \times 4}$$

$$P(E_4) = \frac{n\{\{f\} \times \{f\}\}}{n\{S_1 \times S_2\}} = \frac{1 \times 1}{4 \times 4}$$

With the above example we have demonstrated the important *product rule* for mathematical determination of the probability of a simple event with more than one component. This rule applies for both equally probable and not equally probable spaces. The product rule is stated in the following theorem.

THEOREM 3.1

If E is a simple event whose sample point has n components, $c_1, c_2, c_3, \ldots, c_n$, each with respective assigned probability values $P\{c_1\}, P\{c_2\}, P\{c_3\}, \ldots, P\{c_n\}$, then
$$P(E) = P\{c_1\} \cdot P\{c_2\} \cdot P\{c_3\} \cdot \ldots \cdot P\{c_n\}$$

Example 1. Experiment: Randomly select two letters of the alphabet assuming that a letter may be selected twice, with the sample space

$$S = \{(a,a), (a,b), (a,c), \dots\}$$

(a) What is the probability that both letters selected are vowels?

Solution: Let E_1 be the event both letters are vowels.

$$P(E_1) = \frac{n(E_1)}{n(S)} = \frac{6 \cdot 6}{26 \cdot 26} = \frac{9}{169}$$

(b) What is the probability that the first letter selected is a consonant and the second letter is a vowel?

Solution: Let E_2 be the event a consonant is selected followed by a vowel.

$$P(E_2) = \frac{n(E_2)}{n(S)} = \frac{20 \cdot 6}{26 \cdot 26} = \frac{30}{169}$$

(c) What is the probability that both letters are consonants?

Solution: Let E_3 be the event both letters are consonants.

$$P(E_3) = \frac{n(E_3)}{n(S)} = \frac{20 \cdot 20}{26 \cdot 26} = \frac{100}{169}$$

Example 2. From a national survey, it has been determined that 80% of the population prefers product A.

Experiment: Survey four people in one city block as to their preferences for product A. Assume all four people respond by indicating that they either like or dislike product A. The sample space is

$$S = \{(1,1,1,1), \dots, (d,d,d,d)\}$$

(a) What is the probability that all four people prefer product A?

Solution: Let E_1 be the event four people like product A.

$$E_1 = \{(1,1,1,1)\}$$

$$P(E_1) = P\{(1,1,1,1)\}$$

$$= P\{1\} \cdot P\{1\} \cdot P\{1\} \cdot P\{1\}$$

$$= \frac{4}{5} \cdot \frac{4}{5} \cdot \frac{4}{5} \cdot \frac{4}{5} = \left(\frac{4}{5}\right)^4$$

(b) What is the probability that the first three people surveyed like product A and the fourth person dislikes product A?

Solution: $E_2 = \{(1,1,1,d)\}$

$$P(E_2) = P\{1\} \cdot P\{1\} \cdot P\{1\} \cdot P\{d\}$$

$$= \frac{4}{5} \cdot \frac{4}{5} \cdot \frac{4}{5} \cdot \frac{1}{5} = \frac{4^3}{5^4}$$

EXERCISE 3.6

1. Three bearings are selected for inspection from a continuous production line. It has been determined empirically that the probability that a bearing that is satisfactory is 9/10. Construct a sample space for the three bearings. Determine the probabilities.
   E_1 = all three bearings are acceptable
   $E_2 = \{(s, s, f)\}$
   E_3 = the first two bearings are acceptable and the last is unacceptable

2. Your mathematics teacher is known to pass 90% of the students in each of his classes. Construct a sample space to indicate whether three of his students selected at random from a class of 100 students pass or fail the course. What is the probability of the following events?
   E_1 = no student fails
   E_2 = the first two students fail and the last passes
   E_3 − all three students pass

3. A survey is made of the sex of children in families of six children. How many points are in the sample space? What is the probability of the following events?
   E_1 = all children are boys
   E_2 = the first three are boys, the fourth and fifth are girls, and the sixth is a boy

4. It is known that 80% of the tires manufactured by a given company last more than 30,000 miles. If you purchase three tires, what is the probability that all three tires will last more than 30,000 miles? That all three will last less than 30,000 miles?

5. The records of a broker show that 20% of all prospective buyers will make purchases. What is the probability that the next ten prospects all will make purchases? That the next two will make purchases and, thereafter, the next three will fail to make purchases?

6. Records of a police department show that 20% of all burglaries are solved. What is the probability that the next four burglaries reported will all be solved?

3.10 PROBABILITY OF COMPOUND EVENTS DERIVED FROM UNION OF SIMPLE EVENTS

A compound event is the union of two or more simple events. Consider the experiment *test the acceptability of two transistors from a continuous production line*. Assume that production experience indicates that 90% of all transistors produced are satisfactory. The sample space for this experiment is the set

$$S = \{(s, s), (s, f), (f, s), (f, f)\}$$

Each of the compound events associated with this experiment must contain two, three, or four sample points. The total number of compound events of S is the sum

$$C\left(\frac{4}{2}\right) + C\left(\frac{4}{3}\right) + C\left(\frac{4}{4}\right)$$

Why?

For this experiment, eleven compound events are possible. A compound event is said to occur where the outcome of the experiment is one of the sample points of the compound event. Of the eleven compound events of the transistor experiment, we select three for study.

Let E_1 be the event *the first transistor is acceptable*.

$$E_1 = \{(s, s), (s, f)\}$$

$$P\{(s, s)\} = \frac{9}{10} \cdot \frac{9}{10} = \frac{81}{100}$$

$$P\{(s, f)\} = \frac{9}{10} \cdot \frac{1}{10} = \frac{9}{100}$$

Based on $P\{(s, s)\}$ and $P\{(s, f)\}$, 90% of the time the performance of this experiment will result in (s, s) or (s, f) since either result satisfies the requirement of E_1. This event cannot occur in any other way; hence, we conclude that

$$P(E_1) = P\{(s, s)\} + P\{(s, f)\}$$

Consider another compound event of the transistor experiment. Let E_2 be the event *at least one transistor is acceptable*.

$$E_2 = \{(s, s), (s, f), (f, s)\}$$

$$P\{(s, s)\} = \frac{9}{10} \cdot \frac{9}{10} = \frac{81}{100}$$

$$P\{(s, f)\} = \frac{9}{10} \cdot \frac{1}{10} = \frac{9}{100}$$

$$P\{(f, s)\} = \frac{1}{10} \cdot \frac{9}{10} = \frac{9}{100}$$

When we add the probabilities of the three simple events contained in E_2, we observe that E_2 should occur 99 times of each 100 performances of the experiment.

The concept illustrated in two of the events of the transistor experiment is stated in the following theorem.

THEOREM 3.2

Let E be an event in a sample space S. If E is the empty set, then $P(E) = 0$. If E is not empty, then $P(E)$ is the sum of the probabilities of all of the simple events which are subsets of E.

Application of theorem 3.2 is illustrated in the examples that follow.

Example 1. From past experience, it is known that 80% of all airplanes arriving at an airport are more than one hour late. Let us randomly select and check the arrival time of four airplanes, recording O if a plane is less than one hour late, otherwise recording L. The sample space is

$$S = \{(O,O,O,O),\ldots,(L,L,L,L)\}$$

(a) What is the probability that the first three planes are less than one hour late?

Solution:

$$E_1 = \{(O,O,O,O),\ (O,O,O,L)\}$$

$$P(E_1) = P\{(O,O,O,O)\} + P\{(O,O,O,L)\}$$

$$= \frac{1}{5}\cdot\frac{1}{5}\cdot\frac{1}{5}\cdot\frac{1}{5} + \frac{1}{5}\cdot\frac{1}{5}\cdot\frac{1}{5}\cdot\frac{4}{5}$$

$$= \frac{1}{625} + \frac{4}{625} = \frac{5}{625} = \frac{1}{125}$$

(b) What is the probability that the first plane is late and the last plane is late?

Solution:

$$E_2 = \{(L,L,L,L),\ (L,O,L,L),\ (L,L,O,L),\ (L,O,O,L)\}$$

$$P(E_2) = P\{(L,L,L,L)\} + P\{(L,O,L,L)\} + P\{(L,L,O,L)\} + P\{(L,O,O,L)\}$$

$$= \left(\frac{4}{5}\right)^4 + 2\left(\frac{4}{5}\right)^3\left(\frac{1}{5}\right) + \left(\frac{4}{5}\right)^2\left(\frac{1}{5}\right)^2$$

$$= \frac{400}{625} = \frac{16}{25}$$

3.11 PROBABILITY OF COMPOUND EVENTS DERIVED FROM UNION OF EVENTS NOT ALL SIMPLE

Whenever a compound event is derived from the union of simple events, the probability of the compound event is found by *summing* the probabilities of the simple events. Even when the compound event has not been derived from simple events, the probability of the compound event may still be found by summing the probabilities of the *simple events that are elements of the compound event.* One must merely keep in mind that the compound event is a set composed of *nonrepeated elements.* Sometimes, however, it is not convenient or desirable to find all of the simple events of compound events that are derived from other compound events. The purpose of this section is to develop a procedure for finding $P(E_1 \cup E_2)$ when E_1 and E_2 are any events, either simple or compound.

Consider the experiment *call on three customers for the purpose of selling one product.* Assume that the probability of a sale to an individual customer is $1/10$. The sample space for this experiment is the set

$$S = \{(s, s, s), (s, s, f), \ldots, (f, f, f)\}$$

A total of $2^8 = 256$ events are possible, of which 247 are compound events. We select for study two of the compound events.

Let E_1 be the event *exactly two sales are made.*

$$E_1 = \{(s, s, f), (s, f, s), (f, s, s)\}$$

$$P(E_1) = \left(\frac{1}{10}\right)^2 \cdot \frac{9}{10} + \left(\frac{1}{10}\right)^2 \cdot \frac{9}{10} + \left(\frac{1}{10}\right)^2 \cdot \frac{9}{10} = \frac{27}{1000}$$

Let E_2 be the event *at least two sales are made.*

$$E_2 = \{(s, s, s), (s, s, f), (s, f, s), (f, s, s)\}$$

$$P(E_2) = \left(\frac{1}{10}\right)^3 + \left(\frac{1}{10}\right)^2 \cdot \frac{9}{10} + \left(\frac{1}{10}\right)^2 \cdot \frac{9}{10} + \left(\frac{1}{10}\right)^2 \cdot \frac{9}{10} = \frac{28}{1000}$$

$$(E_1 \cup E_2) = \{(s, s, s), (s, s, f), (s, f, s), (f, s, s)\}$$

$$P(E_1 \cup E_2) = P\{(s, s, s)\} + P\{(s, s, f)\} + P\{(s, f, s)\} + P\{(f, s, s)\}$$

$$= \left(\frac{1}{10}\right)^3 + \left(\frac{1}{10}\right)^2 \cdot \frac{9}{10} + \left(\frac{1}{10}\right)^2 \cdot \frac{9}{10} + \left(\frac{1}{10}\right)^2 \cdot \frac{9}{10}$$

$$= \frac{28}{1000}$$

We have found the probability of the compound event $(E_1 \cup E_2)$ by summing the probabilities of the simple events in $(E_1 \cup E_2)$.

Now let us reexamine $(E_1 \cup E_2)$, recalling that all events are sets. The probability of the event $(E_1 \cup E_2)$ is the sum of the probabilities of the points in $(E_1 \cup E_2)$. $P(E_1) + P(E_2)$ is the sum of the probabilities of the points in E_1 plus the probabilities of the points in E_2. Therefore, $P(E_1) + P(E_2)$ includes the probabilities of the points in $(E_1 \cup E_2)$ twice. Hence, we must subtract $P(E_1 \cap E_2)$ from the sum $P(E_1) + P(E_2)$ to obtain $P(E_1 \cup E_2)$. In the light of this discussion, let us reconsider $P(E_1 \cup E_2)$ for the experiment of calling on three customers to sell a product.

$$P(E_1) = \frac{27}{1000}$$

$$P(E_2) = \frac{28}{1000}$$

$$E_1 \cap E_2 = \{(s,s,f), (s,f,s), (f,s,s)\}$$

$$P(E_1 \cap E_2) = P\{(s,s,f), (s,f,s), (f,s,s)\}$$

$$P(E_1 \cap E_2) = \frac{27}{1000}$$

$$P(E_1 \cup E_2) = P(E_1) + P(E_2) - P(E_1 \cap E_2)$$

$$P(E_1 \cup E_2) = \frac{27}{1000} + \frac{28}{1000} - \frac{27}{1000} = \frac{28}{1000}$$

This is the result found by summing the probabilities of the simple events in $(E_1 \cup E_2)$.

The concept illustrated in the above example is stated in the following theorem.

THEOREM 3.3

If E_1 and E_2 are events of a sample space S, then

$$P(E_1 \cup E_2) = P(E_1) + P(E_2) - P(E_1 \cap E_2)$$

If $E_1 + E_2$ are mutually exclusive,

$$P(E_1 \cup E_2) = P(E_1) + P(E_2)$$

EXERCISE 3.7

1. In a traffic survey, it was found that, on the average, 100 passenger cars and 20 trucks passed an intersection in one hour. For the next 5 cars, what are the probabilities of the following events?
   E_1 = the next 5 vehicles are passenger cars
   E_2 = at least 3 are passenger cars
   E_3 = exactly 3 are passenger cars
   $E_4 = \{E_2 \cup E_3\}$
   $E_5 = \{E_1 \cup E_3\}$

2. Of the patients that visit a medical clinic, it is found that $1/10$ require hospitalization, $2/10$ require outpatient services, and $7/10$ require no treatment. Of the next three patients who visit the clinic, what are the probabilities of the following events? Denote hospitalization by h, outpatient by o, and no treatment by n.
   E_1 = all patients require hospitalization
   $E_2 = (h,h,h), (h,h,o), (h,o,o)$
   E_3 = the first patient requires hospitalization and the last is an outpatient
   $E_4 = E_1 \cup E_2$
   $E_5 = E_1 \cup E_3$
   $E_6 = E_2 \cup E_3$

3. From a city commission of five persons, ten distinct committees of three members each are selected. What is the probability that members m_1 and m_2 are both members of committee A? What is the probability that both m_1 and m_2 are not on committee A? What is the probability that m_1 is on committee A and that m_2 is not on committee A? What is the probability that m_1 and m_2 are both members of committee A or that neither m_1 nor m_2 is a member of committee A?

4. Two cards are drawn at random from a regular deck of 52 playing cards. Find the probability that: (*a*) both cards are spades; (*b*) the first card is a spade; (*c*) the second card is a spade; (*d*) both cards are spades, the first card is a spade, or the second card is a spade.

5. A town has two newspapers, the *Times* and the *Independent*. One-fourth of the people take both papers, one-half take the *Times* only, and one-tenth take the *Independent* only. What is the probability that a person selected at random subscribes to a newspaper? What is the probability that he subscribes to both papers or to the *Times* only, or that he subscribes to both papers or to the *Independent* only?

3.12 PROBABILITY OF E_1 ASSUMING E_2 HAS OCCURRED— CONDITIONAL PROBABILITY

Oftentimes an event E_1 contains sample points that are elements of another event E_2, i.e., $E_1 \cap E_2 \neq \phi$. Because the two events have at least one sample point in common, the two events may occur simultaneously. The purpose of this section is to examine the probability of two events with common sample points, knowing that one of the events has already occurred, i.e., the probability that E_1 occurred under the condition that E_2 is known to have occurred or vice versa. In other words, we wish to answer the question, "If E_2 occurs, what is the probability that E_1 also occurs?"

Consider the experiment: *Survey three television set owners to determine whether program A is being observed. Record s if the answer is yes, f otherwise.* Assume that the probability that a particular person is observing is $1/2$. The equally probable sample space follows.

$$S = \{(s,s,s), (s,s,f), (s,f,s), (f,s,s), (f,f,s), (f,s,f), (s,f,f), (f,f,f)\}$$

Of the 256 possible events, we select arbitrarily the following two events for study.

$$E_1 = \text{the first person is observing } A$$
$$= \{(s,s,s), (s,s,f), (s,f,s), (s,f,f)\}$$

$$E_2 = \text{the second person is observing } A$$
$$= \{(s,s,s), (s,s,f), (f,s,s), (f,s,f)\}$$

$$E_1 \cap E_2 = \{(s,s,s), (s,s,f)\} \neq \phi$$

Let us assume that E_2 has occurred. This means that the outcome of the experiment is one of the four points of E_2. Now, E_1 contains two of the points in E_2; hence, since the outcomes in S are equally probable, definition 3.5 is applicable.

$$P(E_1 \text{ given } E_2) = \frac{n(E_1 \cap E_2)}{n(E_2)} = \frac{2}{4} = \frac{1}{2}$$

Now we assume that E_1 has occurred and find the probability of E_2 given E_1.

$$P(E_2 \text{ given } E_1) = \frac{n(E_1 \cap E_2)}{n(E_2)} = \frac{2}{4} = \frac{1}{2}$$

For equally probable spaces, the probability of "E_1 given E_2" may always be found by the method illustrated for the above experiment. This probability is usually denoted by

$$P(E_1 \mid E_2) = \frac{n(E_1 \cap E_2)}{n(E_2)}$$

The vertical bar is read "given" or "under condition."

It can be shown that the following definition applies to both equally probable and not equally probable spaces.

DEFINITION 3.7

The conditional probability of an event E_1 given that E_2 has occurred is denoted by $P(E_1 \mid E_2)$ and is defined by the expression

$$P(E_1 \mid E_2) = \frac{P(E_1 \cap E_2)}{P(E_2)}$$

Application of definition 3.7 is illustrated in the following examples.

Example 1. A manufacturer conducted a survey of 1,000 TV viewers with the following results: Number who saw his advertisement: 200; number who saw ad and purchased his product: 50; number who did not see ad, but purchased his product: 20.

The above survey results are represented with a Venn diagram.

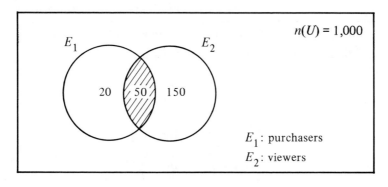

(*a*) Based on this data, what is the probability that a person who saw the ad was also a purchaser? Let E_1 be the event the person makes a purchase, and let E_2 be the event the person viewed the ad.

Solution:

$$P(E_2) = \frac{200}{1000} = \frac{1}{5}$$

$$P(E_1 \cap E_2) = \frac{50}{1000} = \frac{1}{20}$$

$$P(E_1 \mid E_2) = \frac{P(E_1 \cap E_2)}{P(E_2)} = \frac{\frac{1}{20}}{\frac{1}{5}} = \frac{1}{4}$$

(*b*) What is the probability that a person who purchased also saw the ad? Let E_1 represent viewers of ad, and let E_2 represent purchasers.

Solution:

$$P(E_2) = \frac{70}{1000}$$

$$P(E_1 \cap E_2) = \frac{50}{1000} = \frac{1}{20}$$

$$P(E_1 \mid E_2) = \frac{P(E_1 \cap E_2)}{P(E_2)} = \frac{\frac{50}{1000}}{\frac{70}{1000}} = \frac{5}{7}$$

Example 2. In a class of 100 students who studied both mathematics and English, 30 failed math, 20 failed English, and 10 failed both subjects. The results of this survey are shown in the following diagram.

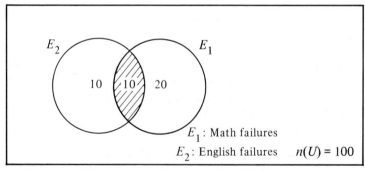

E_1: Math failures
E_2: English failures $n(U) = 100$

What is the probability that a person who fails English also fails math?

Solution: Let E_1 be math failures, and let E_2 represent English failures.

$$P(E_2) = \frac{20}{100} = \frac{1}{5}$$

$$P(E_1 \cap E_2) = \frac{10}{100} = \frac{1}{10}$$

$$P(E_1 \mid E_2) = \frac{\frac{1}{10}}{\frac{1}{5}} = \frac{1}{2}$$

EXERCISE 3.8

1. A card is selected at random from a standard deck of 52 playing cards. If the card selected is red, what is the probability that it is an ace? If the card selected is a king, what is the probability that it is a spade?

2. In a class of 200 students who study both history and English, 20 failed history, 40 failed English, and 10 failed both subjects. What is the probability that a student failed history if he also failed English? If he failed history, what is the probability that he also failed English?

3. A survey was made of 100 customers in a department store. Sixty of the 100 indicated they visited the store because of a newspaper advertisement. The remainder had not seen the ad. A total of 40 customers made purchases; of these customers, 30 had seen the ad. What is the probability that a person who did not see the ad made a purchase? What is the probability that a person who saw the ad made a purchase?

4. A company purchases and inspects 100 items of which 4 are known to be defective. If the first item inspected is defective, what is the probability that the second item is not defective? What is the probability that both of the first two items inspected are defective?

5. A family moves next door to your home. You have heard that they have three children. If you observe that one of the children is a boy what are the following probabilities? (a) that all three are boys; (b) that two are girls; (c) that two are boys and the third is a girl.

6. Two boys and two girls line up for a picture. If a girl is on one end of the line, what is the probability that a girl is on the opposite end?

7. A committee is composed of six Democrats and five Republicans. Three of the Democrats are men, and three of the Republicans are men. If a man is chosen for chairman, what is the probability that he is a Republican?

3.13 INDEPENDENT AND MUTUALLY EXCLUSIVE EVENTS

The concept of independent events is directly related to the concept of conditional probability. When the occurrence of one event in no way affects the probability of another event's occurring, the two events are said to be independent.

DEFINITION 3.8

Two nonempty events E_1 and E_2 are *independent* if

$$P(E_1 \mid E_2) = P(E_1) \quad \text{and} \quad P(E_2 \mid E_1) = P(E_2)$$

From definition 3.6 and definition 3.7, we derive another form for the definition of independent events. Assume E_1 and E_2 independent. Then,

$$P(E_1 \mid E_2) = \frac{P(E_1 \cap E_2)}{P(E_2)} = P(E_1)$$

Hence,

$$P(E_1 \cap E_2) = P(E_1) \cdot P(E_2)$$

This latter formula provides us with a "test" for the independence of two events as illustrated in the following example.

Example. The sample space for three-children families is as follows:

$$S = \{(b,b,b), (b,b,g), (b,g,b), (g,b,b), (g,g,b), (g,b,g), (b,g,g), (g,g,g)\}$$

(a) Consider the events: E_1, *the first child is a boy*, and E_2, *the second child is a girl*. Are E_1 and E_2 independent events?

Solution:

$$P(E_1) = \frac{4}{8} = \frac{1}{2}$$

$$P(E_2) = \frac{4}{8} = \frac{1}{2}$$

$$P(E_1 \cap E_2) = P\{(b,g,b), (b,g,g)\} = \frac{1}{4}$$

$$P(E_1) \cdot P(E_4) = \frac{1}{2} \cdot \frac{1}{2} = \frac{1}{4}$$

Hence, we conclude that E_1 and E_2 are independent.

(b) Consider the events: E_3, *at least two children are boys* and E_4, *the last child is a girl*. Are E_3 and E_4 independent events?

Solution:

$$P(E_3) = \frac{4}{8} = \frac{1}{2}$$

$$P(E_4) = \frac{1}{2}$$

$$P(E_3 \cap E_4) = P\{(b,b,g)\} = \frac{1}{8}$$

$$P(E_3) \cdot P(E_4) = \frac{1}{2} \cdot \frac{1}{2} = \frac{1}{4}$$

Hence, we conclude that E_3 and E_4 are not independent.

When two events have no common sample points they are said to be *mutually exclusive*, i.e., $E_1 \cap E_2 = \phi$. Two nonempty events cannot be both mutually exclusive and independent at the same time. However, as illustrated in the examples of this section, events that are not mutually exclusive may either be or not be independent.

3.14 ALTERNATE CONDITIONAL PROBABILITY—
   BAYES' THEOREM

The concepts of conditional probability and mutually exclusive events provide the basis for assigning probabilities to a series of events that may result from prior events. Consider the following example. Suppose that a manufacturer produces tires at two plants, A and B. From prior experience, it is known that the probability that plant A produces a defective tire is $1/100$ and the probability that plant B produces a defective tire is $5/1000$. A shipment of 100 tires contains 60 tires from A and 40 tires from B. If a defective tire is found in the shipment, what is the probability that the tire was produced at plant A? At plant B?

We begin our search for a method to use in solving this problem by setting up the sample space for the experiment in the usual manner.

Experiment: Test a tire in a shipment of 100 tires for acceptability. Record sA if an acceptable tire is from plant A; record sB if an acceptable tire is from plant B. Record fA if an unacceptable tire is from plant A; record fB if an unacceptable tire is from plant B. The sample space S is

$$S = \{sA, sB, fA, fB\}$$

Let E be the event *the tire is defective*, $E = \{fA, fB\}$. Let E_1 be the event *the tire is from plant A*, $E_1 = \{sA, fA\}$. Let E_2 be the event *the tire is from plant B*, $E_2 = \{sB, fB\}$. We are seeking the following.

$$P(E_1 \mid E) \qquad \text{and} \qquad P(E_2 \mid E)$$

From the known information about the tires in the shipment, these two probabilities are not readily determinable. However we are given $P(E \mid E_1)$ and $P(E \mid E_2)$.

$P(E \mid E_1)$ is the probability that a tire from plant A is defective;
$P(E \mid E_1) = .01$
$P(E \mid E_2)$ is the probability that a tire from plant B is defective;
$P(E \mid E_2) = .005$

We interrupt our solution to construct a Venn diagram of events E, E_1, and E_2.

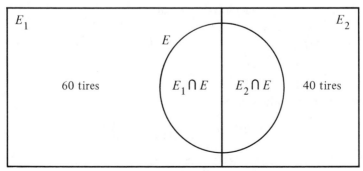

From the diagram and our knowledge of sets we are able to establish the relationship between $P(E_1 | E)$ and $P(E | E_1)$.

$$E = S \cap E = (E_1 \cup E_2) \cap E \tag{1}$$

hence, by the distributive laws of set theory

$$E = (E_1 \cap E) \cup (E_2 \cap E) \tag{2}$$

It is apparent that $(E_1 \cap E)$ and $(E_2 \cap E)$ have no points in common (are mutually exclusive); hence,

$$P(E) = P(E_1 \cap E) + P(E_2 \cap E) \tag{3}$$

From the definition of conditional probability,

$$P(E | E_1) = \frac{P(E_1 \cap E)}{P(E_1)} \tag{4}$$

and

$$P(E_1 \cap E) = P(E_1)P(E | E_1) \tag{5}$$

also

$$P(E_2 \cap E) = P(E_2)P(E | E_2) \tag{6}$$

We now substitute (5) and (6) in (3) above.

$$P(E) = P(E_1)P(E | E_1) + P(E_2)P(E | E_2) \tag{7}$$

Recall that

$$P(E_1 | E) = \frac{P(E_1 \cap E)}{P(E)} \tag{8}$$

Now substituting (5) and (7) in (8), we get

$$P(E_1 | E) = \frac{P(E_1) \cdot P(E | E_1)}{P(E_1)P(E | E_1) + P(E_2)P(E | E_2)} \tag{9}$$

Thus, we have established the relationship between $P(E | E_1)$ and $P(E_1 | E)$ that we were seeking.

We now employ (9) to solve the defective tire problem utilizing the information given in the problem.

$P(E_1 | E) = $ the probability that a defective tire was produced at plant A

$P(E_1) = .6$

$P(E | E_1) = .01$

$P(E_2) = .4$

$P(E | E_2) = .005$

Substituting these values in (9),

$$P(E_1 | E) = \frac{.6(.01)}{.6(.01) + .4(.005)}$$

$$= \frac{.006}{.008} = \frac{3}{4}$$

In a similar manner it follows that,

$$P(E_2 \mid E) = \frac{.4(.005)}{.6(.01) + .4(.005)} = \frac{1}{4}$$

The probability that a defective tire is from plant A is $3/4$; the probability that the defective tire is from plant B is $1/4$.

The method that we have developed for the tire experiment can be extended to any number of events as illustrated in the following Venn diagram.

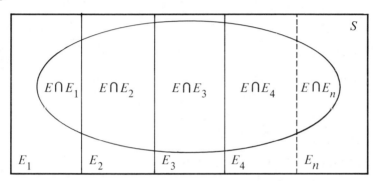

Events E_1 through E_n, as shown in the above diagram, must be mutually exclusive and the union of these events must constitute the sample space, i.e.,

$$E_1 \cup E_2 \cup E_3 \cup \ldots \cup E_n = S$$

There is no requirement that these events be simple (as illustrated in the tire experiment). The event E which is assumed to have occurred must include points from one or more of the events E_1 through E_n. Under these conditions, we are ready to state a theorem for obtaining $P(E_1 \mid E)$, $P(E_2 \mid E)$, $\ldots$, $P(E_n \mid E)$. This theorem is called Bayes' Theorem.

THEOREM 3.4

Let $E_1, E_2, E_3, \ldots, E_n$ be mutually exclusive events of S such that $E_1 \cup E_2 \cup E_3 \cup \ldots \cup E_n = S$, and let E be any event of S. Then for any $i = 1, 2, 3, \ldots, n$,

$$P(E_i \mid E) = \frac{P(E_i)P(E \mid E_i)}{P(E_1)P(E \mid E_1) + P(E_2)P(E \mid E_2) + \ldots + P(E_n)P(E \mid E_n)}$$

Application of theorem 3.4 is illustrated in the following example.

Example 1. Three machines A, B, and C, produce the same item at a factory. Of the total quantity of the item produced, 50% is from A, 40% from B, and 10% from C. The probability that machine A produces a defective item is .01, that machine B produces a defective item is .005, and that machine C produces a defective item is .02. One item selected at random is found to be defective. Find the probability that the item was produced by A, by B, by C.

Solution: The experiment is the random selection of one item for test; record SA, SB, or SC if item is acceptable; otherwise record FA, FB, FC.

$$S = \{SA, SB, SC, FA, FB, FC\}$$

Let E be the event the item is defective.

$$E = \{FA, FB, FC\}$$

Let E_1 be the event *the item is from A.*

$$E_1 = \{SA, FA\}$$

$$P(E_1) = .5$$

$$P(E \mid E_1) = .01$$

Let E_2 be the event *the item is from B*

$$E_2 = \{SB, FB\}$$

$$P(E_2) = .4$$

$$P(E \mid E_2) = .005$$

Let E_3 be the event *the item is from C*

$$E_3 = \{SC, FC\}$$

$$P(E_3) = .1$$

$$P(E \mid E_3) = .02$$

$$P(E) = P(E_1)P(E \mid E_1) + P(E_2)P(E \mid E_2) + P(E_3)P(E \mid E_3)$$

$$= .5(.01) + .4(.005) + (.1)(.02)$$

$$= .005 + .002 + .002$$

$$= .009$$

Now using Bayes' Theorem to solve for $P(E_1 \mid E)$, $P(E_2 \mid E)$, and $P(E_3 \mid E)$,

$$P(E_1 \mid E) = \frac{P(E_1)P(E \mid E_1)}{P(E)}$$

$$= \frac{.5(.01)}{.009} = \frac{5}{9}$$

$$P(E_2 \mid E) = \frac{P(E_2)P(E \mid E_2)}{P(E)}$$

$$= \frac{.4(.005)}{.009} = \frac{2}{9}$$

$$P(E_3 \mid E) = \frac{P(E_3)P(E \mid E_3)}{.009} = \frac{2}{9}$$

EXERCISE 3.9

1. Twenty percent of the employees of a company are college graduates. Of these, 75% are in supervisory positions. Of those who did not attend college, 20% are in supervisory positions. What is the probability that a randomly selected supervisor is a college graduate?

2. In a given city 20% of the families have incomes of $12,000 or more, and of these 80% own homes valued at $24,000 or more. Of the families with less than $12,000 income, 30% own homes valued at $18,000 or more. If a randomly selected house has a value of $24,000 or more, what is the probability that the family that owns the house has an income of $12,000 or more?

3. In a factory four machines produce the same product. Machine A produces 10% of the output, machine B, 20%, machine C, 30%, and machine D, 40%. The proportion of defective items produced by these follows: Machine A: .001; Machine B: .0005; Machine C: .005; Machine D: .002. An item selected at random is found to be defective. What is the probability that the item was produced by A? by B? by C? by D?

4. In a given city, it is known that 30% of the population is age 60 or older. It is also known that 55% of the population is female and that 40% of the females are 60 years or older. If a man is randomly selected, what is the probability that he is 60 or older?

5. In the St. Petersburg Community College, 30% of the men and 20% of the women are studying mathematics. Further, 45% of the students are women. If a student selected at random is studying mathematics, what is the probability that the student is a woman?

3.15 BINOMIAL PROBABILITIES

Many important experiments consist of several repeated identical and independent acts. Each performance of the repeated act is called a *trial* of the experiment. The experiment itself is called a *repeated trials experiment*. When each performance of a trial may result in one of two possible outcomes, the experiment is called a *binomial experiment*. The properties of a binomial experiment are summarized as follows.

   (1) There must be a definite number of trials.
   (2) Each trial must result in one of two possible outcomes.
   (3) The probabilities assigned to each of the two outcomes must be the same for each trial.
   (4) Each of the trials must be independent of the others.

   Binomial experiments abound in many fields: a student passes or fails; a business succeeds or fails; an electric current is on or off; a housewife buys or fails to buy; a boy or a girl is born; a product passes or fails a

quality control test; a patient requires treatment or does not require treatment. It is customary to designate one of the two outcomes a *success* and
the other a *failure*, with success being denoted by s and failure denoted by
f. Examples of binomial experiments follow.

Example 1. Three students take a standardized test. From past
experience it is known that 3/4 of the students who take the test will pass it.
Record s if a student passes a test; otherwise record f. The sample space for
this experiment is

$$S = \{(s,s,s), (s,s,f), (s,f,s), (f,s,s), (f,f,s), (f,s,f), (s,f,f), (f,f,f)\}$$

Find the probabilities of the following events.

(*a*) Let E_1 be the event *all students pass.*

$$E_1 = \{(s,s,s)\}$$

$$P(E_1) = P\{(s,s,s)\} = \left(\frac{3}{4}\right)^3 \qquad \text{Why?}$$

(*b*) Let E_2 be the event *exactly two students pass.*

$$P(E_2) = P\{(s,s,f), (s,f,s), (f,s,s)\}$$

$$P(E_2) = 3\left(\frac{3}{4}\right)^2\left(\frac{1}{4}\right)^1 \qquad \text{Why?}$$

(*c*) Let E_3 be the event *exactly two students fail.*

$$P(E_3) = P\{(f,f,s), (f,s,f), (s,f,f)\}$$

$$P(E_3) = 3\left(\frac{3}{4}\right)^1\left(\frac{1}{4}\right)^2$$

(*d*) Let E_4 be the event *all students fail.*

$$P(E_4) = P\{(f,f,f)\}$$

$$P(E_4) = \left(\frac{1}{4}\right)^3$$

Example 2. Four electric motors are given a quality control test.
From past experience, it is known that the probability that a motor is
acceptable is 9/10. When a motor is acceptable, s is recorded; otherwise,
f. The sample space is

$$\begin{aligned}
S = \{&(s,s,s,s), (s,s,s,f), (s,s,f,s), (s,f,s,s), (f,s,s,s),\\
&(s,s,f,f), (s,f,s,f), (s,f,f,s), (f,s,f,s), (f,s,s,f),\\
&(f,f,s,s), (f,f,f,s), (f,f,s,f), (f,s,f,f), (s,f,f,f),\\
&(f,f,f,f)\}
\end{aligned}$$

Find the probabilities of the following events.

(*a*) Let E_1 be the event *exactly four successes.*

$$P(E_1) = \left(\frac{9}{10}\right)^4$$

(b) Let E_2 be the event *exactly three successes.*

$$P(E_2) = 4\left(\frac{9}{10}\right)^3\left(\frac{1}{10}\right)^1$$

(c) Let E_3 be the event *exactly two successes.*

$$P(E_3) = 6\left(\frac{9}{10}\right)^2\left(\frac{1}{10}\right)^2$$

(d) Let E_4 be the event *exactly one success.*

$$P(E_4) = 4\left(\frac{9}{10}\right)\left(\frac{1}{10}\right)^3$$

(e) Let E_5 be the event *exactly zero successes.*

$$P(E_5) = \left(\frac{1}{10}\right)^4$$

With the above and similar binomial experiments we are able to conclude by theorem 2.2 that the number of distinct permutations of r successes and $n - r$ failures in the n repeated trials is

$$P\left(\frac{n}{r, n - r}\right) = \frac{n!}{r!(n - r)!} = C\left(\frac{n}{r}\right)$$

The number $C\left(\frac{n}{r}\right)$ is the number of simple events (sample points) of the sample space S that yields the required number of successes. If p is the probability of success for each ($1 - p$ is the probability of failure), the probability that any given one of these simple events occurs is $p^r(1 - p)^{n-r}$, as the trials are independent. Hence, the following theorem:

THEOREM 3.5

If a binomial experiment of n trials is performed and the probability of success for each trial is p, then the probability that the experiment results in exactly r successes and $n - r$ failures is

$$C\left(\frac{n}{r}\right)p^r(1 - p)^{n-r}$$

The above probability is the $(n - r + 1)$-st term of the expansion by the binomial theorem of $[p + (1 - p)]^n$. Application of this theorem is illustrated in the following examples.

Example 1. On a true-false test consisting of ten questions, what is the probability of getting at least six answers correct by guessing?

Solution:

P(at least 6 successes) $= P(6, 7, 8, 9, \text{ or } 10 \text{ successes})$

$$= P(\text{exactly 10 successes}) + P(\text{exactly 9}$$
$$\text{successes}) \ldots + P(\text{exactly 6 successes})$$

$$= \binom{10}{0}\left(\frac{1}{2}\right)^{10} + \binom{10}{4}\left(\frac{1}{2}\right)^{9}\left(\frac{1}{2}\right)^{1}$$
$$+ \binom{10}{3}\left(\frac{1}{2}\right)^{8}\left(\frac{1}{2}\right)^{2} + \binom{10}{7}\left(\frac{1}{2}\right)^{7}\left(\frac{1}{2}\right)^{3}$$
$$+ \binom{10}{6}\left(\frac{1}{2}\right)^{6}\left(\frac{1}{2}\right)^{4}$$

Example 2. The records of an automobile insurance company show that 1/10 of the accidents involve bodily injury. Of 100 accidents reported, what is the probability that exactly 20 involve bodily injury?

Solution:

$$P(s) = \frac{9}{10}, \qquad P(f) = \frac{1}{10}$$

Let S be the event *a reported accident does not involve bodily injury.*

$$P(s) = \frac{9}{10}$$

$$= P \text{ (exactly 20 accidents involve bodily injury)}$$

$$= P \text{ (exactly 80 successes occur)}$$

$$= C\binom{100}{80}\left(\frac{9}{10}\right)^{80}\left(\frac{1}{10}\right)^{20}$$

This last probability may be easily evaluated using program 3.1.

3.16 COMPUTER SOLUTION OF BINOMIAL PROBABILITIES

In chapter 2, programs are included for computation of factorials, permutations, combinations, and the binomial expansion. A review of these programs should enable you to understand program 3.1 for computing probabilities for binomial experiments.

Program 3.1

```
10 PRINT "PROBABILITY OF N - R SUCCESS IN
   N TRIALS"
15 REM A IS PROB OF SUCCESS
20 INPUT N,R,A
25 LET B = 1 - A
30 LET W = 1
40 FOR X = 1 TO R
50 LET W = W * X
60 NEXT X
70 LET P = 1
80 FOR Y = (N - R + 1) TO N
90 LET P - P * Y
```

```
100 NEXT Y
110 LET C = P/W
120 LET Z = C * A (N - R) * B R
130 PRINT "N", "R", "PROB OF SUCCESS"
140 PRINT N,R,A
150 PRINT
160 PRINT "THE PROB OF N - R SUCCESSES IS,"
    Z
9999 END
```

EXERCISE 3.10

1. Three samples are withdrawn from a production line. The sample is marked *A* if acceptable and *R* if rejected. Construct a sample space showing all possible outcomes of the three samples.

2. Experience has shown that if twelve samples from a factory are inspected, on the average eight of the twelve will be accepted and four rejected. Determine the following.
   (*a*) The probability that any one sample is acceptable.
   (*b*) The probability that if six samples are inspected, four will be rejected.
   (*c*) The probability that if four samples are inspected, none will be rejected.

3. Records of an insurance company show that 3/1000 of the accidents reported to the company involve a fatality. Determine:
   (*a*) the probability that no fatality is involved in thirty accidents reported.
   (*b*) the probability that four fatal accidents are included in twenty accidents reported.

4. The records of a broker show that 20% of all prospective buyers make purchases. Determine:
   (*a*) the probability that the next ten prospects all make purchases.
   (*b*) the probability that at least nine of the ten will make purchases.

5. John Reeves completed 60% of his passes this season. Assuming he is as good a quarterback next fall, what is the probability that he will complete 80 of his first 100 passes?

6. Last year 90% of students passed a given course. Of the 30 students in a class, what is the probability that all will pass? That 20 will pass?

7. Three electric motors from a factory are tested. A motor is discarded, returned to the factory, or accepted. Using *d* for discard, *r* for return, and *a* for accept, write the term in the multinomial expansion of $(d + r + a)^3$ in which (d, r, a) appears. If the probability of acceptance is 7/10, the probability of return is 2/10, and the probability of discard is 1/10, what

is the probability that one motor is discarded, and two motors are accepted?

8. A survey was made of the patients who visit a clinic. The following dispositions are made:
(*a*) patient is pronounced fit (*F*)
(*b*) patient is asked to return for treatment (*T*)
(*c*) patient is hospitalized (*H*).

The probability for each disposition is $P(F) = \dfrac{7}{10}$, $P(T) = \dfrac{2}{10}$, $P(H) = \dfrac{1}{10}$.

What is the probability that 16 of the next 20 patients who visit the clinic will be hospitalized?

9. A survey was made of the number of people who read classified ads in a newspaper. Thirty people were asked to indicate which one of the following best applies to them: (1) read no ads (*N*); (2) read "articles for sale" ads (*S*); (3) read "help wanted" ads (*H*); (4) read all ads (*A*).
(*a*) Use the multinomial theorem for the expansion of

$$(N + S + H + A)^{30}$$

to find the coefficients of the terms involving
(1) _____ $N^{10}A^{10}H^{10}$
(2) _____ $N^{5}S^{10}H^{10}A^{5}$

(*b*) Assuming the following probabilities, what is the probability that 10 read no ads, 10 read "articles for sale" ads, and 10 read "help wanted" ads?

$$P\{N\} = \frac{30}{100}$$

$$P\{S\} = \frac{40}{100}$$

$$P\{H\} = \frac{20}{100}$$

$$P\{A\} = \frac{10}{100}$$

CHAPTER 4

Basic Statistical Concepts

4.1 THE NATURE OF STATISTICS

As a beginning student in statistics, you may have been overwhelmed by this word *statistics* and intimidated by the term *statistician*. You may not be sure of the meaning of either word; perhaps you only vaguely understand the role statistics and the statistician play in modern life. This chapter and the succeeding chapters in this textbook are intended to give an insight into the modern concepts of statistics and how statistics and probability are applied by the statistician.

The word *statistics* is derived from the word *state*. Governments, from the ancient civilizations of Greece and Rome down to the present-day civilizations, have collected and interpreted data. The early civilizations were mainly interested in statistics for purposes of war and taxes and, unfortunately, those same reasons seem to apply to some governments today. The Constitution of the United States, in the first article, requires that the government collect statistics each ten years on the population of the nation for purposes of apportioning the proper representation of the different states in the lower house of Congress. The federal government collects vast amounts of statistics and publishes an excellent collection in *Statistical Abstract of the United States*.

Often statistics are thought of only as collections of numerical facts, such as populations of cities and states, batting averages of baseball players, the number of families that have two-bathroom houses, or the number of students who are attending college. Numerical facts are not all of statistics, but it is true that they are important, just as formulas and experiments are important in chemistry. In this textbook, we shall consider the subject of statistics to consist of procedures for obtaining, processing, and analyzing data in an orderly manner and for making logical decisions based on the data. Much of the credit for the adaptation of scientific methods to phenomena that can be described numerically or by counting is given to a British statistician, Sir Ronald Fisher.

4.2 STATISTICS AND THE STATISTICIAN

The two categories under which most statistical data can be grouped are (1) data that pertains to practical problems of business, education, and industry and (2) data that pertains to problems of scientific knowledge. The practical problems range from lot acceptance sampling for goods received by a company to courses of study for students to pursue to meet degree requirements. In such cases, it is usually possible to state, in theory at least, the consequences of a proposed course of action and to evaluate each set of possible consequences. The problems of scientific knowledge, embracing such things as testing a new serum for some virus or a new therapy for mental or physical disorder, do not always lend themselves to clear-cut alternatives. Hence, the difference between practical and scientific problems may be of kind as well as of degree.

Any statistical decision—and, indeed, any decision—should be based on the right kind of data. The two general requirements are that the data must be reliable and valid. Data is considered reliable if each time the process of gathering data is repeated on the same subjects, the results are approximately the same. The data is considered valid if it provides a true measure of the characteristic it is supposed to measure. Therefore, the more reliable and valid the data obtained for a particular study, the less chance for error in the decision based on the data.

There are several stages that occur in arriving at decisions in a statistical study. The order in which the stages occur may not always be the same, but for simplification we may think of them as follows, keeping in mind that the stages are interrelated.

(1) The problem to be studied is selected and the scope of the study determined. The type and scope of the problem depend on the needs and desires of the person or company that initiates the study.

(2) The data is collected, processed, and summarized. The processing and summarization may take the form of tables, charts, and graphs, or a combination of all. The tables, charts, and graphs are means of

describing the data; hence, this part of the statistical study is referred to as *descriptive statistics*.

(3) The description of the data may reveal trends that appear to be relevant to the study. On the basis of these trends, hypotheses are formulated.

(4) The hypotheses that have been formulated are tested, and inferences or predictions are made. The formulation and testing of hypotheses and the predictions made on this basis are referred to as *statistical inference*.

The statistician uses his knowledge of statistics to decide how much and what kind of data is needed. Statistics provide ways of processing the data and methods by which predictions can be made about a larger set of data, based on the partial data obtained in a sample.

4.3 POPULATIONS AND SAMPLES

Probability, which was discussed in Chapter 3, and statistics are closely related fields of study, for each investigates the same basic situation from a different point of view. Each involves a large set, called the *population* or *sample space*, and one of its subsets, called the *sample* or *event*.

DEFINITION 4.1

A *population* is the total collection of elements under discussion having one or more common characteristics.

Example 1. If the students entering the first year of college are under statistical investigation, the *population* consists of all the students entering the first year of college.

Example 2. If the families living in a certain city are under investigation, the population is all families living in that city.

DEFINITION 4.2

A *sample* is that part of the population that is examined in a statistical investigation.

Example 1. If the population is all students entering the first year of college, then the students entering the first year of college at Gulf State College would be a *sample* from that population.

Example 2. If the population is the incomes of the families of a certain city, then the family incomes above $10,000 would be a sample.

DEFINITION 4.3

A sample is a *random sample* when each element in the population has the same chance of being included in the sample.

Example 1. If the speed of vehicles passing a checkpoint is being investigated, then the sample of vehicles selected is a *random sample* only if each vehicle (no matter what its speed) traveling past the checkpoint has an equal chance of being included in the sample.

Example 2. If the incomes of families living in a certain city is being investigated, then the sample of families selected is a random sample only if a family with a given income has an equal chance of selection with families having all other incomes.

Observations is the term which refers to the data of a statistical population or sample. Frequently other terms, such as *items, scores, values, measurements*, etc., are also used. Observations that may be described numerically—measured, counted, etc.—are called *quantitative data*. The individual values of quantitative data are called *variates*.

For example, in a study of absenteeism among 500 workers in a plant during a 30-day period, an investigator obtains the total number of hours each worker has been absent. The number of hours that a specified worker has been absent is a single observation. There are 500 single observations in the study $(x_1, x_2, \ldots, x_{500})$ and each single value is a *variate*.

In another case, an investigator might obtain the ages of 1,000 students entering Gulf State College. The age of each student is a single observation. There are 1,000 single observations, or variates, $(x_1, x_2, \ldots, x_{1000})$.

Whenever the observations describe a particular *quality*, the data is called *qualitative data*. The single observations are called *attributes*. These attributes tell only that a particular quality, such as "acceptable item," "registered Republican," "red hair," etc., is present or absent. We may assign a *quantitative* value to the variable to represent the presence or absence of a quality or attribute. To illustrate: a defective item taken from an assembly line may be valued at 0, while a nondefective item may be valued at 1. Also, in the treatment of disease, the *number* of cures achieved can be treated statistically, but a particular individual who undergoes the treatment is either cured or not cured (either 1 for cured or 0 for not cured).

The size of the sample selected for a statistical study is dependent upon the purpose and scope of the study. The sample may contain a few observations or it may contain thousands. The descriptive measures for both a small sample and a large sample carry the same meaning, but these measures may be calculated differently depending on the size of the sample.

A numerical value computed from the data in a sample is called a *statistic*. When these same values are computed from the data of a population they are called *parameters*. Parameters, being characteristic of an entire population, are not usually known. Statistics, on the other hand, being characteristics of a sample, are subject to change from one sample to another.

EXERCISE 4.1

1. Distinguish between reliability and validity for statistical data.

2. What are the stages of a statistical study?

3. Distinguish between population and sample.

4. Give an example of a population and specify at least two samples of that population.

5. Distinguish between sample and random sample.

6. What are some of the difficulties that may be encountered in selecting a random sample?

7. How does a sample of variates differ from a sample of attributes?

8. How does a statistic differ from a parameter?

9. What is the role of statistics and the statistician in conducting a statistical study?

4.4 DESCRIBING A SAMPLE OF UNGROUPED DATA— MEASURES OF CENTRAL TENDENCY

Once the data has been collected, it is organized and values that describe the sample—and thus the population—are computed. The calculation of the descriptive measures of a sample that consists of a small number of observations usually involves each of the observations. However, if the number of observations is large, they may be grouped and the measures calculated from the grouped data. Since the methods employed in computing these descriptive measures are less complicated in a small sample of ungrouped data, we shall first consider ungrouped data and then proceed to samples of grouped data.

DEFINITION 4.4

Any measure indicating a center of a set of data, arranged in order of magnitude, is called a *measure of central tendency*.

The most commonly used measures of central tendency are the arithmetic mean, median, and mode. These measures indicate how the observations tend to "cluster" about some interior value and serve to locate the "middle" of the sample. The most important measure of central tendency and the one we shall consider first is the *arithmetic mean*. The arithmetic mean is often referred to as the *mean* or as the *average*.

DEFINITION 4.5

The arithmetic sum of the observations in a sample (not necessarily distinct) divided by the number of observations in the sample is called the *arithmetic mean* and is denoted by $\bar{x}$.

Example 1. Find the mean of the sample whose observations are 7, 12, and 17.

Solution: $\bar{x} = \dfrac{7 + 12 + 17}{3} = \dfrac{36}{3} = 12$

Example 2. Find the average (mean) weight of five babies whose weights are 7.5 lbs., 7.75 lbs., 8.5 lbs., 8.5 lbs., and 8.25 lbs.

Solution:

$$\bar{x} = \frac{7.5 + 7.75 + 8.5 + 8.5 + 8.25}{5} = \frac{40.5}{5} = 8.1 \text{ lbs.}$$

For convenience, the sum of the n terms in an array of numbers $x_1, \ldots, x_n$ may be written in a *summation notation*, symbolized by $\sum_{i=1}^{n} x_i$. This is perhaps your first encounter with this notation, and a brief explanation is in order. The symbol $\sum$ is the capital Greek letter sigma, used to indicate the sum of numbers in an array. The general, or "ith" term, is written x_i. In an array of n numbers, the first number is denoted by x_i, the second by x_2, and the last by x_n. The $i = 1$ below the sigma indicates the sum is to begin with the first term and the n above indicates that it ends with the term denoted by x_n. That is,

$$\sum_{i=1}^{n} x_i = x_1 + x_2 + x_3 + \ldots + x_n$$

The symbol $\sum_{i=1}^{n} x_i$ is read "the summation of x_i, where i assumes all integral values from 1 to n inclusive." The mean of a sample when expressed in summation notation is

$$\bar{x} = \frac{\sum_{i=1}^{n} x_i}{n}$$

Example 3. Find the mean of the sample whose observations are 5, 8, 12, 15.

Solution: $x_1 = 5, \quad x_2 = 8, \quad x_3 = 12, \quad x_4 = 15.$ Therefore,

$$\bar{x} = \frac{\sum_{i=1}^{4} x_i}{4} = \frac{x_1 + x_2 + x_3 + x_4}{4} = \frac{5 + 8 + 12 + 15}{4} = \frac{40}{4} = 10$$

Example 4. Find the mean of the sample whose observations are 2, 3, 6, 8, 9.

Solution: $x_1 = 2$, $x_2 = 3$, $x_3 = 6$, $x_4 = 8$, $x_5 = 9$. Therefore,

$$\bar{x} = \frac{\sum_{i=1}^{n} x_i}{5} = \frac{x_1 + x_2 + x_3 + x_4 + x_5}{5} = \frac{2 + 3 + 6 + 8 + 9}{5} = \frac{28}{5}$$

$$= 5.6$$

A program for calculating the mean of a sample appears in program 4.1.

Program 4.1

```
10 PRINT  "MEAN"
20 DIM X(N)
30 DATA N
40 DATA X(1),X(2),X(3),...,X(N)
50 LET M = 0
60 READ N
70 FOR I = 1 TO N
80 READ X(I)
90 LET M= M + X(I)/N
100 NEXT I
110 PRINT M
990 END
```

The mean of a sample is easily computed and is widely used as a reference point in comparing the individual observations to the sample as a whole. Its greatest disadvantage is that a few extreme observations in the sample may cause it to become almost meaningless if the sample size is small. To illustrate: consider the sample A, whose observations are 2, 4, 6, 8, and sample B, whose observations are 2, 4, 6, 28. The mean of sample A is 5 and the mean of sample B is 10. Although A and B contain three observations that are the same, the fourth observation in B is extreme and changes the mean from 5 to 10. For many purposes, the mean of B is almost useless because it is larger than any observation in B except 28. For the mean to be useful as a measure of central tendency, it must be fairly close to the middle of the sample.

The *median* is the second most used measure of central tendency. The median of a sample is defined as follows.

DEFINITION 4.6

In a sample whose observations are arranged in order of magnitude, that is $x_1, x_2, \ldots, x_n$, if n is odd, then $x_{(n+1)/2}$ is the *median*. If n is even, then the *median* is $\dfrac{x_{n/2} + x_{(n+2)/2}}{2}$.

Example 1. Find the median of the sample whose observations are 5, 8, 3, 6, 9, 4, 10.

Solution: Arranging the observations in order of magnitude, we have 3, 4, 5, 6, 8, 9, 10. There are seven observations in the sample, and the fourth observation, $x_{(n+1)/2}$, or the number 6, is the median.

Example 2. Find the median of the sample whose observations are 3, 6, 4, 7, 9, 8.

Solution: Arranging the observations in order of magnitude, we have 3, 4, 6, 7, 8, 9. There are six observations in the sample, and the median, $\dfrac{x_{n/2} + x_{(n+2)/2}}{2}$, is $\dfrac{6+7}{2} = 6\frac{1}{2}$. The median, like the mean, is not always an observation in the sample of data.

The third measure of central tendency that we shall discuss is called the *mode*.

DEFINITION 4.7

The *mode* of a sample of observations is the observation which occurs at least as many times as any other observation.

Example 1. Find the mode for the sample composed of the observations 4, 5, 6, 6, 6, 7, 7, 8.

Solution: The observation 6 appears most often and is the mode.

Example 2. Find the mode for the sample composed of the observations 2, 3, 4, 5, 5, 6, 7, 7, 10.

Solution: The observations 5 and 7 both appear twice in the data, while the other observations appear only once. Both observations 5 and 7 are modes, and the sample is said to be *bimodal*.

The question often arises as to which of the measures of central tendency should be used. There is no way that this question can be answered to fit all occasions. The mean is easy to calculate and contains all available information, but, as we have shown, it is affected by extreme values in the sample. The median is not affected by extreme values, and for this reason it is sometimes a better measure of central tendency than the mean. However, the sample mean is likely to be closer to the population mean than the sample median is to the population median. The mode is almost useless as a measure of central tendency when the sample contains only a small number of observations. It becomes more significant as the number of observations increases. Its one advantage is that it requires no calculation. The arithmetic mean, the median, and the mode are all statistics, as they are numerical values based on the sample values.

4.5 MEASURES OF VARIABILITY (DISPERSION)

The measures of central tendency discussed in the previous section describe how the data seems to cluster about some central value. However, they tell nothing about how close together or how far apart the observations in the sample may be. That is, we have no indication of how the observations are scattered. Statistics measuring this characteristic of the data are termed *measures of variation* or *measures of dispersion*. Since several samples may have the same measures of central tendency but the observations in the sample may vary considerably, we get a more complete description of the data when we look at the measures of variation.

DEFINITION 4.8

Any statistic indicating how a set of data is scattered about a center is called a *measure of dispersion*.

Consider the following observations of the percentages of butterfat content for two samples of milk, bottled by Dairy *A* and Dairy *B*.

Sample from Dairy *A*: 4.1, 4.3, 4.2, 4.4, 4.0.

Sample from Dairy *B*: 4.0, 3.8, 4.2, 4.4, 4.6.

Both samples have the same mean, 4.2, but it is apparent that the milk bottled by Dairy *A* is much more uniform in its content of butterfat than is the milk bottled by Dairy *B*. Also, the contents from Dairy *A* do not vary as much from the mean, 4.2, as the contents from Dairy *B* and, as a result, we would feel more confident that the butterfat content in a bottle of milk from Dairy *A* would exceed the government standard minimum of 4.0% than would a bottle from Dairy *B*.

The measures of variability or dispersion that we shall discuss are the *range, variance,* and *standard deviation*.

DEFINITION 4.9

The *range* of a sample is the difference between the largest and the smallest observation in the sample.

Example 1. Find the range of the sample composed of the observations 3, 12, 15, 7, 9.

Solution: The largest observation is 15 and the smallest is 3. The range is $15 - 3 = 12$.

Example 2. Find the range of the sample composed of the observations 33, 53, 35, 37, 49.

Solution: The largest observation is 53 and the smallest is 33. The range is $53 - 33 = 20$.

The range of the butterfat content in the samples of milk bottled by Dairy *A* is $4.4 - 4.0 = .4$. The range of the sample from Dairy *B* is $4.6 - 3.8 = .8$. This difference in the ranges of the two samples indicates the greater spread in the butterfat content of milk from Dairy *B*.

Although the range is easy to calculate, it is not generally satisfactory as a measure of variation. For one thing, it involves only two of the observations, the largest and the smallest, regardless of the number of observations in the sample. As a result, it reveals nothing about the scatter of the other observations. Consider the two samples of observations:

$$A = \{3,5,7,9,11,13\}$$
$$B = \{3,4,5,11,12,13\}$$

The range of each is 10. The mean and median of each are 8. However, the observations in sample A tend to cluster about the mean and median more closely than those of sample B.

This disadvantage of the range as a measure of variation limits its usefulness, and we must consider more adequate measures. Since the mean can be considered a balance point, we can get a better description of variation by finding the difference between each observation and the mean. These differences or deviations from the mean are also referred to as *distance scores*.

Other measures that describe the variation of the observations in a sample are the *variance* and the *standard deviation*.

DEFINITION 4.10

If the data values in a sample of observations are $x_1, x_2, x_3, \ldots, x_n$, then the variance, denoted s^2, of the sample is the sum of the squares of the deviations from the mean divided by the number of observations, n, in the sample. That is,

$$s^2 = \frac{\sum\limits_{i=1}^{n} (x_i - \bar{x})^2}{n}$$

Example 1. Find the variance of the sample of observations 2, 5, 7, 9, 12.

Solution:

$$\bar{x} = \frac{35}{5} = 7$$

$$s^2 = \frac{(2-7)^2 + (5-7)^2 + (7-7)^2 + (9-7)^2 + (12-7)^2}{5}$$

$$= \frac{(-5)^2 + (-2)^2 + (0)^2 + (2)^2 + (5)^2}{5}$$

$$= \frac{25 + 4 + 0 + 4 + 25}{5}$$

$$= \frac{58}{5} = 11.6$$

Example 2. A man and wife have six children whose ages are 6, 8, 10, 12, 14, and 16. Find the variance in ages.

Solution:

$$\bar{x} = \frac{66}{6} = 11$$

$$s^2 = \frac{(6-11)^2+(8-11)^2+(10-11)^2+(12-11)^2+(14-11)^2+(16-11)^2}{6}$$

$$= \frac{(-5)^2 + (-3)^2 + (-1)^2 + (1)^2 + (3)^2 + (5)^2}{6}$$

$$= \frac{25 + 9 + 1 + 1 + 9 + 25}{6}$$

$$= \frac{70}{6} \doteq 11.7$$

The calculation of the variance using definition 4.10 can be long and tedious, as the deviation of each measurement from the mean is involved. In example 2 we found the sum of the squares of the deviations to be

$$\sum_{i=1}^{6} (x_i - \bar{x})^2 = 70$$

Fortunately, when the work is to be done manually there is an alternate and much shorter method for finding $\sum_{i=1}^{n} (x_i - \bar{x})^2$. To illustrate this alternate method, we tabulate the data of example 2 in the table below. The first column contains the individual measurements, and the second column contains the squares of the measurements.

x_i	x_i^2
6	36
8	64
10	100
12	144
14	196
16	256
$\sum_{i=1}^{6} x_i = 66$	$\sum_{i=1}^{6} x_i^2 = 796$

Our calculations show that

$$\sum_{i=1}^{n} x_i^2 - \frac{\left(\sum_{i=1}^{n} x_i\right)^2}{n} = 796 - \frac{(66)^2}{6}$$

$$= 796 - 726$$

$$= 70.$$

You will note that the two sums, $\sum_{i=1}^{6} (x_i - \bar{x})^2$ and

$$\left(\sum_{i=1}^{n} x_i^2 = \frac{\left(\sum_{i=1}^{n} x_i \right)^2}{n} \right),$$

yield the same results. This is no accident, and we shall show that in general

$$\sum_{i=1}^{n} (x_i - \bar{x})^2 = \sum_{i=1}^{n} x_i^2 - \frac{\left(\sum_{i=1}^{n} x_i \right)^2}{n}$$

Proof:

$$\sum_{i=1}^{n} (x_i - (\bar{x})^2) = \sum_{i=1}^{n} (x_i^2 - 2\bar{x}x_i + \bar{x}^2)$$

$$= \sum_{i=1}^{n} x_i^2 - 2\bar{x} \sum_{i=1}^{n} x_i + \sum_{i=1}^{n} \bar{x}^2$$

$$= \sum_{i=1}^{n} x_i^2 - \left(\frac{2 \sum_{i=1}^{n} x_i}{n} \right)\left(\sum_{i=1}^{n} x_i \right) + n\bar{x}^2$$

$$= \sum_{i=1}^{n} x_i^2 - \frac{2}{n}\left(\sum_{i=1}^{n} x_i \right)^2 + n\frac{\left(\sum_{i=1}^{n} x_i \right)^2}{n^2}$$

$$= \sum_{i=1}^{n} x_i^2 - \frac{\left(\sum_{i=1}^{n} x_i \right)^2}{n}$$

Using the alternate formula for finding the sum of the squares of the deviations, the variance of the data in example 2 is

$$s^2 = \sum_{i=1}^{n} x_i^2 - \frac{\left(\sum_{i=1}^{n} x_i \right)^2}{n} \bigg/ n$$

$$= \frac{796 - 726}{6}$$

$$= 11.7$$

A program to compute the variance is given in program 4.2.

Program 4.2

```
10 READ N
20 FOR I = 1 TO N
```

```
 30 READ X
 40 LET A = A + X
 50 LET B = B + X ↑ 2
 60 NEXT I
 70 LET P = (A ↑ 2)/N
 80 LET M = A/N
 90 LET V = (B - P)/N
100 PRINT   "THE MEAN IS";   M
110 PRINT   "THE VARIANCE IS";   V
120 END
```

The variance has several properties that make it useful as a measure of dispersion even though its practical significance at this point may seem almost nil. One property that makes the variance useful is that it is independent of the mean. We are interested in how the observations are scattered; measures of central tendency tell us nothing about this, whereas the variance does. A second property is that the measure of variance is not related to the number of observations; that is, it reflects the dissimilarity of the observations and not the number of observations. (*Note:* This property does not hold for the range; as the number of observations increases, the range cannot get smaller.) A third property is that the measure of variance is small when the data are clustered closely about the mean, becoming larger as the data are scattered. The larger the measure of variability, the more scattered are the observations.

These properties enable us to compare the variability of samples and to determine which sample is more variable. To illustrate, consider two samples A and B and their variance, as shown:

$$A = \{3, 4, 7, 9, 11, 13\} \qquad \bar{x} = 8 \qquad s^2 = 11.7$$

$$B = \{3, 4, 5, 11, 12, 13\} \qquad \bar{x} = 8 \qquad s^2 = 16.7$$

We see that sample A has a mean of 8 and a variance of 11.7, while sample B has a mean of 8 and a variance of 16.7. Thus, the measurements in B are more scattered than the measurements in A, and we say that B is more variable than A.

Variance is an excellent measure of dispersion, but it has one disadvantage. When the data is scattered over a wide range, the measure of variance may be quite large and unwieldly. To overcome this disadvantage another measure of variability, called the *standard deviation*, is preferred by many who work with statistics.

The standard deviation, denoted by s, is derived from the variance and, as such, has all the properties ascribed to the variance. The variance has been defined as the average of the squares of the deviations from the mean, and the standard deviation is the positive square root of this average.

DEFINITION 4.11

The *standard deviation* is the positive square root of the variance, i.e.,

$$s = \sqrt{s^2} = \sqrt{\frac{\sum_{i=1}^{n}(x_i - \bar{x})^2}{n}}$$

Example 1. Find the standard deviation of the sample of measurements $1, 3, 7, 10, 14$.

    Solution: $\bar{x} = 7$ $s^2 = 22$ $s = \sqrt{22} \doteq 4.7$

Example 2. Find the standard deviation of the sample of measurements $3, 10, 10, 11, 15, 15, 26, 30$.

    Solution: $\bar{x} = 15$ $s^2 = 69.5$ $s = \sqrt{69.5} \doteq 8.4$

Program 4.3 calculates the standard deviation, along with the mean and variance.

Program 4.3

```
10 PRINT   "MEAN",   "VARIANCE", "STANDARD
   DEVIATION"
20 DIM X(N)
30 DATA N
40 DATA X(1),X(2),X(3),...,X(N)
45 LET M = 0
46 LET V = 0
50 READ N
60 FOR I = 1 TO N
70 READ X(I)
80 LET M = M + X(I)/N
90 NEXT I
100 FOR I = 1 TO N
110 LET V = V + ((X(I) - M) * (X(I) - M))/N
120 NEXT I
130 LET S = V ↑ .5
140 PRINT M,V,S
990 END
```

    The variance is measured in terms of the squares of the original data. That is, if the given measurements are expressed in units of feet, then the variance is expressed in units of square feet. Taking the square root of the variance, we obtain the standard deviation and our unit of measure of variability is expressed in the original units of measure. For this reason the standard deviation is a more meaningful and useful measure of variation than the variance. However, both have an important role in statistics, as will be brought out in future discussion.

EXERCISE 4.2

1. The numbers of touchdowns scored in the games of a season by a football team were 2, 3, 0, 3, 4, 1, 3, 0.
   (a) What is the mean number of touchdowns scored?
   (b) What is the median?
   (c) What is the mode?

2. In a freshman class the absences of a sample of 20 students for the semester were 1, 3, 0, 2, 1, 0, 4, 5, 0, 3, 2, 6, 2, 1, 0, 2, 3, 5, 4, 1.
   (a) What is the mean number of absences?
   (b) What is the median?
   (c) What is the mode?

3. Calculate the range, variance, and standard deviation for problem 1.

4. Calculate the range, variance, and standard deviation for problem 2.

5. On a fishing trip, eight fish were caught, with lengths of 9, 11, 8, 15, 14, 12, 17, 14 measured to the nearest inch.
   (a) Find the measures of central tendency for the data.
   (b) Find the measures of dispersion for the data.

6. An importer of foreign cars advertises that the cars average 23 miles per gallon of gasoline.
   (a) Would you interpret this advertisement to refer to the mean, median, or mode?
   (b) If you were considering a purchase of one of those cars, would you be more impressed if the advertisement referred to the mean, the median, or the mode?

7. A manufacturer of outboard motors receives a shipment of shearpins to be used in the assembly of its motors. A random sample of ten pins is selected and tested to determine the amount of pressure required to cause the pin to break. When tested, the required pressures to the nearest pound are 19, 23, 27, 19, 23, 28, 27, 28, 29, 27.
   (a) Calculate the measures of central tendency.
   (b) Calculate the measures of variation.

8. Show that the samples of observations $A = \{3, 6, 2, 1, 7, 5\}$ and $B = \{6, 7, 3, 2, 8, 4\}$ have different means but the same standard deviation. Why is this possible?

9. The following observations represent a random sample of the grades of

two students in a mathematics class: Vera—75, 80, 85, 84, 83, 86, 84, 86, 88, 85; John—60, 95, 61, 90, 96, 85, 100, 70, 94, 85.

(a) What is the mean score of each?

(b) What is the difference in the variance of the grades of Vera and John?

(c) If you were selecting either Vera or John to represent the class in a scholarship contest, which person would you choose? Why?

10. The standard deviation has been defined as $s = \sqrt{s^2}$.

(a) If the variance of a sample is 1,600, what is the standard deviation?

(b) If the variance of a sample is 1/4, what is the standard deviation?

(c) Under what condition is the variance larger than the standard deviation?

11. What can be said about a sample of observations whose standard deviation is zero?

4.6 DESCRIBING A SAMPLE OF GROUPED DATA

Statistical data consists of observations that have been collected and recorded. A better description of a sample containing a large number of observations can be obtained by grouping the individual observations into *classes* or *class intervals*. When the data in a sample has been divided into classes, it is referred to as *grouped data*.

The grouping of data into classes minimizes the difficulty in describing the sample. The advantage gained by grouping more than offsets the loss of identity of the individual observations in the data. When the data has been divided into classes, the number of observations in each class is called the *class frequency* of that class and for the ith class interval is denoted by f_i. The arrangement of the data in such a manner is called a *frequency distribution*.

The following observations are a listing of the weights of 100 sixth-grade students recorded to the nearest pound, arranged in order of magnitude.

59	64	67	69	71	73	74	76	79	82
60	64	67	69	71	73	74	76	79	82
60	65	67	70	72	73	74	76	79	82
61	65	67	70	72	73	74	77	79	82
62	65	68	70	72	73	75	77	79	83
62	65	68	70	72	73	75	77	80	83
63	66	68	70	72	73	75	77	80	84
63	66	68	71	72	73	75	78	80	85
63	66	68	71	72	74	75	78	81	86
63	67	69	71	72	74	75	78	81	87

A description of the sample is obtained more easily by grouping the data. For our purpose we choose to divide the data into ten class intervals of equal width: 59–61, 62–64, 65–67, 68–70, 71–73, 74–76, 77–79, 80–82, 83–85, and 86–88. In a sample of this size, ten to twelve classes are desirable but not mandatory. If the number of classes is too small, the accuracy of the summary obtained is questionable; if the number of classes is too large, the summary may be too extensive to be of practical value. The number of classes into which the data is divided is optional, and the statistician must decide upon and use the number best suited to his purpose.

The *class limits* of the ten classes are denoted by the smallest and largest values in the class interval. The smallest value in a class represents the *lower class limit*, and the largest represents the *upper class limit*. The lower class limit of the class 59–61 is 59, and the upper class limit is 61. The lower class limit of the second class is 62, and the upper class limit is 64.

When a distribution is to be described graphically, *class boundaries* are used to enclose the class intervals. Returning to the weights of the students, the upper class limit of the first class is 61 and the lower class limit of the second class is 62. The midpoint between these two classes is 61.5. This midpoint is called the *upper class boundary* of the first class interval and the *lower class boundary* of the second class interval. In like manner, 64.5 is the upper boundary of the second class and the lower boundary of the third class. The remaining class boundaries are determined in the same way. All observations in a given class must be greater than its lower boundary and less than its upper boundary. In order for class boundaries to be halfway between intervals, their values must be carried to one more decimal place than the observations that are grouped. Class boundaries eliminate the possibility of an observation falling into two classes.

The difference between the lower class boundary and the upper class boundary is called the *class width*. The width of the first class in table 4.1 is 3 (61.5 − 58.5), and the width of the second class is 3 (64.5 − 61.5). The successive class bounds can be found by adding the class widths, 3, to the upper class boundary of the preceeding class interval. It is not necessary but usually good practice for all classes to have the same width.

The midpoint of the ith class interval is called the *class mark*, and is denoted by x_i. It is found by dividing the sum of either the class boundaries or the class limits by 2. The class mark for the first interval in table 4.1 is 60, determined through class boundaries $\left(\dfrac{58.5 + 61.5}{2} = 60\right)$ or class limits $\left(\dfrac{59 + 61}{2} = 60\right)$.

When the appropriate class intervals have been determined, the number of observations falling in each class is counted and regarded as the frequency of that class. The entries in table 4.1 form a frequency distribution of the weights of our 100 sixth-grade students.

Table 4.1 Frequency Distribution Table of the Weights of 100 Sixth-Grade Students

Class Interval	Class Boundary	Tally	Class Mark (x_i)	Class Frequency (f_i)
59–61	58.5–61.5	1111	60	4
62–64	61.5–64.5	HHI 111	63	8
65–67	64.5–67.5	HHI HHI 11	66	12
68–70	67.5–70.5	HHI HHI 111	69	13
71–73	70.5–73.5	HHI HHI HHI HHI 1	72	21
74–76	73.5–76.5	HHI HHI HHI	75	15
77–79	76.5–79.5	HHI HHI 11	78	12
80–82	79.5–82.5	HHI 1111	81	9
83–85	82.5–85.5	1111	84	4
86–88	85.5–88.5	11	87	2
				100

The steps in making a frequency distribution table are summarized as follows:

(1) Determine the number of class intervals to be formed.
(2) Establish the class intervals and class boundaries.
(3) Make a tally of the elements in each class interval.
(4) Calculate the class marks.
(5) Record the frequency of each class interval.
(6) Find the sum of the class frequencies to check against the number of observations in the sample.

The *relative frequency* of a class is found by dividing the class frequency by the total number of observations in the sample. The results, when multiplied by 100, form a *percentage distribution*. The class relative frequencies and the percentage distribution of the weights of the 100 sixth-grade students are given in table 4.2.

The relative frequency of a class is the empirical probability that a random observation from the population will fall into that class. The relative frequency of the class 59–61 in table 4.2 is 4/100 and, therefore, the empirical probability of a random observation falling in this interval is 4/100. As was shown in chapter 3, the empirical probability of the union of the class events in the distribution must be equal to one.

Table 4.2 enables us to determine quickly the percentage of the observations in a sample that lie in a particular class interval. When we want to know the percentage of observations that is above or below a specified interval boundary, the cumulative frequency distributions can be used to advantage. The total number of observations that are less than the upper boundary of a particular class is called the *cumulative frequency* of that class. These frequencies, when expressed as percentages, form a *cumulative percentage distribution*.

Table 4.2 Relative Frequency and Percentage Distribution of 100 Sixth-Grade Students

Class	Frequency (f_i)	Relative Frequency	Percentage Distribution
59–61	4	4/100	4
62–64	8	8/100	8
65–67	12	12/100	12
68–70	13	13/100	13
71–73	21	21/100	21
74–76	15	15/100	15
77–79	12	12/100	12
80–82	9	9/100	9
83–85	4	4/100	4
86–88	2	2/100	2
	100		100%

The data in a frequency distribution may be represented graphically by a bar graph called a *histogram*. The histogram is constructed by marking off the class boundaries along a horizontal axis and drawing a rectangle to represent each class. The base of the rectangle corresponds to the class width, and the height of the rectangle corresponds to the frequency of that class. (The frequency is also referred to as class density.) Figure 4.1 is a histogram of the data in table 4.1. It should be pointed out that the areas above the various classes are proportional to the frequency of those classes.

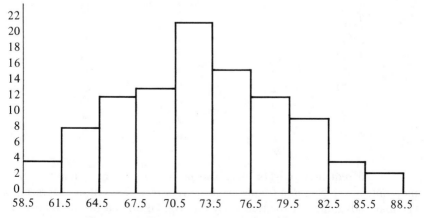

Figure 4.1 Frequency Histogram of the Weights of the 100 Sixth-Grade Students

Occasionally, a *frequency polygon* is used instead of a frequency histogram. In constructing a frequency polygon, the points (x_i, f_i) are plotted on horizontal and vertical axes. The polygon is completed by adding a class mark with 0 frequency to each end of the distribution and joining all the points with line segments. The frequency polygon for the data in table 4.1 is shown in figure 4.2.

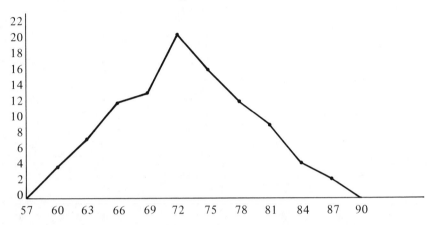

Figure 4.2 Frequency Polygon of the Weights of 100 Sixth-Grade Students

Table 4.3 Cumulative Frequency and Cumulative Percentage Distribution of the 100 Sixth-Grade Students

Class	Frequency (f_i)	Cumulative Frequency	Cumulative Percentage
59–61	4	4	4
62–64	8	12	12
65–67	12	24	24
68–70	13	37	37
71–73	21	58	58
71–76	15	73	73
77–79	12	85	85
80–82	9	94	94
83–85	4	98	98
86–89	2	100	100%
	100		

A frequency polygon may also be constructed by connecting the midpoints of the bars in a frequency histogram by a series of line segments. The main advantage of the frequency polygon compared to the frequency histogram is that it indicates that the observations in the class interval are not all the same. Also, when several sets of data are to be shown on the same graph, it is clearer to superimpose frequency polygons than to super-impose frequency histograms, especially if class boundaries coincide.

It is often advantageous and desirable to make a graph showing the cumulative frequency within a sample. The data for such a graph depicting the cumulative frequency of the weights of the 100 sixth-grade students are found in column three of table 4.3. The graph, called an *ogive*, (pronounced o-jive), is illustrated in figure 4.3. To avoid the confusion of less than or greater than, the class boundaries are plotted on the horizontal axis instead of the class marks.

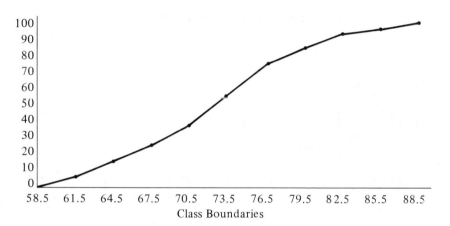

Figure 4.3 Cumulative Frequency Graph
of the Weights of 100 Sixth-Grade Students

The cumulative frequency graph makes it easy to read such items as the number of students whose weights are less than or greater than a specified weight. If the cumulative percentage had been plotted, the graph would appear the same but would be called a *percentage ogive*. The percentage ogive is more useful in many fields using statistics than is the cumulative frequency ogive. The percentage ogive will be dealt with in discussing percentiles later in the chapter.

The description of a sample of attributes, both numerically and graphically, is a simple task. The frequency distribution table is constructed by listing the various attributes together with their frequencies.

Example 1. Twenty students are enrolled in the foreign language department, and their major fields are as follows: Spanish, Spanish, French, Italian, French, Spanish, German, German, Russian, Russian, French, German, German, German, Spanish, Russian, German, Italian, German, Spanish.

(*a*) Make a frequency distribution table.

(*b*) Make a frequency histogram.

Solution:

(*a*) Frequency distribution table.

Major field	Number of students
German	7
Russian	3
Spanish	5
French	3
Italian	2
Total	20

(*b*) The frequency histogram is shown in figure 4.4.

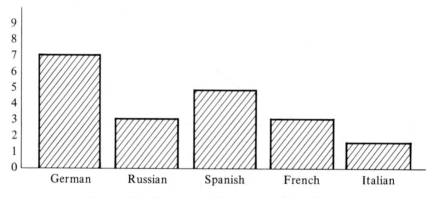

Figure 4.4 Frequency Histogram of Attributes

In the histogram the attributes are listed and spaced evenly along the horizontal axis. Each specific attribute is represented by a rectangle, and all of these rectangles have the same width. The height of each rectangle, identified by a number on the vertical axis, corresponds to the frequency of that attribute.

4.7 MEAN OF GROUPED DATA

The mean of ungrouped data has been defined as the arithmetic average of the individual observations. When the data is grouped, the individual measurements lose their identity, and to find the mean we assume that all of the observations in a class are represented by the class mark. This, of course, is slightly inaccurate, but it is reasonable since some values may fall below the class mark and some above. The mean for grouped data is defined as follows.

DEFINITION 4.12

If $x_1, x_2, x_3, \ldots, x_n$ are class marks in a sample of grouped data with corresponding frequencies of $f_1, f_2, f_3, \ldots, f_n$, then the mean of the sample is

$$\bar{x} = \frac{\displaystyle\sum_{i=1}^{n} x_i f_i}{\displaystyle\sum_{i=1}^{n} f_i}$$

Example. Find the mean weight of the 100 sixth-grade students as tabulated in table 4.1.

Solution: As an aid in computing the mean, the following table is utilized. This table is an extension of table 4.1 and includes the column $x_i f_i$.

Class Boundaries	Class Marks (x_i)	Frequencies (f_i)	$x_i f_i$
58.5–61.5	60	4	240
61.5–64.5	63	8	504
64.5–67.5	66	12	792
67.5–70.5	69	13	897
70.5–73.5	72	21	1,512
73.5–76.5	75	15	1,125
76.5–79.5	78	12	936
79.5–82.5	81	9	729
82.5–85.5	84	4	336
85.5–88.5	88	2	174
		$\displaystyle\sum_{i=1}^{100} f_i = 100$	$\displaystyle\sum_{i=1}^{100} x_i f_i = 7{,}245$

The total of the third column is $\displaystyle\sum_{i=1}^{n} f_i$, and the total of the fourth column is $\displaystyle\sum_{i=1}^{n} x_i f_i$. Thus we have $\bar{x} = \dfrac{7245}{100} = 72.45$.

A computer program for calculating the mean of grouped data is given in program 4.4.

Program 4.4

```
10 PRINT "MEAN"
20 DIM X(N),F(N)
30 DATA N
40 DATA X(1),F(1),X(2),F(2),X(3),F(4),....,
   X(N), F(N)
50 LET T = 0
60 LET C = 0
70 READ N
80 FOR I = 1 TO N
90 READ X(I),F(I)
```

```
100 LET T = T + (X(I) * F(I))
110 LET C = C + F(I)
120 NEXT I
130 LET M = T/C
140 PRINT M
990 END
```

4.8 MEDIAN AND PERCENTILE FOR GROUPED DATA

The median for grouped data is the value that divides the cumulative frequencies into two equal parts so that one half of the observations are below and one half above it. Geometrically, the median is that point on the horizontal axis where a vertical line intersecting it divides the area of the histogram into two equal parts or areas. Also, the empirical probability of a random observation taken from the population falling above the median is 1/2, and the probability of it falling below is 1/2.

Example. Find the median weight of the 100 sixth-grade students as tabulated in table 4.1.

Solution: There are 100 observations (students' weights) in the sample. The cumulative frequency table 4.3 shows that the first four intervals contain 37 observations and the first five contain 58. Obviously, the 50th observation is contained in the fifth class interval. The width of the fifth class is 3, and, since it contains 21 observations, we say that each observation has a width of 3/21, or 1/7, of the width of the interval. We are looking for the 13th observation (the 50th in the cumulative column); therefore, we multiply 1/7 by 13, obtaining 13/7 as the required width. Adding the required width to the lower boundary of the fifth interval, we have 70.5 + 13/7 = 72.36, which is the median.

In general, the median of a sample of grouped data can be found by adding the proportional part of the interval containing the median to the lower boundary of that interval. We can now define the median M for grouped data as follows.

DEFINITION 4.13

$$M = L + C \frac{\left[\dfrac{N}{2} - S_f\right]}{F_m}$$

where L = lower class boundary of the median class, i.e., the class containing the median;

N = number of observations in the sample, i.e., the total frequency;

S_f = sum of the frequencies of all classes lower than the median class;

F_m = frequency of the median class;

C = width of the median class.

Solution of the previous example by the formula:

$$L = 70.5$$
$$N = 100$$
$$S_f = 37$$
$$F_m = 21$$
$$C = 3$$

The median $= 70.5 + 3\dfrac{\left[\dfrac{100}{2} - 37\right]}{21}$

$$= 70.5 + 3\dfrac{[50 - 37]}{21}$$

$$= 70.5 + \dfrac{13}{7}$$

$$= 72.36$$

The formula for finding the median, or 50th percentile, is easily adjusted for finding any percentile. In many of the sciences dealing with human behavior, and especially in education, the terms *quartile, decile,* and *percentile* are used. Percentiles refer to a division of the percentage distribution into intervals of 1%, deciles into intervals of 10%, and quartiles into intervals of 25%. The cumulative percentage ogive is illustrated in figure 4.5 for the data contained in table 4.3 under the heading *Cumulative Percentage*. The formula, in its adjusted form, for finding the *n*th percentile is:

$$n\text{th percentile} = L + C\frac{[N\frac{n}{100} - S_f]}{F_n}$$

where n denotes the desired percentile, F_n denotes the frequency of the class containing the desired percentile, N denotes the number of elements of data, and S_f denotes the frequency of all classes lower than the *n*th percentile class.

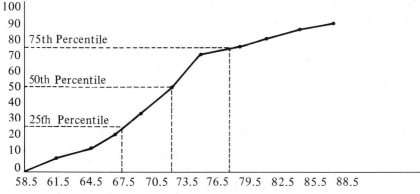

Figure 4.5 Cumulative Percentage Ogive

The first quartile, or 25th percentile, is the value that divides the cumulative frequency such that $\frac{1}{4}$ of the measurements lie below and $\frac{3}{4}$ lie above.

Example 1. Find the 25th percentile of the data given in table 4.2.

$$\text{Solution: 25th percentile} = 67.5 + 3\frac{[100(\frac{25}{100}) - 24]}{13}$$

$$= 67.5 + 3\frac{(1)}{13}$$

$$= 67.5 + 3/13$$

$$= 67.73$$

Example 2. Find the 75th percentile of the data given in table 4.2.

$$\text{Solution: 75th percentile} = 76.5 + 3\frac{[100(\frac{75}{100}) - 73]}{12}$$

$$= 76.5 + 3\frac{(2)}{12}$$

$$= 76.5 + .5$$

$$= 77$$

Percentiles are values that divide a distribution into 100 equal parts. These values, denoted by $P_1, P_2, P_3, \ldots, P_n$, are often more meaningful and useful than the actual values. To illustrate: suppose that two students, John and James, are enrolled in different sections of the same class. They take the same test, and each receives a grade mark of 76. In John's section there are 30 students, and 20 of them scored higher than he did. James's section also contained 30 students, but only 5 scored higher than he did. The percentage breakdown shows that John's mark was below the 35th percentile for his section, while James's mark was above the 80th percentile for his. Even though they made the same score, John was in the lower $\frac{1}{3}$ of his group, while James's score was better than $\frac{5}{6}$ of those in his.

In a frequency distribution of grouped data, the interval with the greatest frequency is called the modal class. For the data in table 4.2 the modal class is the class 71–73.

4.9 MEASURES OF VARIABILITY FOR GROUPED DATA

The range of a sample of ungrouped data was defined to be the difference between the largest and smallest measurements. For grouped data, where the individual measurements cannot be identified, the range is defined in the following way.

DEFINITION 4.14

The *range* for a sample of grouped data is the difference between the upper boundary of the highest class and the lower boundary of the lowest class.

The range of the data in table 4.2 is $88.5 - 58.5 = 30$. From this one can infer that for sixth-grade students the heaviest student will weigh about 30 pounds more than the lightest student.

The variance for grouped data in which the individual observations in the sample have been replaced with class marks defined as follows.

DEFINITION 4.15

If $x_1, x_2, x_3, \ldots, x_n$ are the class marks of a sample of observations corresponding to frequencies of $f_1, f_2, f_3, \ldots, f_n$, then the *variance* is given by the formula

$$s^2 = \frac{\sum_{i=1}^{n} f_i x_i^2}{n} - \left(\frac{\sum_{i=1}^{n} f_i x_i}{n}\right)^2$$

The standard deviation s is the positive square root of the variance.

Example. Find the variance and standard deviation of the weights of the sixth-grade students as given in table 4.1.

Solution: The following table is an extension of the data in table 4.1 with the columns x_i^2, $f_i x_i$ and $f_i x_i^2$.

Class Marks (x_i)	*Frequency* (f_i)	x_i^2	$f_i x_i$	$f_i x_i^2$
60	4	3,600	240	14,400
63	8	3,969	504	31,752
66	12	4,356	792	52,272
69	13	4,761	897	61,893
72	21	5,184	1,512	108,864
75	15	5,625	1,125	84,375
78	12	6,084	936	74,008
81	9	6,561	729	59,049
84	4	7,056	336	28,224
87	2	7,569	174	15,138
	100		7,245	528,975

$$\sum_{i=1}^{n} f_i x_i^2 = 528{,}975, \quad \sum_{i=1}^{n} f_i x_i = 7245$$

$$s^2 = \frac{528,975}{100} - \left(\frac{7245}{100}\right)^2$$

$$= 5289.75 - 5249$$

$$= 40.75$$

and $$s = \sqrt{40.75} = 6.4$$

A program for calculating the mean, variance, and standard deviation of grouped data is given in program 4.5.

Program 4.5

```
10 PRINT "MEAN", "VARIANCE", "STANDARD
   DEVIATION"
20 DIM X(N),F(N)
30 READ N
40 FOR I = 1 TO N
50 DATA N
60 DATA X(1),F(1),X(2),F(2),X(3),F(3),...,
   X(N),F(N)
70 READ X(I),F(I)
80 LET T = T + (X(F) * F(I))
90 LET C = C + F(I)
100 NEXT I
110 LET M = T/C
120 FOR I = 1 TO N
130 LET R = R + (F(I) * X(I) * X(I))/C
140 NEXT I
150 LET V = R - M ↑ 2
160 LET S = V ↑ .5
170 PRINT M,V,S
180 END
```

EXERCISE 4.3

1. Determine the class marks, class boundaries, and class widths for the class intervals:
   (a) 3–10   (c) 1.35–3.24
   (b) 6.5–12.5   (d) 7.312–10.105

2. A frequency distribution has class marks of 75, 82, 89, 96, 103, 110.
   (a) What are the class intervals?
   (b) What are the class boundaries?
   (c) What are the class widths?

3. The following data is a sample of the accounts receivable of a small merchandising firm.

37	42	44	47	46	50	48	52	90
54	56	55	53	58	59	60	62	92
60	61	62	63	67	64	64	68	
67	65	66	68	69	66	70	72	
73	75	74	72	71	76	81	80	
79	80	78	82	83	85	86	88	

Using a class interval of 5, i.e., 35–39,
- (a) Make a frequency distribution table.
- (b) Construct a frequency histogram.
- (c) Construct a frequency polygon.
- (d) Make a cumulative frequency distribution.
- (e) Construct a cumulative percentage ogive.

4. Using the data in problem 3 find:
- (a) the mean
- (b) the median
- (c) the variance
- (d) the standard deviation

5. The IQ scores for a sample of 24 students who are entering their first year of high school are:

115	119	119	134
121	128	128	152
97	108	98	130
108	110	111	122
106	142	143	140
141	151	125	126

- (a) Make a cumulative percentage ogive using 96–102 as the lowest class interval.
- (b) What scores are below the 25th percentile?
- (c) What scores are above the 75th percentile?
- (d) What is the median score?

6. In a certain state, each political candidate for a state office is required to file a list of campaign contributions with the state treasurer. One candidate, for a one-month period, filed the following contributions.

Contributions in dollars	Number of such gifts
5	200
10	150
25	100
50	10
100	4
500	5
1000	1

(*a*) Find the mean of the contributions for that month.

(*b*) Find the standard deviation.

7. The highway patrol set up a radar checkpoint and recorded the speed in miles per hour of a random sample of 50 cars that passed the checkpoint in one hour. The speeds of the cars were recorded as follows.

74	66	65	55	48
56	50	65	75	67
76	68	50	65	60
65	60	51	68	76
68	77	63	65	52
52	63	65	80	70
65	81	70	63	53
45	65	55	71	64
55	70	64	45	66
64	40	66	55	71

(*a*) Make a frequency distribution chart, using 5 as a class width, e.g., 39.5–44.5.

(*b*) Find the mean and standard deviation.

(*c*) What value represents the median? The 40th percentile?

8. Thirty coeds attend a meeting, and the colors of their hair are as follows: blonde, red, red, blonde, brown, brown, red, black, black, blonde, red, brown, brown, brown, red, blonde, black, brown, brown, red, blonde, black, brown, red, brown, red, black, blonde, red, blonde.

(*a*) Make a frequency distribution.

(*b*) Make a frequency histogram.

CHAPTER 5

Random Variables and Distributions

5.1 INTRODUCTION TO RANDOM VARIABLES

To introduce the concept of a random variable, let us return to the bulb-testing experiment that we have employed in several previous discussions. Consider the experiment "select and test two light bulbs from a continuous production line and record the results." The sample space S is

$$S = \{(s,s), (s,f), (f,s), (f,f)\}$$

Assume that our primary interest is the number of acceptable bulbs found in each of the sample points. We list below the simple events of S, together with the number of acceptable bulbs for each of the events.

Simple Event	Number of Acceptable Bulbs
$E_1 = \{(s,s)\}$	2
$E_2 = \{(s,f)\}$	1
$E_3 = \{(f,s)\}$	1
$E_4 = \{(f,f)\}$	0

The numbers 2, 1, and 0, representing the number of acceptable bulbs in the simple events of S, form a set which we denote by R_X. In this instance, $R_X = \{0, 1, 2\}$. Each of the sample points in S is associated with exactly one element in R_X; however, there is no restriction on the number of sample points in S which may be associated with the same element of R_X. In this instance, two sample points, (s, f) and (f, s), are associated with the element 1 of R_X.

In mathematics, a function is defined as a correspondence associating each element of one set (called the *domain* of the function) with exactly one element of a second set. In the example just given, each element of S corresponds to exactly one element of the set $R_X = \{0, 1, 2\}$. Thus, this correspondence between S and R_X determines a function X which has domain S, and associates each outcome in S with the number of acceptable bulbs in that outcome. The set R_X is called the range space of X and consists of all real numbers into which X maps elements of S. In the study of probability and statistics, functions such as X are called *random variables*.

DEFINITION 5.1

A *random variable* X is a function from the sample space of an experiment to a set of real numbers. If $a \in S$, then $X(a)$ represents the number which the random variable X associates with a. The *range space* of X is the set of real numbers $R_X = \{b \mid b = X(a) \text{ and } a \in S\}$.

In the light bulb example, we see $X(s, s) = 2$, $X(s, f) = 1$, $X(f, s) = 1$, and $X(f, f) = 0$.

Previously we have learned to associate probability with the events of an experiment. We shall continue to do this. Now, however, the events will be identified with one or more of the elements in R_X. For example, the event consisting of the two points $\{(s, f), (f, s)\}$ is associated with 1. Because of the focus of attention on the values in R_X, the reference to the original elements in S is often dropped, and one simply writes X in place of $X(a)$ where $a \in S$. Thus, the set $\{a \in S \mid X(a) = 1\} = \{(s, f), (f, s)\}$ may be referred to as the event $X = 1$, and the other events may be referred to in like manner. With this thought in mind we may write

$$P\{(s, f), (f, s)\} = P(X = 1)$$

We call X a random variable since each value of R_X represents a random event associated with the experiment. The set of probabilities associated with the range space of a random variable is known as a *probability distribution*. Table 5.1 shows the probability distribution of the

Table 5.1 Probability Distribution for X

Values of X in R_X	Corresponding Sample Points	Probability
2	(s, s)	1/4
1	$(s, f), (f, s)$	1/2
0	(f, f)	1/4

random variable X representing the number of acceptable bulbs. We shall assume for this illustration that the probability of an acceptable bulb is $1/2$. It should be noted that if $b \in R_X$, then $P(X = b) = P[a \in S \mid X(a) = b]$, and consequently all values in the probability distribution are nonnegative and their sum is 1.

A few examples of random variables associated with the events of experiments are shown below.

Random Variable	*Range Space*
1. Let X be the number of observers of a TV program in a survey of 10 people.	$R_X = \{0, 1, 2, \ldots, 10\}$
2. Let X be the number of correct answers a student makes in a test of 20 questions.	$R_X = \{0, 1, 2, \ldots, 20\}$
3. Let X be the number of passes thrown by a quarterback in a football game.	$R_X = \{0, 1, 2, \ldots\}$

If the range space of a random variable contains a finite number of elements, as in experiments 1 and 2 above, or a countable sequence, as in experiment 3, we say that the random variable is *discrete*.

DEFINITION 5.2

A random variable is *discrete* if its range space is a discrete set.

If the range space is composed of an interval of the set of real numbers, e.g., $\{x \mid 2 < x < 4\}$, or the union of such intervals, we say that the random variable is *continuous*.

DEFINITION 5.3

A random variable is *continuous* if its range space is a continuous set.

The following are examples of continuous random variables.

Random Variable	*Range Space*
1. Let X be the percentage of voters who will vote in the next presidential election.	$R_X = \{x \mid 0 \le x \le 100\}$
2. Let X be the amount of rainfall at each weather station on a certain day.	$R_X = \{x \mid x \ge 0\}$
3. Let X be the hair length of the men on campus.	$R_X = \{x \mid x > 0\}$

The assignment of probabilities to events associated with continuous random variables will be discussed in section 5.5.

5.2 DISCRETE RANDOM VARIABLES AND
THE BINOMIAL DISTRIBUTION

A discrete random variable may be closely associated with the binomial probabilities which were discussed in chapter 3. This relationship may be illustrated with the bulb-testing experiment of section 5.1, the results of which are shown below. X represents the number of acceptable bulbs.

Values of X in R_x	Corresponding Sample Points in S	Probability
2	(s, s)	1/4
1	$(s, f), (f, s)$	1/2
0	(f, f)	1/4

The entries in column 3 for the probability for each of the several values in R_X may be computed using the binomial theorem as shown below.

$$P(X = x_i) = C\binom{2}{x_i}\left(\frac{1}{2}\right)^{x_1}\left(\frac{1}{2}\right)^{2-x_1}$$

where x_i is an element of the set $R_X = \{0, 1, 2\}$.

Let us calculate the three entries in the probability column of the above table.

$$P(X = 0) = P\{(s, s)\} = C\binom{2}{0}\left(\frac{1}{2}\right)^0\left(\frac{1}{2}\right)^2 = \frac{1}{4}$$

$$P(X = 1) = P\{(s, f), (f, s)\} = C\binom{2}{1}\left(\frac{1}{2}\right)^1\left(\frac{1}{2}\right)^1 = \frac{1}{2}$$

$$P(X = 2) = P\{(f, f)\} = C\binom{2}{2}\left(\frac{1}{2}\right)^2\left(\frac{1}{2}\right)^0 = \frac{1}{4}$$

The probability distribution which we have developed may be represented graphically, as shown in figure 5.1. This graph is called a *probability distribution histogram*.

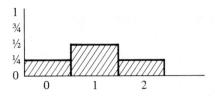

Figure 5.1 Probability Distribution

Let us illustrate the random variable concept with another example. Assume, now, that three bulbs are selected and tested, and our primary interest is the number of defectives. The sample space for this experiment is

$$S = \{(s, s, s), (s, s, f), (s, f, s), (s, f, f), (f, s, s), (f, s, f), (f, f, s), (f, f, f)\}$$

If the random variable X now represents the number of defective bulbs selected, then

$$R_X = \{0, 1, 2, 3\}$$

The probabilities of the simple events for this experiment are given in table 5.2.

Table 5.2 Probabilities for the Three-Bulb Experiment

Simple Events	Number of Defective Bulbs (x_i)	Corresponding Probability
$E_1 = \{(s, s, s)\}$	0	1/8
$E_2 = \{(s, s, f)\}$	1	1/8
$E_3 = \{(s, f, s)\}$	1	1/8
$E_4 = \{(s, f, f)\}$	2	1/8
$E_5 = \{(f, s, s)\}$	1	1/8
$E_6 = \{(f, s, f)\}$	2	1/8
$E_7 = \{(f, f, s)\}$	2	1/8
$E_8 = \{(f, f, f)\}$	3	1/8

It is obvious from the table that $X = 0$ would be assigned to the event E_1; $X = 1$ assigned to the events E_2, E_3, and E_5; $X = 2$ assigned to the events E_4, E_6, E_7; and $X = 3$ assigned to the event E_8. Assuming that the simple events are equally probable, the probability distribution of X is

$$P(X = 0) = P\{(s, s, s)\} = 1/8$$

$$P(X = 1) = P\{(s, s, f), (s, f, s), (f, s, s)\} = 3/8$$

$$P(X = 2) = P\{(s, f, f), (f, s, f), (f, f, s)\} = 3/8$$

$$P(X = 3) = P\{(f, f, f)\} = 1/8$$

It should be noted that $\sum_{i=0}^{3} P(X = i) = 1$, where $i \in R_X = \{0, 1, 2, 3\}$.

DEFINITION 5.4

Suppose a binomial experiment of n trials is performed, and the probability of success is p. Let X be the number of successes in the n repetitions. Then X is a *binomial random variable* with parameters n and p.

In a binomial experiment, we observe that $R_X = \{0, 1, 2, 3, \ldots, n\}$ and $P(X = i) = C\binom{n}{i} p^i (1 - p)^{n-i}$, where $i \in R_X$. For the preceding bulb experiment,

$$P(X = 0) = C\binom{3}{0}\left(\frac{1}{2}\right)^0\left(\frac{1}{2}\right)^3 = \frac{1}{8}$$

$$P(X = 1) = C\binom{3}{1}\left(\frac{1}{2}\right)^1\left(\frac{1}{2}\right)^2 = \frac{3}{8}$$

$$P(X = 2) = C\binom{3}{2}\left(\frac{1}{2}\right)^2\left(\frac{1}{2}\right)^1 = \frac{3}{8}$$

$$P(X = 3) = C\binom{3}{3}\left(\frac{1}{2}\right)^3\left(\frac{1}{2}\right)^0 = \frac{1}{8}$$

5.3 THE MEAN, VARIANCE, AND STANDARD DEVIATION OF A DISCRETE RANDOM VARIABLE

Let us return to the two-bulb experiment, with X the number of defective bulbs selected. The probability distribution of X follows.

Table 5.3 Probabilities for Two-Bulb Experiment

Sample Points	x_i	$P(X = x_i)$
(s, s)	0	1/4
$(s, f), (f, s)$	1	1/2
(f, f)	2	1/4

Suppose this two-bulb experiment is repeated 100 times. Since the number of repetitions is fairly large, we might expect the events "two defective bulbs are selected" to occur about 25 times, "one defective bulb is selected" to occur about 50 times, and "no defective bulbs are selected" to occur about 25 times, as the empirical probabilities of these events should be close to their true probability of occurrence. If the respective events occurred exactly 25, 50, and 25 times, the average number of defectives found over the 100 repetitions would be

$$\frac{(0 \cdot 25) + (1 \cdot 50) + (2 \cdot 25)}{100} = 1$$

Such an idealized average is used to define the expected value of a random variable.

DEFINITION 5.5

Let X be a discrete random variable with range space $\{x_1, x_2, \ldots, x_n\}$ and probability distribution $P(X = x_i)$, $x_i \in R_X$. The expected value of X, denoted by $E(X)$ is given by

$$E(X) = \sum_{i=1}^{n} x_i P(X = x_i)$$

The expected value of the distribution in table 5.3 is

$$E(X) = \sum_{i=1}^{n} x_i P(X = x_i)$$

$$= 0\left(\frac{1}{4}\right) + 1\left(\frac{1}{2}\right) + 2\left(\frac{1}{4}\right)$$

$$= 1$$

The expected value of a random variable is defined in such a way that if the experiment were repeated many times, the average value of X over all repetitions should be close to the expected value. The expected value of a random variable is also called the *mean* of the random variable.

Example 1. Consider the random variable X representing the number of defective radios in a shipment of four radios to a local appliance store. Assume that the outcomes are equally probable. Find $E(X)$.

Solution: The probability distribution is:

Number of Defective
Radios

x_i	$P(X = x_i)$	$x_i P(X = x_i)$
0	1/16	0
1	4/16	4/16
2	6/16	12/16
3	4/16	12/16
4	1/16	4/16

The expected value of X is

$$E(X) = \sum_{i=1}^{n} x_i P(X = x_i)$$

$$= 0 + \frac{4}{16} + \frac{12}{16} + \frac{12}{16} + \frac{14}{16}$$

$$= 2$$

Having calculated the expected value, we are now ready to calculate the variance of the random variable. The variance is defined as follows.

DEFINITION 5.6

Let X be a discrete random variable with expected value $E(X)$ and with probability distribution $P(X = x_i)$, $x_i \in R_X$. The *variance* of X, denoted by σ^2, is

$$\sigma^2 = \sum_{i=1}^{n} (x_i - E(X))^2 \, P(X = x_i)$$

The calculation of the variance is illustrated in the following example.

Example 2. Find the variance of the random variable X, representing the number of defective radios in the shipment of four radios in the preceding example.

Solution: We shall use the expected value 2 previously found for this example.

x_i	$P(X = x_i)$	$(x_i - P(x))$	$(x_i - E(X))^2$	$(x_i - E(X))^2 P(X = x_i)$
0	1/16	−2	4	4/16
1	4/16	−1	1	4/16
2	6/16	0	0	0
3	4/16	1	1	4/16
4	1/16	2	4	4/16

Using definition 5.6,

$$\sigma^2 = \sum_{i=1}^{5} (x_i - E(X))^2 P(X = x_i) = \frac{4}{16} + \frac{4}{16} + 0 + \frac{4}{16} + \frac{4}{16}$$

$$= \frac{16}{16}$$

$$= 1$$

The standard deviation σ of the random variable X is

$$\sigma = \sqrt{\sigma^2}$$

$$= \sqrt{1}$$

$$= 1$$

5.4 THE MEAN, VARIANCE, AND STANDARD DEVIATION OF THE BINOMIAL RANDOM VARIABLE

The binomial is one of the most widely used distributions in statistics. Since it occupies such an important place, it is desirable to find formulas for calculating the mean, variance, and standard deviation without constructing the probability distribution for each experiment. Our approach in finding the formula will be to find the expected value when $n = 1$ and $n = 2$ and to state the general formula on this intuitive basis.

In the previous section, the expected value of a discrete random variable with range space $x_1, \ldots, x_n$ was defined as

$$E(X) = \sum_{i=1}^{n} x_i P(X = x_i)$$

The expected value of the binomial random variable X for $n = 1$ trials, where the probability of success is p and the probability of failure is $1 - p = q$, is

$$E(X) = \sum_{i=0}^{1} iP(X = i)$$

$$= (0 \cdot q) + (1 \cdot p)$$

$$= p$$

For $n = 2$,

$$E(X) = \sum_{i=0}^{2} iP(X = i)$$

$$= 0(q)^2 + 1(2pq) + 1(p)^2$$

$$= 2pq + p^2$$

$$= 2p(q + p)$$

$$= 2P \qquad [Note: p + q = 1]$$

It is easy to show that $E(X)$ for $n = 3$ is

$$E(X) = 3p$$

In general, it can be shown that the expected value of a binomial experiment consisting of n trials is

$$E(X) = np$$

Similarly, the variance of X for $n = 1$ is

$$\sigma^2 = \sum_{i=0}^{1} (i - E(X))^2 P(X = i)$$

$$= (0 - p)^2 q + (1 - p)^2 p$$

$$= p^2 q + q^2 p \qquad [Note: (1 - p)^2 = q^2]$$

$$= pq(p + q) \qquad [Note: p + q = 1]$$

$$= pq$$

For $n = 2$,

$$\sigma^2 = \sum_{i=0}^{2} (i - 2p)^2 P(X = i)$$

$$= (0 - 2p)^2 q^2 + (1 - 2p)^2(2pq) + (2 - 2p)^2 p^2$$

$$= 4p^2 q^2 + (1 - 4p + 4p^2)(2pq) + 4(1 - p)^2 p^2$$

Substituting $q = 1 - p$ in the above expression, it can be shown through algebraic manipulation that

$$\sigma^2 = 2pq$$

It can also be shown that the variance of X for $n = 3$ trials is

$$\sigma^2 = 3pq$$

In general, the variance of X for n trials is

$$\sigma^2 = npq$$

and the standard deviation is

$$\sigma = \sqrt{npq}$$

Example 1. Suppose that 75% of the students taking statistics pass the course. In a class of 40 students, what is the expected number who will pass. Find the variance and standard deviation.

Solution: $n = 40$, $p = .75$, $q = .25$

The expected number who pass is

$$E(X) = np$$
$$= 40(.75)$$
$$= 30$$

The variance is

$$\sigma^2 = npq$$
$$= 40(.75)(.25)$$
$$= 7.5$$

The standard deviation is

$$\sigma \doteq 2.74$$

Example 2. A new insecticide is advertised as being 90% effective in killing ants with one application. If 10,000 ants are treated with one application of the insecticide, find the expected value, variance, and standard deviation of the number of ants killed.

Solution: $n = 10,000$, $p = .9$, $q = .1$

The expected number killed is

$$E(X) = np$$
$$= 10,000(.9)$$
$$= 9,000$$

The variance is

$$\sigma^2 = npq$$
$$= 10,000(.9)(.1)$$
$$= 900$$

The standard deviation is 30.

EXERCISE 5.1

1. Compute the expected value and standard deviation of each of the following binomial distributions.
   (a) $n = 100$; probability of success is .5
   (b) $n = 672$; probability of success is .75
   (c) $n = 400$; probability of success is .10

2. If the probability of a defective switch is .10, what is the expected number of defective switches in a shipment that contains 144 switches?

3. It is known that 2% of the batteries produced by a certain company will not last until the guarantee expires. If 10,000 of these batteries are sold, find the number that the company must expect to replace.

4. Three tires are selected at random from the production line and inspected. If a tire passes the inspection it is marked s for acceptance, and if it fails it is marked f for rejection. The probability of a tire being acceptable is .5. Let X equal the number of accepted tires in a sample of three tires, and use the formulas for the binomial probability distribution to:
   (a) Calculate the probability distribution of X.
   (b) Calculate the mean and standard deviation of x by using the formulas $E(x) = np$ and $\sigma = \sqrt{npq}$.
   (c) Construct a probability histogram and find the probability that the number of acceptable tires in a sample of three tires lies within two standard deviations of the mean.

5. Suppose that it is known that one-fourth of the students who enroll in a certain subject do not complete the course. If a class of 24 students is enrolled in this subject, what is the expected value and standard deviation of X, the number of students who will complete the course?

5.5 CONTINUOUS RANDOM VARIABLES AND THE NORMAL CURVE

The normal probability distribution is the most important probability distribution in the field of probability and statistics. This type of distribution was first discovered by the English mathematician De Moivre (1667–1754). Later the French mathematician Laplace (1749–1827) applied it to the study of the sciences and other practical problems. The German mathematician Gauss (1777–1855) further developed and used the normal curve in his study of physics and astronomy.

As noted in section 5.1, a continuous random variable can assume any value in an interval of real numbers. The normal probability distribution provides a means of assigning probabilities to intervals of real numbers associated with certain continuous random variables. The mathematical equation that generates the normal curve for the normal probability distribution depends upon the two parameters of the population μ and σ. The equation for the normal curve* is

$$f(x) = \frac{1}{\sqrt{2\pi}\sigma}e^{-\frac{1}{2}(x-\mu)^2/\sigma}, \quad -\infty < x < \infty$$

where $\pi = 3.1416$, $e = 2.7183$, μ is a real number, and σ is positive.

The graph of the normal curve is illustrated below for $\mu = 50$ and $\sigma = 10$. For illustration, we have arbitrarily selected a few values for x, as shown in figure 5.2.

$$x = 35, 40, 45, 50, 55, 60, 65$$

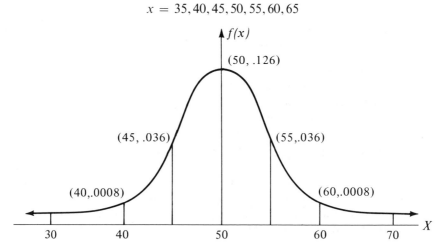

Figure 5.2 The Normal Curve

It should be noted that different scores are used on the vertical and horizontal axes.

The shape of the normal curve relative to μ is determined by σ. A smalll σ indicates that the area under the curve is closely concentrated about μ; the curve will have a high peak and drop off sharply to the left and right. A large σ produces a curve with a low peak which descends gradually to the horizontal axis as we consider measurements that are more distant from μ (see figure 5.3).

The normal curve is characterized by the following properties:
(1) the measurements tend to cluster about μ;
(2) the curve is symmetrical about a vertical axis drawn through μ;
(3) as the curve moves away in either direction from this vertical axis it approaches but never touches the horizontal axis.

It may be shown that a normal distribution with parameters μ and σ has an expected value μ and variance σ^2. Many populations taken from natural

---

* This equation is derived in more advanced courses of study.

or man-made phenomena are normally distributed. A few such populations are

> (1) the life span of certain species of insects;
> (2) the lengths of time storage batteries will successfully operate;
> (3) the heights of college students.

The mathematical equation which we have given varies with μ and σ. When the random variable X with a normal distribution is transformed into a special type of normal random variable called the *standard normal random variable*, the normal curve becomes "standardized" for all values of μ and σ. The standard normal distribution is called the *Z-distribution*.

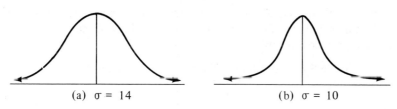

(a) $\sigma = 14$ (b) $\sigma = 10$

Figure 5.3

The procedure for transforming each score, x_i, of a normal random variable X with parameters μ and σ into the corresponding score z_i for the standard normal random variable Z is given by the formula

$$z_i = \frac{x_i - \mu}{\sigma}$$

With this transformation, each x_i in a normal distribution is associated with a standard score z_i in the standard normal distribution.

The following example will illustrate the procedure for transforming the X-scores into Z-scores. Suppose the following scores were selected from a normal distribution with $\mu = 5$ and $\sigma = 2$: $-3, 1, 5, 7, 13$. If we let $x_i = -3$, $x_2 = 1$, $x_3 = 5$, $x_4 = 7$, and $x_5 = 13$, then the corresponding Z-scores are calculated as follows.

$$z_1 = \frac{-3 - 5}{2} = -4$$

$$z_2 = \frac{1 - 5}{2} = -2$$

$$z_3 = \frac{5 - 5}{2} = 0$$

$$z_4 = \frac{7 - 5}{2} = 1$$

$$z_5 = \frac{13 - 5}{2} = 4$$

$$X\text{-scores}: \quad -3, \quad 1, \quad 5, \quad 7, \quad 13$$

$$Z\text{-scores}: \quad -4, -2, \quad 0, \quad 1, \quad 4$$

It can be shown that the expected value of the standard normal random variable Z is 0 and the variance and standard deviation are both 1.

The equation of the standard normal curve is derived from the equation of the normal curve by replacing μ and σ with 0 and 1 respectively. The standard normal equation then becomes,

$$f(x) = \frac{1}{\sqrt{2\pi}}e^{-x^2/2}, \quad -\infty < x < \infty$$

Using the equation, we can determine approximate values for $f(x)$ for any value of x. Sufficient values for sketching the standard normal curve are provided in table 5.4.

Table 5.4 Coordinates of Points on the Standard Normal Curve

x	$f(x)$
-4	.000
-3	.004
-2	.054
-1	.242
0	.400
1	.242
2	.054
3	.004
4	.000

It is customary as well as convenient to use a different scale for the horizontal and vertical axes when sketching a normal curve. When the same scales are used, the standard normal curve appears almost flat.

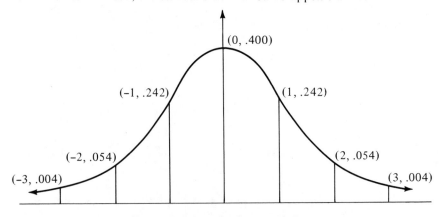

Figure 5.4 Standard Normal Curve

The standard normal curve has the following characteristics:
(1) it is symmetrical about $z_i = 0$;
(2) it has its highest point at the ordered pair (0, .400);
(3) it has inflection points 1 and -1; for $x > 1$ or $x < -1$ it curves upward, and in the interval $-1 > x > 1$ it curves downward;
(4) it has one square unit of measure between the curve and the horizontal axis.

The standard normal distribution enables us to assign probabilities to any normal random variable X with parameters μ and σ. For example, when X has a value in the interval (x_1, x_2), then the standard normal random variable Z will assume a value in the interval (z_1, z_2) where $z_1 = \dfrac{x_1 - \mu}{\sigma}$ and $z_2 = \dfrac{x_2 - \mu}{\sigma}$ (see figure 5.5).

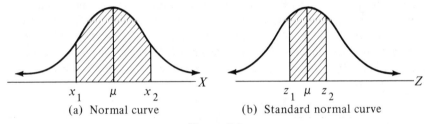

(a) Normal curve   (b) Standard normal curve

Figure 5.5

Since all values of X in the interval x_1, x_2 have corresponding Z-values in the interval z_1, z_2, the proportion of area under the X-curve between x_1 and x_2 in figure 5.5 is equal to the area under the Z-curve between z_1 and z_2. Therefore, we have

$$P(x_1 < X < x_2) = P(z_1 < Z < z_2)$$

The probability that a standard normal random variable will assume a value in a specified interval is equal to the area over that interval. The area, and thus the probability, can be found by using tables II and III in the appendix.

The Z-scores in table II are listed in steps of .1, beginning with -4.0 and ending with 4.0. The area associated with each Z-score is rounded off to three decimal places and is the area under the curve to the left of the respective Z-score. For example, the area associated with a Z-score of 0.0 is .500; that is, 50% of the area under the normal curve is to the left of the mean (figure 5.6).

The Z-scores in table III are listed in steps of .01, beginning with 0.00 and ending with 3.99. Table III lists only nonnegative Z-scores; however, the symmetry of the curve can be used to find the area associated with a negative Z-score. The column headed by Z gives the values. The area corresponding to a Z-score in table III is the area to the left of the Z-score

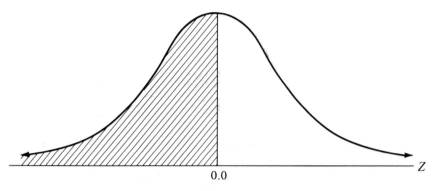

Figure 5.6

but to the right of 0.00. The column headed by Z gives the values of Z in increments of .1. The other columns are headed by the one-hundredth increment of Z. For example, the area associated with $z = 1.25$ is found by reading down in the Z-column to the number 1.2 and then finding the intersection of this line with the column headed by .05. The intersection is the number .3944 and is the area associated with $z = 1.25$. This area is shown in figure 5.7.

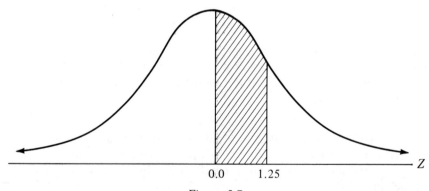

Figure 5.7

Example 1. Given a normal population with $\mu = 25$ and $\sigma = 5$, find the probability that an assumed value of the variable will fall in the interval $(20, 30)$.

Solution: The Z-scores associated with $x_1 = 20$ and $x_2 = 30$ are

$$z_1 = \frac{20 - 25}{5} = -1$$

and

$$z_2 = \frac{30 - 25}{5} = 1$$

We are asked to find the probability (area) over the interval $(20, 30)$, as shown in figure 5.8.

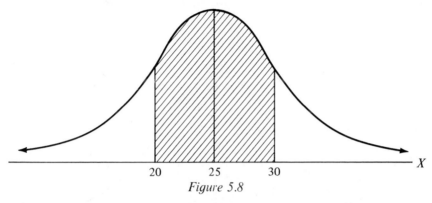

Figure 5.8

Using table III, we find the area bounded by $z = 0$ and $z = 1$, and since the curve is symmetrical, this area is equal to the area bounded by $z = -1$ and $z = 0$. Thus,

$$P(20 < X < 30) = P(-1 < Z < 1)$$
$$= 2P(0 < Z < 1)$$
$$= 2(.3413)$$
$$= .6826$$

Solution using table II: The area to the left of $z_1 = -1$ is .159, and the area to the left of $z_2 = 1$ is .841. Then

$$P(20 < X < 30) = P(-1 < Z < 1)$$
$$= P(Z < 1) - P(Z < -1)$$
$$= 841 - .159$$
$$= .682$$

Example 2. A television company manufactures transistors that have an average life-span of 1,000 hours and a standard deviation of 100 hours. Find the probability that a transistor selected at random will have a life-span between 875 hours and 1,075 hours. Assume the distribution is normal.

Solution: The Z-scores corresponding to the X-scores are

$$z_1 = \frac{875 - 1000}{100} = \frac{-125}{100} = 1.25$$

and

$$z_2 = \frac{1075 - 1000}{100} = \frac{75}{100} = .75$$

$$P(875 < X < 1025) = P(-1.25 < Z < .75)$$
$$= P(0 < Z < .75) + P(0 < Z < 1.25)$$
$$= .2734 + .3944$$
$$= .6678$$

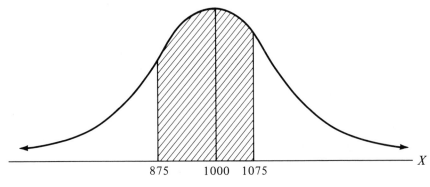

Figure 5.9 P(1075 > X > 875)

Example 3. The average life of a certain type of automobile battery is 2 years with a standard deviation of .25 year. Assuming that the length of useful life of the batteries is normally distributed, find the probability that a battery selected at random will last

(*a*) less than 1.8 years;
(*b*) less than 2.5 years but greater than 2.2 years;
(*c*) at least 1.6 years but no more than 1.75 years.

Solution: (*a*) To find the probability that the battery will last less than 1.8 years, we need to know the area under the normal curve to the left of $X = 1.8$. The Z-score corresponding to $X = 1.8$ is

$$z = \frac{1.8 - 2}{.25} = \frac{-.2}{.25} = -.8$$

Using table III and the symmetry of the curve, we find

$$P(X < 1.8) = P(Z < -.8)$$
$$= P(Z > .8)$$
$$= .500 - P(0 < Z < .8)$$
$$= (.5000 - .2881)$$
$$= .2119$$

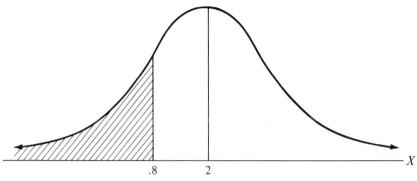

Figure 5.10 P(X < 1.8)

(b) For the solution to 3(b) we shall find the area bounded by $x_1 = 2.5$ and $x_2 = 2.2$. The corresponding Z-scores are

$$z_1 = \frac{2.5 - 2}{25} = \frac{.5}{.25} = 2 \quad \text{and} \quad z_2 = \frac{2.2 - 2}{.25} = \frac{.2}{.25} = .8$$

Therefore,

$$P(2.2 < X = 2.5) = P(.8 < Z < 2)$$

$$= P(0 < Z < 2) - P(0 < Z < .8)$$

$$= .4772 - .2881$$

$$= .1891$$

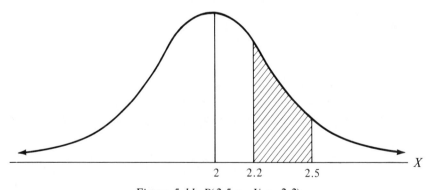

Figure 5.11 P(2.5 > X > 2.2)

(c) In 3(c) we are asked to find the area bounded by $x_1 = 1.6$ and $x_2 = 1.75$. The corresponding Z-scores are

$$z_2 = \frac{1.75 - 2}{.25} = \frac{-.25}{.25} = -1 \quad \text{and} \quad z_1 = \frac{1.6 - 2}{.25} = \frac{-.4}{.25} = -1.6$$

Since both Z-scores are negative, we must use the symmetric property of the curve (or else table II) to find the probability. That is,

$$P(1.6 < X < 1.75) = P(-1.6 < Z < -1)$$
$$= P(1.6 > Z > 1)$$
$$= .4452 - .3413$$
$$= P(0 < Z < 1.6) - P(0 < Z < 1)$$
$$= .1039$$

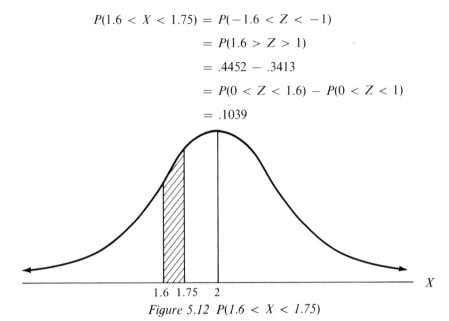

1.6 1.75   2

Figure 5.12 P(1.6 < X < 1.75)

In the preceding examples, we were given the mean and standard deviation of a distribution and asked to find probabilities of a random variable, assuming values in specified intervals. These probabilities were calculated by transforming the X-scores into Z-scores and using tables II and III in the appendix. The procedure can be reversed. Let us solve the following equation for x_i.

If

$$z_i = \frac{x_i - \mu}{\sigma}$$

then

$$x_i = \sigma z_i + \mu$$

Example 4. The average grade on a mathematics test is 82, with a standard deviation of 5. If the instructor assigns A's to the highest 12% and the grades follow a normal distribution, what is the lowest grade that will be assigned A?

Solution: We are asked to find the X-score that has 12% of the area underneath the curve to its right; hence there will be 50% − 12%, or 38%, of the area between the mean and the desired X-score. Using table III, we find that the Z-score such that $P(0 < Z < z_i) = .3800$ is $z_i = 1.175$, i.e., $P(0 < Z < 1.175) = .3800$ or $P(Z > 1.175) = .1200$.

Using the formulas

$$x_i = \sigma z_i + \mu \qquad \text{and} \qquad z_i = 1.175$$

we find

$$x = 5(1.175) + 82 = 87.875$$

The lowest grade to be assigned an A is 88.

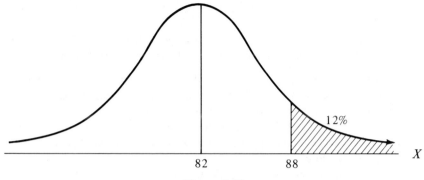

Figure 5.13

EXERCISE 5.2

1. A normal distribution has a mean of 50 and a standard deviation of 6. Find:
   (a) the percentage of measurements below 47.
   (b) the percentage of measurements above 60.
   (c) the percentage of measurements between 41 and 58.
   (d) the value of the random variable such that 30% of the measurements are below it.
   (e) the value of the random variable such that 28% of the measurements are above it.

2. Let X be a continuous normal random variable with $\mu = 400$ and $\sigma = 20$; find the indicated probability.
   (a) $P(X < 375)$
   (b) $P(X > 440)$
   (c) $P(385 < X < 410)$
   (d) $P(355 < X < 375)$

3. Let X be a continuous normal random variable with $\mu = 16$ and $\sigma = 2.2$; find
   (a) $P(X > 19)$
   (b) $P(13 < X < 14)$
   (c) $P(19 > X > 17.5)$

4. (a) Find z_i such that $P(Z > z_i) = .5$
   (b) Find z_i such that $P(Z < z_i) = .8643$

5. Let X be a normally distributed random variable with $\mu = 7$ and $\sigma = 1.5$. If a value of x is chosen at random, find the probability that X falls between $x_i = 8$ and $x_2 = 9$.

6. The grade-point average of college students is 2.5, and the standard deviation is .8. (Assume normal distribution.)

(a) What fraction of the students have a grade-point average less than 2.0?

(b) If students whose grade-point average is less than 1.5 are put on probation, what percent of the students are on probation?

7. A soft-drink machine can be regulated to discharge an average of 7 ounces per cup. If the amount of drink dispensed per cup is normally distributed with a standard deviation of .3 ounce,

(a) what fraction of the cups will contain more than 7.1 ounces?

(b) if the cups hold exactly 8 ounces, what is the probability that a cup will overflow?

(c) what should be the setting so that the cups will overflow only 1% of the time?

8. The life of a certain brand of automobile tire is 25,000 miles with a standard deviation of 710 miles. Assuming normal distribution, what is the probability that a tire will have to be replaced if it is guaranteed for 24,000 miles?

9. The hourly rate scale in a certain craft is $4.25 per hour with a standard deviation of $.75 per hour. Assuming normal distribution,

(a) what percentage of the workers receive hourly wages between $3.50 and $4.90?

(b) what hourly wage represents the 95th percentile?

10. The average life of a small kitchen appliance is five years with a standard deviation of one year. Assuming normal distribution, if the manufacturer replaces free any appliance that fails while under guarantee, how long a guarantee should be offered if his profit depends on not more than 2% being replaced?

5.6 THE NORMAL CURVE APPROXIMATION FOR THE BINOMIAL DISTRIBUTION

Let E be the event that exactly r successes occur in n repetitions of a binomial experiment, with probability of success p and the probability of failure $q = 1 - p$. Then

$$P(E) = C\binom{n}{r}(p)^r(q)^{n-r}$$

The arithmetical computation involved in calculating $P(E)$ when n is large is monumental. Binomial probabilities for a limited number of values of n when n is small and for limited values of p are given in table IV in the appendix. If the desired values of n and p are not listed in the table, then we may use the computer program for binomial probability given in Chapter 3.

If the desired values of n and p are not listed in the table and a computer is not available, then, for certain binomial distributions, the normal distribution can be used to give approximate probabilities. If n is large and p is close to $1/2$, then the normal distribution gives a very accurate approximation of the binomial distribution. Actually, even if n is small and p is not extremely close to 0 or 1, the approximation is fairly good and usable.

To illustrate: suppose we have a binomial distribution with $n = 10$ and $p = .6$. To investigate this binomial distribution, we construct the histogram and then superimpose upon it the particular normal curve having the same mean and standard deviation as the binomial distribution. That is, we draw a normal curve (figure 5.14) with the parameters

$$\mu = np = (10)(.6) = 6$$
$$\sigma = \sqrt{npq} = \sqrt{(10)(.6)(.4)} = 1.55$$

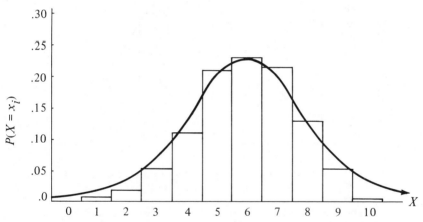

Figure 5.14 Normal Curve Approximation to a Binomial Distribution with $n = 10$ and $p = .6$

The exact probability that the binomial random variable X will equal x_i is equal to the area of the rectangle whose base is centered at x_i. For example, the exact probability that X assumes the value 7 is equal to the area of the rectangle whose base is centered at 7. (See Fig. 5.15.) Using the following formula or table IV in the appendix, we find the exact probability to be .2150.

$$P(X = 7) = C\binom{10}{7}(.6)^7(.4)^3$$

The approximation of the binomial probability by the normal curve with parameters $\mu = np = 10(.6) = 6$ and $\sigma = \sqrt{npq} = \sqrt{10(.6)(.4)} = 1.55$ is the area under the curve bounded by $x_1 = 6.5$ and $x_2 = 7.5$. The corresponding Z-scores are

$$z_1 = \frac{6.5 - 6}{1.55} = .32 \quad \text{and} \quad z_2 = \frac{7.5 - 6}{1.55} = .97$$

Thus,

$$P(X = 7) = P(.32 < Z < .97)$$
$$= P(0 < Z < .97) - P(0 < Z < .32)$$
$$= .3340 - .1255$$
$$= .2085$$

The approximation by the normal curve is very close to the exact probability.

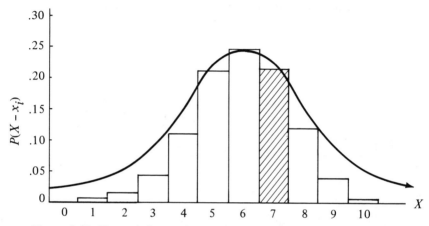

Figure 5.15 Normal Curve Approximation to a Binomial Distribution with $n = 10$, $p = .6$ for $P(X = 7)$

    The normal approximation is most useful in calculating binomial sums. This is especially true when n is large, for without tables or the assistance of a computer, the task can be nearly impossible. Suppose that we want to find the probability that the binomial random variable X in the preceding problem assumes either of the values 7, 8, or 9. The exact probability is given by

$$P(X = 7 \text{ or } 8 \text{ or } 9) = P(X = 7) + P(X = 8) + P(X = 9)$$
$$= C\binom{10}{7}(.6)^7(.4)^3 + C\binom{10}{8}(.6)^8(.4)^2 + C\binom{10}{9}(.6)^9(.4)^1$$
$$= .2150 + .1209 + .0404$$
$$= .3763$$

The value .3763 is equal to the sum of the area of the rectangles whose bases are centred at 7, 8, and 9.

    The approximation by the normal curve with parameters $\mu = 6$ and $\sigma = 1.55$ is the area under the curve bounded by $x_1 = 6.5$ and $x_2 = 9.5$. The corresponding Z-scores are

$$z_1 = \frac{6.5 - 6}{1.55} = .32 \quad \text{and} \quad z_2 = \frac{9.5 - 6}{1.55} = 2.26$$

Thus,

$$P(X = 7 \text{ or } 8 \text{ or } 9) = P(.32 < Z < 2.26)$$
$$= P(0 < Z < 2.26) - P(0 < Z < .32)$$
$$= .4881 - .1255$$
$$= .3626$$

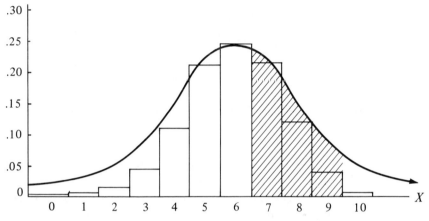

Figure 5.16 Normal Curve Approximation for $\sum_{i=7}^{9} P(X = x_i)$

The accuracy of the binomial probabilities approximated by the normal curve will increase as n becomes larger; on the other hand, the approximations will become less accurate when n is small. When p is close to 0 or 1 and n is small, the probability distribution will be skewed to the right or left and the histogram will no longer be symmetric. The histogram for the binomial distribution when $n = 5$ and $p = .2$ is shown in figure 5.17. The normal curve with $\mu = np = 1$ and $\sigma = \sqrt{npq} = 1$ is superimposed over the histogram.

It is evident that the normal curve in figure 5.17 does not fit the histogram as well as the normal curve fits the histogram for $n = 10$ and $p = .6$ as shown in figure 5.15. A "rule of thumb" used by many statisticians as a guide to determine whether the normal approximation is usable or not is the value of both np and npq. If both np and npq are greater than 5, then the approximation is usable.

Example 1. The student body of a large school has approximately an equal number of boys and girls. If a committee of 8 is selected at random, what is the probability that it will contain exactly 5 girls?

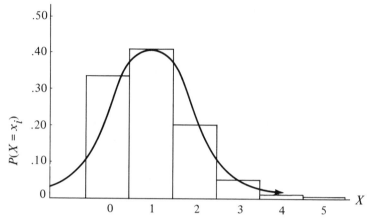

*Figure 5.17 Normal Curve Approximation to a Binomial Distribution
with n = 5 and p = .2*

Solution: (*a*—By the binomial formula). Let *X* be the binomial random variable. Since $n = 8$ and $p = .5$, the probability of exactly 5 girls is

$$P(X = 5) = C\binom{8}{5}(.5)^5(.5)^3 = .2188$$

Solution: (*b*—Normal curve approximation). Since $p = .5$, we should obtain fairly accurate results by approximation, using the normal curve with parameters

$$\mu = np = 8(.5) = 4 \quad \text{and} \quad \sigma = \sqrt{npq} = \sqrt{8(.5)(.5)} = 1.4$$

The approximate probability is the area under the curve bounded by $x_1 = 4.5$ and $x_2 = 5.5$. The corresponding Z-scores are

$$z_1 = \frac{4.5 - 4}{1.4} = .36 \quad \text{and} \quad z_2 = \frac{5.5 - 4}{1.4} = 1.07$$

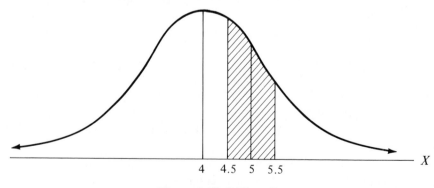

Figure 5.18 P(X = 5)

Thus,

$$P(X = 5) = P(.36 < Z < 1.07)$$
$$= P(0 < Z < 1.07) - P(0 < Z < .36)$$
$$= .3577 - .1406$$
$$= .2171$$

Example 2. What is the probability that the committee of 8 in example 1 consists of at least 3 but not more than 5 girls?

Solution: (a) The exact probability by the binomial formula is

$$P(X = 3 \text{ or } 4 \text{ or } 5) = P(X = 3) + P(X = 4) + P(X = 5)$$
$$= C\binom{8}{3}(.5)^3(.5)^5 + \binom{8}{4}(.5)^4(.5)^4 + C\binom{8}{5}(.5)^5(.5)^3$$
$$= .2185 + .2734 + .2188$$
$$= .7110$$

Solution: (b) The probability may be approximated by the normal distribution X with parameters $\mu = 4$ and $\sigma = 1.4$. The approximate probability is the area under the curve bounded by $x_1 = 2.5$ and $x_2 = 5.5$. The corresponding Z-scores are

$$z_1 = \frac{2.5 - 4}{1.4} = -1.07 \quad \text{and} \quad z_2 = \frac{5.5 - 4}{1.4} = 1.07$$

Thus, as shown in figure 5.19,

$$P(X = 3 \text{ or } 4 \text{ or } 5) = P(-1.07 < Z < 1.07)$$
$$= 2P(0 < Z < 1.07)$$
$$= 2(.3577)$$
$$= .7154$$

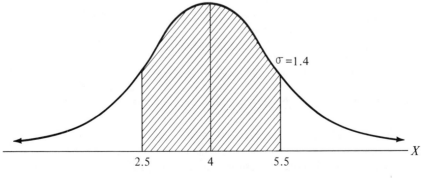

Figure 5.19 $P(X = 3 \text{ or } 4 \text{ or } 5)$

Example 3. What is the probability that the number of girls on the committee of 8 in example 1 will be less than 3?

Solution: (*a*) The exact probability by the binomial formula is

$$P(X = 0 \text{ or } 1 \text{ or } 2) = P(X = 0) + P(X = 1) + P(X = 2)$$

$$= C\binom{8}{0}(.5)^0(.5)^8 + C\binom{8}{1}(.5)^1(.5)^7 + \binom{8}{2}(.5)^2(.5)^6$$

$$= .0039 + .0313 + .1093$$

$$= .1445$$

Solution: (*b*) The probability may be approximated by the normal distribution X with parameters $\mu = 4$ and $\sigma = 1.4$. The approximate probability is the area under the curve bounded on the right by $x = 2.5$. The corresponding Z-score is

$$z = \frac{2.5 - 4}{1.4} = -1.07$$

Thus,

$$P(X = 0 \text{ or } 1 \text{ or } 2) = P(Z < -1.07)$$

$$= .5000 - P(0 < Z < 1.07)$$

$$= .5000 - .3577$$

$$= .1423$$

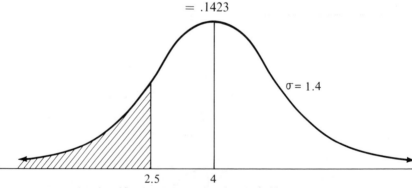

Figure 5.20 $P(X = 0 \text{ or } 1 \text{ or } 2)$

When n is relatively small, the exact probabilities computed by the binomial formula and the probabilities using normal curve approximation will vary somewhat. As n becomes larger, the difference between the actual and approximate probabilities becomes insignificant.

EXERCISE 5.3

1. A binomial random variable has a mean of 6 and a standard deviation of 1.5. What percent of the area under the probability histogram is to the left of 5; to the right of 7.25?

2. The quarterback for a professional football team completed 60% of the passes attempted during the first 10 games of the season. What is the probability that of the next 50 passes he attempts,
   (a) he will have 35 or more completions?
   (b) he will have less than 20 completions?

3. The probability that an electronic switch will operate successfully is .98. A random sample of 1,000 switches were tested and 30 were found to be defective. What is the probability of finding 30 or more defective switches in the sample?

4. A salesman has found that on the average, 3 out of every 10 contacts he makes result in a sale. If he makes 50 contacts, what is the probability that at least 10 will result in a sale?

5. A new car was designed on the assumption that 60% of its sales would be to female customers. If a random sample of 500 purchasers is selected, what is the probability that at least 275 of them are female?

6. The manufacturer of an electronics part has found that 98% of the parts are acceptable. A random sample of 500 parts is tested. What is the probability that 12 or more defective parts will be found?

7. A large advertising sign is made up of 1,000 light bulbs, whose average life-span is 500 hours with a standard deviation of 50 hours. The entire set of bulbs is replaced periodically to minimize the number of bulbs that burn out while the sign is operating. If the owner wishes that no more than 1% of the bulbs burn out between replacements, how often should the bulbs be replaced?

8. A multiple choice test consists of 50 questions, each with 4 possible answers of which only 1 is correct. What is the probability that by sheer guesswork a student will answer between 20 and 30 of the questions correctly?

9. A new serum is 90% effective in preventing colds. If 100 people take the serum, what is the probability that between 7 and 12 will catch a cold?

10. An automatic lathe for producing metal washers is said to be out of adjustment if a random sample of 100 washers contains 14 or more that are defective. If, in normal operation, 10% of its output is defective, what is the probability that the lathe will be declared out of adjustment after a given sample is checked?

11. The lathe in problem 10 produces washers whose internal diameters are normally distributed with mean equal to .373 inch and standard deviation of .002 inch. If specifications require that the internal diameters be .375 inch plus or minus .004 inch, what percentage of the production will be unacceptable?

CHAPTER 6

Sampling Distributions

6.1 INTRODUCTION

The primary objective of a statistical study is to make inferences about unknown population parameters based on statistics calculated from random samples taken from the population under study. Often several random samples are taken from a population and the value of a statistic is found for each sample. The distribution of the statistic computed from several random samples taken from the same population or from similar populations is our major concern in this chapter.

The parameters of a small finite population can often be calculated by inspecting the entire population. To illustrate: if we want to know the mean age at the time of taking office of the presidents of the United States, it can easily, and perhaps best, be done by using the whole population. However, in most situations, computing the parameters in this way is either impracticable or impossible.

Random sampling usually has advantages even when complete inspection is possible. A small number of measurements that have been carefully and accurately made will represent the population better than a large number that have been made hurriedly. Also, the cost of a complete investigation may be prohibitive, or the study may deal with a population that is either infinite or partially inaccessible. In such cases, a complete investigation is impossible.

We should always distinguish clearly between *parameter* and *statistic*. The parameters of a population, usually denoted by Greek letters, are constant and if they were known there would be no need for a study. On the other hand, a statistic, usually denoted by a lowercase letter, is a random variable whose value depends on the sample.

As additional samples are taken from the same population, the value of the statistic will fluctuate. The fluctuation will depend on the size of the sample, the method of selecting the sample, and the population from which the samples are taken.

Sampling may be done in either of two ways: (1) With replacement: the elements in the sample are selected, identified, and returned to the population; (2) Without replacement: the elements are selected, identified, and not returned to the population. If the size of the population is large or infinite, the distribution of the statistic computed from random samples is the same whether the sampling is done with or without replacement. When the size of the population is small, sampling without replacement gives a slightly different distribution for the statistic than if the sampling is done with replacement. The difference in the value of the statistic for different random samples is our major concern in this chapter.

DEFINITION 6.1

The probability distribution of a statistic is called a *sampling distribution*.

DEFINITION 6.2

The standard deviation of the sampling distribution of a statistic is called the *standard error* of the statistic.

6.2 SAMPLING DISTRIBUTION OF THE MEAN

The probability distribution of the sample mean $\bar{x}$ and its relationship to the population mean μ is illustrated by an actual sampling from a known population.

Suppose that our known population is $\{6, 8, 10, 12\}$. The individual observations are identified as:

$$x_1 = 6, \quad x_2 = 8, \quad x_3 = 10, \quad \text{and} \quad x_4 = 12$$

The mean of the population is

$$\mu = \frac{6 + 8 + 10 + 12}{4} = 9$$

the variance is

$$\sigma^2 = \frac{(6-9)^2 + (8-9)^2 + (10=9)^2 + (12=9)^2}{4} = 5$$

and the standard deviation is

$$\sigma = \sqrt{5}$$

Since the population is small, it will be a simple task to select all 16 possible distinct samples of size 2, with replacement, and compute the mean for each sample. The samples and their means are shown in table 6.1.

Table 6.1 Means of Random Samples with Replacements

Sample No.	Possible Samples	Weights	Mean ($\bar{x}$)	Sample No.	Possible Samples	Weights	Mean ($\bar{x}$)
1	x_1, x_1	6, 6	6	9	x_3, x_1	10, 6	8
2	x_1, x_2	6, 8	7	10	x_3, x_2	10, 8	9
3	x_1, x_3	6, 10	8	11	x_3, x_3	10, 10	10
4	x_1, x_4	6, 12	9	12	x_3, x_4	10, 12	11
5	x_2, x_1	8, 6	7	13	x_4, x_1	12, 6	9
6	x_2, x_2	8, 8	8	14	x_4, x_2	12, 8	10
7	x_2, x_3	8, 10	9	15	x_4, x_3	12, 10	11
8	x_2, x_4	8, 12	10	16	x_4, x_4	12, 12	12

The range space of the discrete random variable $\bar{X}$ is

$$R_{\bar{X}} = \{6, 7, 8, 9, 10, 11, 12\}$$

The distribution of means can be assigned as,

$$\bar{x}_1 = 6, \quad \bar{x}_2 = 7, \quad \bar{x}_3 = 8, \quad \bar{x}_4 = 9, \quad \bar{x}_5 = 10, \quad \bar{x}_6 = 11, \quad \bar{x}_7 = 12$$

The frequency distribution of the means is shown in table 6.2.

Table 6.2 Frequency Distribution of the Means

$\bar{x}_i$	Frequency
6	1
7	2
8	3
9	4
10	3
11	2
12	1

Suppose just one sample of size 2 were selected from this population with replacement. Since the samples of table 6.1 are random samples, each has probability 1/16 of being the one sample selected. Thus, considering the frequency distribution shown in Table 6.2, the probability distribution of $\bar{X}$ may be found as given in Table 6.3.

Table 6.3 Probability Distribution of $\bar{x}$

$\overline{X}_i$	Samples	$p(\overline{X} = \bar{x}_i)$
6	(6, 6)	1/16
7	(6, 8) and (8, 6)	2/16
8	(6, 10), (8, 8) and (10, 6)	3/16
9	(6, 12), (8, 10), (10, 8) and (12, 6)	4/16
10	(8, 12), (10, 10) and (12, 8)	3/16
11	(10, 12) and (12, 10)	2/16
12	(12, 12)	1/16

The expected value of $\overline{X}$ is given by the formula $E(\overline{X}) = \sum_{i=1}^{n} \bar{x}_i\, P(\overline{X} = \bar{x}_i)$

$$= 6\left(\frac{1}{16}\right) + 7\left(\frac{2}{16}\right) + 8\left(\frac{3}{16}\right) + 9\left(\frac{4}{16}\right) + 10\left(\frac{3}{16}\right) + 11\left(\frac{2}{16}\right) + 12\left(\frac{1}{16}\right) = 9.$$

If the means of the 16 possible samples were averaged, the mean of their means is found to be $\frac{144}{16} = 9$, as was the population mean μ.

The average of the means of all possible samples of size n taken from a finite population is always equal to the expected value of $\overline{X}$ which is equal to the population mean. That is,

$$E(\overline{X}) = \mu$$

and we say that $E(\overline{X})$ is an unbiased estimator of μ.

The variance, denoted by $\sigma_{\overline{X}}^2$, of the sampling distribution of the sample means is

$$\sigma_{\overline{X}}^2 = \sum_{i=1}^{7} (\bar{x}_i - \mu)^2 P(\overline{X} = \bar{x}_i) = \frac{40}{16} = \frac{5}{2}$$

and the standard deviation is

$$\sigma_{\overline{X}} = \sqrt{\frac{5}{2}}$$

The variance of the population has been computed as $\sigma^2 = 5$ and the variance of the sampling distribution of means as $\sigma_{\overline{X}}^2 = \frac{5}{2}$. For all possible random samples of size n drawn, *with replacement*, from a finite population with variance σ^2, the variance of the sampling distribution of means is $\sigma_{\overline{X}}^2 = \frac{\sigma^2}{n}$ and the standard deviation is $\sigma_{\overline{X}} = \frac{\sigma}{\sqrt{n}}$.

Example 1. A population consists of the measurements 2, 3, 3, 4, 4, 4, 5, 5, 5, 6, 6, 7. Compute: (a) μ, (b) σ^2, (c) $E(\overline{X})$, and (d) $\sigma_{\overline{X}}^2$.

Solution: (a) $\mu = \sum\limits_{i=1}^{12} \dfrac{x_i}{n} = \dfrac{54}{12} = 4.5$

(b) $\sigma^2 = \sum\limits_{i=1}^{12} \dfrac{(x_i - \mu)^2}{n} = \dfrac{23}{12} = 1.9$

(c) $E(\overline{X}) = \mu = 4.5$

(d) $\sigma_{\overline{X}}^2 = \dfrac{\sigma^2}{n} = \dfrac{1.9}{12} \doteq .16$

If random samples of size n are drawn without replacement from a small finite population of size N, or if a sample comprises a large part of the population,* the expected value of the sampling distribution of means is

$$E(\overline{X}) = \mu$$

However, the standard deviation is given by

$$\sigma_{\overline{X}} = \frac{\sigma}{\sqrt{n}} \sqrt{\frac{N - n}{N - 1}}$$

Example 2. A population consists of the measurements (1, 2, 4, 6, 8, 9). Find (a) μ, (b) σ, (c) $E(\overline{X})$, and (d). If random samples of size 4 are drawn without replacement, find the standard deviation of the distribution.

Solution: (a) $\mu = \sum\limits_{i=1}^{6} \dfrac{x_i}{n} = \dfrac{30}{6} = 5$

(b) $\sigma = \sqrt{\sum\limits_{i=1}^{6} \dfrac{(x_i - \mu)^2}{n}} = \sqrt{\dfrac{52}{6}} = 2.95$

(c) $E(\overline{X}) = \mu = 5$

(d) $\sigma_{\overline{X}} = \dfrac{\sigma}{\sqrt{n}} \sqrt{\dfrac{N - n}{N - 1}} = \dfrac{2.95}{\sqrt{4}} \sqrt{\dfrac{6 - 4}{6 - 1}}$

$$= \frac{2.95}{2}(.632) = .93$$

When the population size N is relatively large when compared to the sample size n, the quotient $\dfrac{N - n}{N - 1}$ is, for all practical purposes, equal to 1.

Sampling distributions have a tendency to be normally distributed as larger samples are taken. This tendency to become normal occurs in the sampling distributions of many of the statistics which are of practical importance. It may be stated in general that, almost regardless of the shape of the curve of the original population, the shape of sampling distributions of a statistic computed from random samples will be approximately normal. This general rule can be proved mathematically and is known as the Central Limit Theorem.

---

* A rule of thumb is 20% or more, but this is arbitrary and may vary.

THEOREM 6.1

Central Limit Theorem. If random samples of size n are taken from a population with mean μ and standard deviation σ, then the sampling distribution of means is approximately normally distributed with

$$E(\bar{X}) = \mu$$

and

$$\sigma_{\bar{x}} = \frac{\sigma}{\sqrt{n}}$$

The Central Limit Theorem can be applied to the sum of the sample measurements. This sum also has an approximately normal distribution. However, the expected value of the sum is nu, and the standard deviation is $\sqrt{n}\,\sigma$.

A most important consequence of the Central Limit Theorem arises from the fact that the statistic $\bar{X}$ is approximately normally distributed, regardless of the original distribution. When $n > 30$, approximating the distribution by means of the normal distribution gives very good results. If the population is normal, the sampling distribution of $\bar{X}$ is exactly normal for all n.

6.3 SAMPLING DISTRIBUTION OF THE DIFFERENCE BETWEEN TWO MEANS

In the previous discussion of the sampling distribution of means, we found some variability even though the samples were drawn from the same population. This fluctuation was to be expected, and we were able to describe it in terms of the sampling distribution.

Suppose that we select pairs of samples from a population and find the difference between the means of each pair, thus obtaining a distribution of these differences. The resulting distribution is called the *sampling distribution of the difference between means* and is denoted by $(\bar{X}_1 - \bar{X}_2)$.

To illustrate: let the given population be 4, 6, 8, 10, in which $\mu = 7$ and $\sigma = 2.236$. Let us randomly select (with replacement) two samples at a time from the population. Suppose that the first sample contained the values 4, 8 and the second sample contained the values 4, 4, 6. Then

$$\bar{x}_1 = \frac{4 + 8}{2} = 6$$

and

$$\bar{x}_2 = \frac{6 + 8 + 10}{3} = 8$$

and

$$\bar{x}_1 - \bar{x}_2 = -2$$

If we draw a large number of random samples of size $n_1 = 2$ and $n_2 = 3$ from the populations, then the differences between the means of the pairs of samples form a frequency distribution that, by the Central Limit Theorem, will be approximately normally distributed with mean equal to zero.

The distribution of the difference between pairs of sample means may be described even when the samples are not drawn from the same population.

Assume that we have two distinct populations. The first population consists of the number of credit hours taken per semester by college students who do not have regular jobs, and the second population consists of the credit hours taken per semester by college students who have regular jobs. The mean and standard deviation for each of the two populations are:

Population 1	Population 2
$\mu_1 = 16$	$\mu_2 = 15$
$\sigma_1 = 3$	$\sigma_2 = 4$

N_1 independent random samples of size 64 are drawn from population 1, and the mean of each sample is computed. The values obtained might be $12, 18, 17, 16, \ldots, 11$.

In like manner, N_2 independent random samples of size 36 are drawn from population 2, and the mean of each sample is computed. The resulting means might be $12, 14, 15, 11, \ldots, 9$.

A random pairing of the means of the two samples and their difference d is shown below.

Population 1 $\overline{X}_1$	Population 2 $\overline{X}_2$	Difference (d) $(\overline{X}_1 - \overline{X}_2)$
12	12	0
18	14	4
17	15	2
16	11	5
$\vdots$	$\vdots$	$\vdots$
11	9	2

Since $\mu_1 = 16$ and $\mu_2 = 15$, the difference between the two population means is one credit hour per semester. The pairing of 36 sample means shows that the means may or may not be equal. However, by the Central Limit Theorem, we would expect the sampling distribution of $\overline{X}_1 - \overline{X}_2$ to be approximately normally distributed and

$$E(\overline{X}_1 - \overline{X}_2) = (\mu_1 - \mu_2) = 1$$

The standard error of the statistic $\overline{X}_1 - \overline{X}_2$ is the standard deviation of the difference between the two means. To find the standard error of the distribution, we use a theorem from mathematical statistics: *The standard error of the sums or differences of two independent random variables is the square root of the sum of the squares of the standard errors of the separate random variables.* Thus, when n_1 and n_2 are the number of elements in each sample from N_1 and N_2 respectively, the standard error is computed by using the formula

$$\sigma_{(\bar{X}_1 - \bar{X}_2)} = \sqrt{\sigma_{\bar{X}_1}^2 + \sigma_{\bar{X}_2}^2}$$

$$= \sqrt{\frac{\sigma_1^2}{n_1} + \frac{\sigma_2^2}{n_2}}$$

The standard normal random variable Z is

$$Z = \frac{(\bar{X}_1 = \bar{X}_2) - (\mu_1 - \mu_2)}{\sqrt{\frac{\sigma_1^2}{n_1} + \frac{\sigma_2^2}{n_2}}}$$

For the samples taken from the population of students who do not have jobs and the students who do, we have

$$F(\bar{X}_1 - \bar{X}_2) = (\mu_1 - \mu_2) = 1$$

and

$$\sigma_{(\bar{X}_1 - \bar{X}_2)} = \sqrt{\frac{3^2}{64} + \frac{4^2}{36}} = .76$$

Having determined the mean and standard error of the distribution of the differences between the means of paired samples of two student populations, we can use the normal curve approximation to find the probability that the difference between any pair of sample means will lie in a specified interval. Suppose we want to find the probability that the difference $\bar{x}_1 - \bar{x}_2$ between two sample means of the two student populations lies in the interval bounded by .25 and 1.5.

The standard normal values corresponding to $x_1 = .25$ and $x_2 = 1.5$ are

$$z_1 = \frac{.25 - 1}{.76} = \frac{-.75}{.76} = -.99$$

and

$$z_2 = \frac{1.5 - 1}{.76} = \frac{.5}{.76} = .66$$

Thus,

$$P(1.5 > (\bar{x}_1 - \bar{x}_2) > .25) = P(.66 > Z > -.99)$$
$$= P(0 < Z < .66) + P(0 < Z < .99)$$
$$= .2454 + .3389$$
$$= .5843$$

Imagine that we are interested in finding an interval that encloses 95% of the sampling distribution of the differences between the means of the two student populations. From table III,

$$P(-1.96 < Z < 1.96) = .95$$

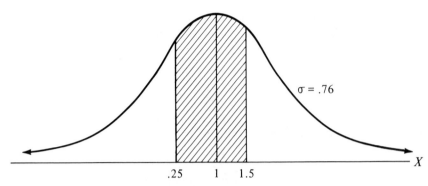

Figure 6.1 $P(1.5 > (\bar{x}_1 - \bar{x}_2) > .25)$

Thus,

$$P\left(-1.96 < \frac{(\bar{x}_1 - \bar{x}_2) - E(\bar{X}_1 - \bar{X}_2)}{\sigma_{(\bar{X}_1 - \bar{X}_2)}} < 1.96\right) = .95$$

$$P\{-1.96(\sigma_{(\bar{X}_1 - \bar{X}_2)}) + E(\bar{X}_1 - \bar{X}_2) < (\bar{x}_1 - \bar{x}_2)$$
$$< 1.96(\sigma_{(\bar{X}_1 - \bar{X}_2)}) + E(\bar{X}_1 - \bar{X}_2)\} = .95$$

$$P[-1.96(.76) + 1 < (\bar{x}_1 - \bar{x}_2) < 1.96(.76)] = .95$$

$$P[-.51 < (\bar{x}_1 - \bar{x}_2) < 2.49] = .95$$

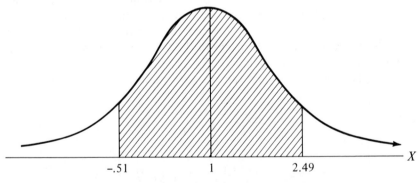

Figure 6.2 $P(2.49 > (\bar{X}_1 - \bar{X}_2) > -.51)$

The results obtained from sampling distributions of $\bar{X}_1 - \bar{X}_2$ are valid when the population is infinite or for finite populations when the sampling is done with replacement. When the sampling is done without replacement from a finite population, the results are valid provided the number of measurements in the population is relatively large when compared to the size of the samples.

Example 1. Car batteries produced by company A have a mean life of 3.5 years with a standard deviation of .4 years. A similar battery produced by company B has a mean life of 3.3 years and a standard deviation of .3 years. What is the probability that a random sample of 25 batteries from company A will have a mean life of at least .4 years more than the mean life of a sample of 36 batteries from company B?

Solution: Population A: $\mu_1 = 3.5,$ $\sigma_1 = .4,$ $n_1 = 36.$
Population B: $\mu_2 = 3.3,$ $\sigma_2 = .3,$ $n_2 = 25.$

Therefore

$$E(\overline{X}_1 - \overline{X}_2) = (\mu_1 - \mu_2) = .2$$

$$\sigma_{(\overline{X}_1 - \overline{X}_2)} = \sqrt{\frac{.16}{25} + \frac{.09}{36}} = .094$$

The probability that the mean of the sample from company A is at least .4 years greater than the mean of the sample from company B, as determined by the standard normal curve, is

$$z = \frac{.4 - .2}{.094} = 2.13$$

$$P\big((\overline{X}_1 - \overline{X}_2) > .4\big) = P(Z > 2.13)$$

$$= .5000 - P(0 < Z < 2.13)$$

$$= .5000 - .4854$$

$$= .0146$$

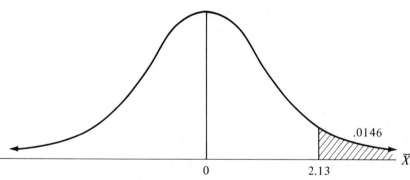

.0146

0   2.13

Figure 6.3 $P(\overline{X}_1 - \overline{X}_2 > .4)$

EXERCISE 6.1

1. A population consists of the number of defective transistors in shipments received by an assembly plant. The number of defectives is 2 in the first, 4 in the second, 6 in the third, and 8 in the fourth.
   (a) Find the mean μ and the standard deviation σ of the given population.
   (b) List all random samples, with replacement, of size 2 that can be formed from the population.

(c) Find the mean and the standard deviation of the sampling distribution of part (b).

2. A kindergarten class has nine members whose ages are 3, 3, 4, 4, 4, 4, 4, 5, and 5.
   (a) Find the mean μ and the standard deviation σ of the population.
   (b) Find the mean $E(\bar{x})$ and the standard deviation $\sigma(\bar{x})$ of a random sample, with replacement of size 36.
   (c) Find the probability that the mean of a random sample (part (a)) will lie between 3.24 and 5.

3. Random samples of size 100 are drawn, with replacement, from two populations, P_1 and P_2, and their means, $\bar{X}$ computed. If
   $\mu_1 = 10$, $\sigma_1 = 2$, $\mu_2 = 8$, and $\sigma_2 = 1$, find
   (a) $E(\bar{X}_1 - \bar{X}_2)$;
   (b) $\sigma_{(\bar{X}_1 - \bar{X}_2)}$;
   (c) the probability that the difference between a given pair of sample means is less than 1.5;
   (d) the probability that the difference between a given pair of sample means is greater than 1.75 but less than 2.5.

4. Two populations, P_1 and P_2, are given. A large number of random samples of size 50 is drawn, with replacement, from population 1. The mean $\bar{x}_1$ of each sample is found. A large number of samples of size 40 is drawn, with replacement, from population 2 and the means of each sample is found. If $\mu_1 = 23$, $\sigma_1 = 1.5$, $\mu_2 = 21$, and $\sigma_2 = 2$, find
   (a) $E(\bar{X}_1 - \bar{X}_2)$;
   (b) $\sigma_{(\bar{X}_1 - \bar{X}_2)}$;
   (c) the probability that the difference between a given pair of sample means is greater than 2.5;
   (d) the probability that the difference between a given pair of sample means is less than 3 but greater than 1.

5. A family has four children whose ages are 5, 8, 11, and 12.
   (a) List all random samples, without replacement, of size 2 that can be formed from the population.
   (b) Find the mean and the standard deviation of the sampling distribution.

6. The average age of all people living in a certain city is 35 years, with a standard deviation of 10 years.
   (a) Suppose that a large number of random samples of size 100 is selected and the average age of each sample is computed. Find the interval within which 95% of all samples means will fall.
   (b) Repeat part (a), except use random samples of size 225.
   (c) Explain the difference in the results of part (a) and part (b).

7. An electrical firm manufactures a certain type of light bulb that has a mean life of 1,800 hours and a standard deviation of 200 hours.

   (a) Find the probability that a random sample of 100 bulbs will have an average life of more than 1,825 hours.

   (b) Find the probability that a random sample of 100 bulbs will have an average life of not more than 1,775 hours and not less than 1,760 hours.

8. The mean cost per week for groceries for a family of three in St. Petersburg is $30 with a standard deviation of $2.40. The mean cost per week for groceries for a family of three in Chicago is $38 with a standard deviation of $3. A large number of samples of size 50 was selected at random from St. Petersburg and the mean $\bar{x}_1$ of each sample was calculated. The same number of random samples of size 60 was randomly selected from Chicago and the mean $\bar{x}_2$ of each sample found. What is the probability that a given sample mean from St. Petersburg is $6 or less than a given sample mean from Chicago?

9. A manufacturing company receives a shipment of ball bearings each month from a supplier. The inspectors apply the following rule in deciding whether to accept or reject each shipment. A random sample of 36 bearings is selected and measured. If the mean diameter of the sample is between .245 and .255, the shipment is accepted; otherwise it is rejected.

   (a) What is the probability of accepting a shipment that has a mean diameter of .24 inches and a standard deviation of .015 inches?

   (b) What is the probability of accepting a shipment that has a mean diameter of .2515 inches and a standard deviation of .005 inches?

10. A company manufactures large numbers of a certain kind of automatic washing machines that has a mean life of 4.5 years with a standard deviation of 1.2 years.

    (a) The company agrees to replace any machine that wears out before the guarantee expires. What length of time should they be guaranteed if the company plans to replace a maximum of 5%?

    (b) If a random sample of 36 machines is selected, what is the probability that the mean life is less than 4 years?

11. A seed company advertises that it has developed an early tomato that will produce ripe tomatoes in 54 days with a standard deviation of 4 days. Another seed company advertises that they have developed an early tomato that will produce ripe tomatoes in 60 days with a standard deviation of 6 days. A gardener makes a number of plantings of seed from each company, and each planting contains 400 seeds. The mean number of days $\bar{X}_1$ before ripe tomatoes for each planting from the first seed company was found. The average number of days $\bar{X}_2$ for each

planting from the second company was found. Assume that the conditions were identical for each planting and find

(a) the probability that the difference between any one sample mean taken from seeds produced by the first company and any one sample mean taken from seeds developed by the second company is less than 5 days;

(b) the probability that there is no difference between the mean of any one sample from the first company and the mean of any one sample from the second company.

6.4 THE T-DISTRIBUTION (SMALL SAMPLES)

In most practical situations, the parameters of the population from which samples are drawn are unknown. For samples of size $n > 30$, a good estimate of the population variance σ^2 is provided by calculating the variance s^2 of a random sample. As long as the computed value of s^2 is about the same for different samples drawn from the population, which is usually the case for samples of size $n > 30$, the substitution of s^2 for σ^2 in describing the sampling distribution of mean results in a Z-distribution that is approximately normally distributed and

$$z = \frac{\bar{x} - \mu}{\dfrac{s}{\sqrt{n}}}$$

is a value in the Z-distribution.

When the sample size is small, i.e., $n < 30$, the values of s^2 change considerably from sample to sample, and the sampling distribution of means is not a normal distribution. In such cases, the normal curve does not provide satisfactory results in describing the distribution. Instead, another distribution, called the *small sample distribution*, is employed.

The small sample was discovered by William Gosset and published by him in 1908 under the name "Student." He referred to the distribution as t, and since that time it has been known as the *t-distribution* or *Student's t*. Gosset determined the values of t as follows.

$$t = \frac{\bar{x} - \mu}{\dfrac{s}{\sqrt{n-1}}}$$

The statistic t is said to have a t-distribution.

The t-distribution, like the Z-distribution, is mound shaped and symmetrical about $t = 0$. Unlike Z, however, it is more variable and tails out rapidly to the left and right of $t = 0$. This results in more observations in the tails of the t-distribution than in the tails of the normal distribution. As a result, the t-distribution has a larger variance than the Z-distribution.

The variability of the t-distribution depends on two random quantities, s and $\bar{x}$. When n is small, the t-distribution is quite variable. However, as n increases in size, s, the estimator of σ, is based on more information and the variability of t decreases. For $n = 30$ the t-distribution is, for all practical purposes, the same as the Z-distribution. When n is infinitely large, the two distributions are identical.

The variability of the t-distribution compared to the Z-distribution is shown in figure 6.4.

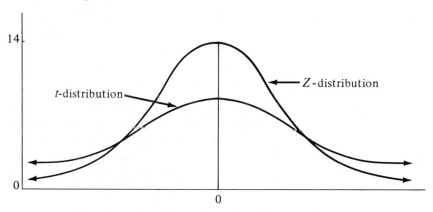

Figure 6.4 Variability of the t- and Z-Distributions

For small samples, the sample variance computed by

$$s^2 = \sum_{i=1}^{n} \frac{(x_i - \bar{x})^2}{n}$$

tends to underestimate the population variance. Thus for small samples, statisticians have found that

$$\tilde{s}^2 = \frac{\sum_{i=1}^{n}(x_i - \bar{x})^2}{n - 1}$$

is a better estimator for the population variance. The divisor $n - 1$ is called the number of *degrees of freedom* associated with $\tilde{s}^2$. The number of degrees of freedom, abbreviated df, refers to the number of values that are free to vary once the restrictions are placed on the data. For example, if the sum of the observation in sample of size 4 is 20 and three of the observations are 4, 5, and 3, then the fourth observation must be 8. This last value is not free to vary if the sum is to be 20.

The shape of the t-distribution is based on the number of degrees of freedom, $n - 1$, instead of the sample size n. As the number of df increases, the t-distribution becomes less variable. As a result, there is a different t-distribution for each value of n. (See Fig. 6.5.)

An examination of the t-distributions in figure 6.5 shows that the percentage of observations in each tail increases as the number of df

decreases. Table V in the back of the book gives the percentages of observations in a *t*-distribution that is to the right of a particular *t*-value.

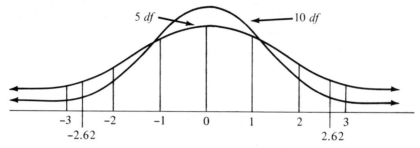

Figure 6.5 t-Distributions with 5 and 10 df and $t_{\alpha/2} = .05$

The table of *T*-values (table V) is different from the table of normal curve areas. In the *t*-distribution table, each row gives the values for one particular *t*-distribution. The left column gives the number of degrees of freedom, the entries in the rows are the *t*-values, and the headings of the columns gives the area to the right of the *t*-entry. To illustrate how the table is read, one line from table V with 10 degrees of freedom is reproduced.

Area for t

df	$t_{.10}$	$t_{.05}$	$t_{.025}$	$t_{.01}$	$t_{.005}$
10	1.383	1.833	2.262	2.821	3.250

Thus, for 10 *df*, 10% of the area underneath the curve lies to the right of $t = 1.383$, 5% to the right of $t = 1.833$, 2.5% to the right of $t = 2.262$, and so on for the other *t* entries. The symmetry of the curve enables us to read the percentage to the left of a negative *t*-value. Consequently, 90% of the curve will lie in the interval $-1.833 < t_i < 1.833$. (See Fig. 6.6.)

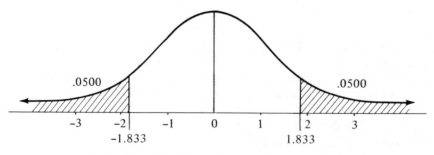

Figure 6.6 t-Distribution for 10 df and $t_{\alpha/2} = .05$

In like manner, for $df = 10$ and $t_{.025}$, we find $t = 2.262$. This indicates 2.5% of the area underneath the curve is to the right of $t = 2.262$ and 2.5% to the left of -2.262, with 95% enclosed within the interval. (See Fig. 6.7.)

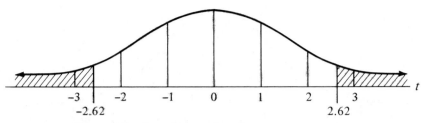

Figure 6.7 t-Distribution for df = 10 and $t_{\alpha/2} = .025$

The *t*-distribution and the values in table V are based on the assumption that $\bar{x}$ and *s* are independent and the sampling is from a normal population. The *t*-value, given by the formula

$$t = \frac{\bar{x} - \mu}{\frac{\tilde{s}}{\sqrt{n}}}$$

is a value of a *t*-distribution with $n - 1$ *df*.

The sampling distribution of means for small samples is investigated in a similar way as are large samples. If σ is known, then use the normal curve. If σ is unknown and the population is normal, use the *t*-curve.

Example 1. A manufacturer of transistors claims that its transistors will last an average of 1,000 hours. To maintain this average, 25 transistors are tested each month. If the computed *t*-value lies between $-t_{.025}$ and $t_{.025}$, the manufacturer is satisfied with his claim. What conclusions should be drawn from a sample that has a mean $\bar{x} = 1,010$ and $\tilde{s} = 60$. Assume the distribution of lifetime of the transistors to be normal.

Solution: From table V we find $t_{.025} = 2.064$ for 24 *df*. Thus the manufacturer will be satisfied if a sample of 25 transistors yield a *t*-value between -2.064 and 2.064. Since, $\mu = 1,000$, $x = 1,010$ and $\tilde{s} = 60$, the computed *t*-value is

$$t = \frac{\bar{x} - \mu}{\frac{\tilde{s}}{\sqrt{n}}}$$

$$= \frac{1010 - 1000}{\frac{40}{\sqrt{25}}}$$

$$= \frac{10}{8}$$

$$= 1.25$$

The computed *t*-value falls between -2.064 and 2.064 (unshaded area). The manufacturer should be satisfied that the sample verifies his claim.

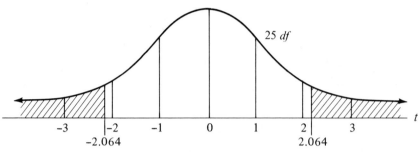

Figure 6.8.

Suppose that we have two normal populations with parameters $\mu_1, \sigma_1{}^2$, and $\mu_2, \sigma_2{}^2$ respectively. If $\sigma_1{}^2$, and $\sigma_2{}^2$ are unknown, then we have no known exact sampling distribution unless we can assume that the two variances are equal. When the two measures can be assumed to be the same, then they can be measured by a common variance σ^2 such that

$$\sigma^2 = \sigma_1{}^2 = \sigma_2{}^2$$

In the sampling distribution of the difference between two means, the estimator of σ could be either $\tilde{s}_1$ or $\tilde{s}_2$. However, we wish to have the best estimate available, so it is reasonable to pool the information from both samples. Since both $\tilde{s}_1$ with $(n_1 - 1)$ degrees of freedom and $\tilde{s}_2$ with $(n_2 - 1)$ degrees of freedom are estimates of σ, it is logical to write the pooled estimate of σ as

$$s = \frac{\sqrt{(n_1 - 1)\tilde{s}_1{}^2 + (n_2 - 1)\tilde{s}_2{}^2}}{n_1 + n_2 - 2}$$

A value of the random variable t with $(n_1 + n_2 - 2)$ degrees of freedom is

$$t = \frac{(\bar{x}_1 - \bar{x}_2) - (\mu_1 - \mu_2)}{\sqrt{\dfrac{s^2}{n_1} + \dfrac{s^2}{n_2}}}$$

$$= \frac{(\bar{x}_1 - \bar{x}_2) - (\mu_1 - \mu_2)}{s\sqrt{\dfrac{1}{n_1} + \dfrac{1}{n_2}}}$$

Example 2. A manufacturer of transistors makes two brands, A and B. Brand A has an average life of 60 hours more than brand B but the variance of the two brands is equal. Each month nine transistors of each brand are tested and a t-value corresponding to the difference of the sample means is computed. The manufacturer is satisfied if the computed t-value falls between $-t_{.05}$ and $t_{.05}$. During one month, the sample of nine transistors from brand A had a mean life-span of 1,000 hours and a standard deviation of 60 hours, while those of brand B had a mean life-span of 925 hours with a standard deviation of 50 hours. Assuming that the life-span of both brand A and brand B is normal, should the manufacturer be satisfied?

Solution: From table V, we find $t_{.05} = 1.746$ for $9 + 9 - 2 = 16$ degrees of freedom. Thus, the manufacturer will be satisfied if the samples yield a t-value between -1.746 and 1.746. Since $n_1 = 9$, $n_2 = 9$, $\tilde{s}_1 = 60$, and $\tilde{s}_2 = 50$, the pooled estimate of σ is

$$s = \sqrt{\frac{(n_1 - 1)\tilde{s}_1{}^2 + (n_2 - 1)\tilde{s}_2{}^2}{n_1 + n_2 - 2}}$$

$$= \sqrt{\frac{8(60)^2 + 8(50)^2}{16}}$$

$$= 50$$

Hence, the computed t-value is

$$t = \frac{(\bar{x}_1 - \bar{x}_2) - (\mu_1 - \mu_2)}{s\sqrt{\dfrac{1}{n_1} + \dfrac{1}{n_2}}}$$

$$= \frac{(1000 - 925) - 60}{50\sqrt{\dfrac{1}{9} + \dfrac{1}{9}}}$$

$$= 1.369$$

The computed t-value falls between -1.746 and 1.746 (unshaded area of Figure 6.9), and the manufacturer should be satisfied.

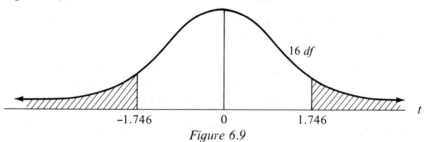

Figure 6.9

EXERCISE 6.2

1. The graph of a t-distribution with 10 degrees of freedom is shown in figure 6.10.
   Find the value of t for which
   (a) the shaded area on the right $= .05$
   (b) the total shaded area $= .10$
   (c) the total unshaded area $= .99$
   (d) the shaded area on the left $= .01$
   (e) the area to the right of $-t$, $= .90$

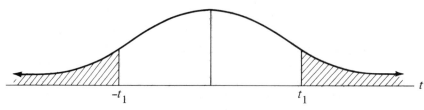

Figure 6.10

2. (a) Find $t_{.05}$ when $df = 15$.
   (b) Find $-t_{.05}$ when $df = 9$.
   (c) Find $t_{.10}$ when $df = 30$.
3. Find the probability that a *t*-distribution has a *t* score
   (a) greater than 1.740 when $n = 18$.
   (b) less than -1.323 when $n = 22$.
   (c) greater than 2.201 or less than -2.201 when $n = 12$.

4. Given a normal population with $\mu = 10$ and a random sample of size 9 from the population, what is the probability that the *t*-value is greater than 1.397?

5. A machine is set to produce metal shims having a thickness of .05 inches. To maintain the proper setting, 10 shims are tested each day. If the computed *t*-value falls between $-t_{.025}$ and $t_{.025}$, the machinist is satisfied that the machine is in adjustment. What should he conclude about the setting on the basis of a sample that has a mean of .053 inches and a standard deviation of .003?

6. A manufacturer of vacuum cleaners produces a machine in which the electric motor has, on the average, a 2-horsepower rating. To maintain the quality of the motor, random samples of six motors are tested each month. If the computed *t*-value falls between $-t_{.05}$ and $t_{.05}$, the manufacturer is satisfied that the motors have the proper horsepower rating. What should be concluded about a sample that has $\bar{x} = 1.9$, and $\tilde{s} = .05$?

7. Random samples of size $n_1 = 12$ and $n_2 = 15$ are selected from two normal populations. The means of the two populations are $\mu_1 = 20$ and $\mu_2 = 24$, and the variances σ_1^2 and σ_2^2 are equal but unknown. If the random sample of size $n_1 = 12$ has statistics $\bar{x} = 20$, $\tilde{s} = 4$ and the random sample of size $n_2 = 15$ has statistics $\bar{x}_2 = 21$, $\tilde{s}_2 = 3.5$, does the computed *t*-value for the difference lie between $-t_{.01}$ and $t_{.01}$?

8. A manufacturer of electric fuses produces two brands, *A* and *B*, such that the average breaking point of brand *A* is 1 amp greater than that of brand *B*. The variance for brand *A* and brand *B* are approximately equal. Each week, random samples of both brands are tested. A random sample of ten fuses from brand *A* has an average breaking point of 15.8

amps with a standard deviation of .02, and a random sample of five fuses of brand B has an average breaking point of 15.2 with a standard deviation of .025 amps. If the manufacturer is satisfied when the computed t-value for the difference between the two samples falls between $-t_{.025}$ and $t_{.025}$, should he be satisfied on the basis of the two samples?

6.5 SAMPLING DISTRIBUTION OF PROPORTIONS

We shall now consider a distribution in which the data is in the form of proportions or percentages. Suppose that we conduct a binomial experiment in which the probability of success for each trial is p and the probability of failure is $1 - p = q$. The sampling distribution of the random variable X, representing the number of successes in n trials of the experiment, can be closely approximated by a normal distribution with parameters $\mu = np$ and $\sigma = \sqrt{npq}$, provided p is not too close to 0 or 1.

If a sample of size n is drawn from this binomial population, we can determine the proportion $\tilde{p}$ of successes in the sample, i.e., $\tilde{p} = x/n$, where x represents the number of successes. The value of $\tilde{p}$ will vary for different samples of size n. The several values of $\tilde{p}$ shall be denoted by $\tilde{P}$. The sampling distribution of $\tilde{P}$ is the same as that of the binomial random variable X except $\tilde{P}$ is written as a proportion. Hence, the sampling distribution of $\tilde{P}$ is approximately normally distributed with expected value being the mean of the several values of $\tilde{P}$. The mean and standard deviation of $\tilde{P}$ are given by

$$\mu_{\tilde{p}} = E(\tilde{P}) = E\left(\frac{x}{n}\right) = \frac{np}{n} = p$$

and

$$\sigma_{\tilde{p}} = \sqrt{\sigma^2_{x/n}} = \sqrt{\frac{npq}{n}} = \sqrt{\frac{pq}{n}}$$

The relationship between the statistics of the binomial distribution and the distribution of proportions is shown in table 6.4.

Table 6.4 Binomial Distribution and Distribution of Proportions

Distribution	Means	Standard Deviation	Z-Value
Binomial	$E(\overline{X}) = \mu = np$	$\sigma = \sqrt{npq}$	$z = \dfrac{x - np}{\sqrt{npq}}$
Proportion	$E(\tilde{P}) = E\left(\dfrac{x}{n}\right)$ $= \mu_{\tilde{p}}$	$\sigma_{\tilde{p}} = \sqrt{\dfrac{pq}{n}}$	$z = \dfrac{\tilde{p} - \mu_{\tilde{p}}}{\sqrt{\dfrac{pq}{n}}}$

To illustrate, the following example will be solved (*a*) as a binomial distribution and (*b*) as a sampling distribution of proportions.

Example 1. A company produces light bulbs and knows that, on the average, 10% are defective and will not pass inspection. What is the probability that more than 15% of a random sample of 100 bulbs is defective.

Solution: (a—As a binomial distribution). The expected number of defective bulbs in the sample is

$$E(X) = np = 100(.10) = 10$$

and the standard deviation is

$$\sigma = \sqrt{npq} = \sqrt{100(.10)(.90)} = 3$$

The normal curve approximation is used to find the probability that more than 15 bulbs (15%) are defective. The Z-value is

$$z = \frac{15.5 - 10}{3} = 1.83$$

and

$$P(X > 15.5) = P(Z > 1.83)$$
$$= .5000 - .4664$$
$$= .0336$$

(b—As a distribution of proportions). Let $\tilde{P}$ be the proportion of defective bulbs in the sample. The expected value of $\tilde{P}$ is

$$E(\tilde{P}) = \mu_P = .10$$

and the standard deviation is

$$\sigma_{\tilde{p}} = \sqrt{\frac{pq}{n}} = \sqrt{\frac{(.10)(.90)}{100}} = .03$$

The Z-value is

$$z = \frac{\tilde{p} - \mu_{\tilde{p}}}{\sigma_{\tilde{p}}} = \frac{.155 - .10}{.03} = 1.83$$

and the probability of $\tilde{P}$ is

$$P(\tilde{P} > .155) = P(Z > 1.83)$$
$$= .5000 - .4664$$
$$= .0336$$

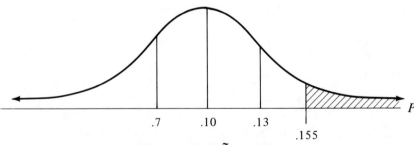

Figure 6.11 $P(\tilde{P} > .155)$

The sampling distribution of the difference between two proportions is essentially the same as the sampling distribution of the difference between two means. The expected value of the difference between two proportions is

$$E(\tilde{P}_1 - \tilde{P}_2) = (\mu_{P_1} - \mu_{P_2})$$

and the standard deviation is

$$\sigma_{(\tilde{P}_1 - \tilde{P}_2)} = \sqrt{\frac{p_1 q_1}{n_1} + \frac{p_2 q_2}{n_2}}$$

Hence, a value of the standard normal random variable Z is given by

$$z = \frac{(\tilde{P}_1 - \tilde{P}_2) - (\mu_{P_1} - \mu_{P_2})}{\sqrt{\dfrac{p_1 q_1}{n_1} + \dfrac{p_2 q_2}{n_2}}}$$

To illustrate, consider the following example.

Example 2. A poultry farmer wished to make a comparison between two feed mixtures. One flock of hens was fed from mixture 1 and another flock from mixture 2. In a six-week period, the flock being fed from mixture 1 increased egg production by 25%, while those fed from mixture 2 increased egg production by 20%. Random samples of 200 and 300 hens were selected from the respective flocks. Let $\tilde{p}_1$ be the proportion of the sample from the first flock with increased egg production, and let $\tilde{p}_2$ be the proportion of the sample from the second flock. Find

    (a) the expected difference between the two proportions,
    (b) the standard error of this difference,
    (c) the probability that hens fed from mixture 1 increased their egg production more than those fed from mixture 2.

Solution: (a) The expected difference between the two proportions is

$$E(\tilde{P}_1 - \tilde{P}_2) = \mu_{p1} - \mu_{p2}.25 - .20 = .05$$

    (b) The standard error of this difference is

$$\sigma_{(\tilde{P}_1 - \tilde{P}_2)} = \sqrt{\frac{p_1 q_1}{n_1} + \frac{p_2 q_2}{n_2}}$$

$$= \sqrt{\frac{(.25)(.75)}{200} + \frac{(.20)(.80)}{300}}$$

$$= .038$$

    (c) The probability that the hens fed from mixture 1 increased their egg production more than those fed from mixture 2 is

$$P(\tilde{P}_1 > \tilde{P}_2) = P(Z > z_i)$$

where

$$z_i = \frac{.05}{.038} = 1.31$$

Thus

$$P(\tilde{P}_1 > \tilde{P}_2) = P(Z > 1.31)$$
$$= .5000 - .4049$$
$$= .0951$$

6.6 THE CHI-SQUARE DISTRIBUTION

If random samples are withdrawn from a normal population, the variance of the samples s^2 forms a distribution that is independent of the mean of the population. However, for each sample size n and for each standard deviation σ, the shape of the distribution will change. If the distributions are to be useful, they must be standardized, as was the case of the Z-scores.

The standardization is accomplished through the use of the formula

$$\chi^2 = \frac{(n-1)\tilde{s}^2}{\sigma}$$

where

$$\tilde{s}^2 = \sum_{i=1}^{n} \frac{(x_i - \bar{x})^2}{n-1}$$

The distribution of χ^2 is called a *chi-square probability distribution* with $(n-1)$ degrees of freedom.

The shape of the chi-square distribution, like the t-distribution, varies according to the number of degrees of freedom associated with $\tilde{s}^2$. Table IV in the back of the book is constructed in the same manner as the table for the t-distribution. The left column gives the number of degrees of freedom, the column heading gives the area to the right of the chi-square values that are entered in the table.

The chi-square distribution is not symmetrical, and the extreme values of χ^2 must be tabulated for both tails. For a sample with 10 *df*, 99.5% of the distribution will be to the right of $\chi^2 = 2.15585$ and only .5% to the right of $\chi^2 = 25.1882$. The interval $(2.15585, 25.1882)$ will contain 99% of the distribution.

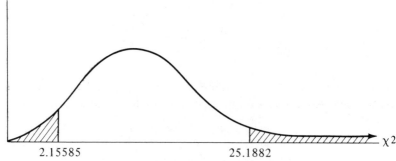

Figure 6.12 Chi-square Distribution with 10 df

Example 1. A manufacturer of kitchen clocks claims that a certain model will last 5 years on the average with a standard deviation of 1.2 years. A random sample of six of the clocks lasted $6, 5.5, 4, 5.2, 5$, and 4.3 years

Compute the χ^2 value for this distribution.

Solution: The sample mean is

$$\bar{x} = \frac{\sum\limits_{i=1}^{6} x_i}{n} = 5$$

the sample variance is

$$\tilde{s}^2 = \frac{\sum\limits_{i=1}^{6} (x_i - \bar{x})^2}{n - 1} = \frac{2.78}{5} = .556$$

and

$$\chi^2 = \frac{(n - 1)\tilde{s}^2}{\sigma^2} = \frac{5(.556)}{(1.2)^2} = 1.9305$$

is a value from a chi-square distribution with 5 degrees of freedom.

6.7 THE F-DISTRIBUTION

The final distribution that will be introduced in this chapter was developed by Sir Ronald Fisher and is known as the F-distribution. This distribution provides a procedure to determine if the variance of sample means is greater than could be expected from chance alone. If so, then we can conclude that the population means differ significantly.

Suppose that we select a random sample of size n, from a normal population with variance σ^2 and compute $\tilde{s}_1^2/\sigma_1^2$. Then from a second normal population with variance σ_2^2, we select another sample of size n_2 and compute $\tilde{s}_2^2/\sigma_2^2$. The ratio of the two quantities produce an f-value. That is,

$$f = \frac{\tilde{s}_1^2/\sigma_1^2}{\tilde{s}_2^2/\sigma_2^2}$$

The distribution of all possible f-values with numerator $\tilde{s}_1^2/\sigma_1^2$ and denominator $\tilde{s}_2^2/\sigma_2^2$ is known as an F-distribution with $n_1 - 1$ and $n_2 - 1$ degrees of freedom. In an F-distribution, the number of degrees of freedom associated with the numerator is always stated first. Since we are at liberty to designate either population as population 1, it is usually desirable to designate the population with the larger variance as population 1. That is, we always place the larger sample variance in the numerator of

$$f = \frac{\tilde{s}_1^2/\sigma_1^2}{\tilde{s}_2^2/\sigma_2^2}$$

To illustrate: suppose that from population 1 with $\sigma_1{}^2 = 5$ we select a sample of size 10 and find that $\tilde{s}_1{}^2 = 4$. Then from population 2 with $\sigma_2{}^2 = 6$, we select a sample of size 12 and find that $\tilde{s}_2{}^2 = 3$. Then we can compute an f-value by

$$f = \frac{\tilde{s}_1{}^2/\sigma_1{}^2}{\tilde{s}_2{}^2/\sigma_2{}^2} = \frac{4/5}{3/6} = 1.6$$

The graph of an F-curve with 9 and 11 degrees of freedom is shown in figure 6.13.

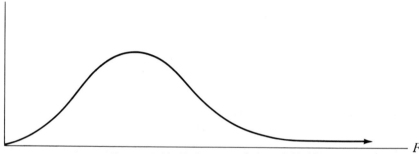

Figure 6.13 F-Curve with 9 and 11 df

The F-distribution will be further discussed in chapter 7, where it will be used in the analysis of variation of two normal populations.

EXERCISE 6.3

1. The records of a large university shows that 40% of the student body are classified as freshmen. A random sample of 50 students is selected. Find
   (a) the expected number of freshmen in the sample.
   (b) the standard error of the expected number.
   (c) the probability that more than 45% are freshmen.

2. An honest coin is tossed 400 times. Compute
   (a) the expected number of heads.
   (b) the standard error of the expected number.
   (c) the probability that more than 55% of the tosses will result in heads.
   (d) the probability that at least 47% and at most 54% of the tosses will result in heads.

3. A professional basketball player is successful in 60% of the shots he takes from the field. In one game, he takes 36 shots from the field. What is the probability that
   (a) he is successful in less than 50% of his attempts?
   (b) between 48% and 72% of his shots are successful?

4. In a certain city it has been found that an average of 56% of the eligible voters actually vote in city elections. What is the probability that in a

random sample of 200 eligible voters the percentage who vote in the next city election is

(a) more than 65%,
(b) less than 48%,
(c) between 48% and 65%?

5. In a random sample of 10,000 claims filed against an automobile insurance company, 75% exceeded $300. What is the probability that of the next 400 claims filed more than 72% will be above $300?

6. For a chi-square distribution, find
   (a) χ^2 .025 with 10 degrees of freedom.
   (b) χ^2 .01 with 25 degrees of freedom.
   (c) χ^2 .05 with 6 degrees of freedom.
   (d) χ_α^2 such that $P(\chi^2 < \chi_\alpha^2) = .995$ with 12 degrees of freedom.

7. What is the probability that a chi-square value with 12 degrees of freedom will be greater than
   (a) 21.0261?
   (b) 26.2170?
   (c) 3.57065?

8. For an *F*-distribution, find
   (a) $f_{.05}$ with 4 and 6 degrees of freedom.
   (b) $f_{.05}$ with 9 and 17 degrees of freedom.
   (c) $f_{.01}$ with 7 and 12 degrees of freedom.
   (d) $f_{.01}$ with 8 and 20 degrees of freedom.

CHAPTER 7

Estimation and Decision-Making

7.1 INTRODUCTION

We have come to one of the main areas of statistical inference—the estimation of parameters and decision-making. In this chapter we shall be concerned with estimating the unknown parameters of a population and testing hypotheses. The estimations of the population parameters will be based on the computed values of statistics of random samples taken from the population.

Our discussion will be confined to the population parameters associated with the sampling distributions of chapter 6. We shall see how estimates are made and how they are interpreted.

We shall be concerned with two types of estimation—*point estimation* and *interval estimation*. The first type, a point estimate, is a single number that is associated with a point on a line. The second type of estimation is associated with the interval of numbers between two points on a line.

Even though a point estimate is based on information contained in a sample, it is very unlikely that a single number will coincide exactly with the parameter of interest. The actual estimation is accomplished through the use of an *estimator*, a statistic calculated from a random sample. To illustrate, the mean of a random sample

$$\bar{x} = \frac{\displaystyle\sum_{i=1}^{n} x_i}{n}$$

is an estimator of the population mean μ. Other estimators are available for estimating the population mean including the sample median and the average value of the range. Each would generate a probability distribution in repeated sampling and for certain populations would possess certain advantages and disadvantages. However, the sample mean $\bar{x}$ is usually superior because for some populations its variance is a minimum and, regardless of the population, it is unbiased.

Since a point estimate is unlikely to be precisely equal to the parameter, we need to specify an interval within which we are confident that the parameter does lie. This specified interval is called a *confidence interval*, and the probability that the parameter lies in the interval is called the *confidence coefficient*. A good interval estimate will successfully inclose the desired parameter a large percentage of the time.

7.2 ESTIMATING THE POPULATION MEAN

We have seen that a sampling distribution of means is approximately normally distributed with expected value, $E(\bar{X})$, equal to μ and standard error $\sigma_{\bar{x}} = \dfrac{\sigma}{\sqrt{n}}$. A few calculations will enable us to place bounds on the error in using $\bar{X}$ as an estimate of μ and determine the confidence interval within which we expect μ to be.

Even though the sample mean is an unbiased estimator of μ, it is possible that $\bar{X}$ might lie either above or below the population mean. However, since the sampling distribution of means is approximately normally distributed according to the Central Limit Theorem, we would not expect the sample mean to deviate more than $2\sigma_{\bar{x}}$ in either direction from μ. Hence, we can place a bound of $2\sigma_{\bar{x}}$ on the error of the point estimate. The bounds placed on the error establish a confidence interval for the point estimate.

The point $(\bar{X} - 2\sigma_{\bar{x}})$ is the lowest point of the confidence interval and is called the *lower confidence limit*, or *LCL*, of the mean. The point $(\bar{X} + 2\sigma_{\bar{x}})$ is the highest point of the confidence interval and is called the *upper confidence limit*, or *UCL*, of the mean. Since the distribution of means is approximately normal, we would expect the interval,

$$\bar{X} \pm 2\sigma_{\bar{x}}$$

to inclose the population mean about 95% of the time.

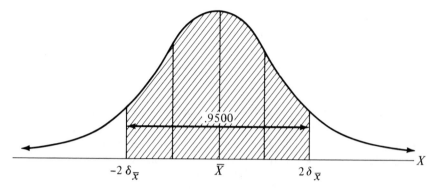

Figure 7.1 .95 Confidence Interval for μ

The confidence interval we have described is called a large sample confidence interval, for n must be large enough for the Central Limit Theorem to apply and for the sample means to be approximately normally distributed. Also, if the standard deviation of the population is unknown, the sample standard deviation, $\tilde{s}$, must be used to estimate σ.

A confidence coefficient of .95 corresponds approximately to the confidence interval $\overline{X} \pm 2\sigma_{\overline{X}}$. To be more exact, $\overline{X} \pm 1.96\sigma_{\overline{x}}$ should be used to establish the confidence interval, since 95% of the area under the normal curve lies between $Z = \pm 1.96$. Hence a .95 confidence interval for μ has limits $\overline{X} \pm 1.96\sigma_{\overline{x}}$, i.e.,

$$.95 = P(-1.96 < Z < 1.96)$$

$$= P(-1.96 < \frac{\overline{X} - \mu}{\sigma_{\overline{X}}} < 1.96)$$

$$= P(\overline{X} - 1.96\sigma_{\overline{x}} < \mu < \overline{X} + 1.96\sigma_{\overline{x}})$$

Thus,

$$LCL = \overline{X} - 1.96\sigma_{\overline{X}}$$

$$= \overline{X} - 1.96\frac{\sigma}{\sqrt{n}}$$

$$UCL = \overline{X} + 1.96\sigma_{\overline{x}}$$

$$= \overline{X} + 1.96\frac{\sigma}{\sqrt{n}}$$

and the .95 confidence interval for μ is

$$\overline{X} - 1.96\frac{\sigma}{\sqrt{n}} < \mu < \overline{X} + 1.96\frac{\sigma}{\sqrt{n}}$$

Similarly, a .90 confidence coefficient corresponds to the interval $\overline{X} \pm 1.645 \frac{\sigma}{\sqrt{n}}$. The confidence limits are

$$LCL = \overline{X} - 1.645 \frac{\sigma}{\sqrt{n}}$$

and

$$UCL = \overline{X} + 1.645 \frac{\sigma}{\sqrt{n}}$$

A confidence interval for any desired confidence coefficient denoted by $(1 - \alpha)$ can be constructed by using

$$\overline{X} \pm z_{\alpha/2} \frac{\sigma}{\sqrt{n}}$$

where $z_{\alpha/2}$ is the value in the Z table such that the area under the Z-curve to the right of $z_{\alpha/2}$ equals $\frac{\alpha}{2}$ (see figure 7.2).

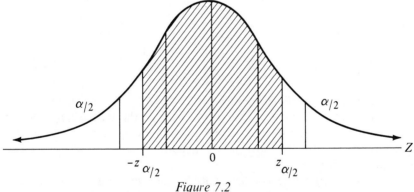

Figure 7.2

A confidence coefficient of .95 implies that $\alpha = .05$ and $z_{\alpha/2} = z_{.025} = 1.96$. In like manner, a .90 confidence coefficient implies that $\alpha = .10$ and $z_{\alpha/2} = z_{.05} = 1.645$.

Example. A random sample of 36 people employed by a large industry showed the average number of days absent in a one-year period of time resulted in the statistics $\overline{x} = 12$ and $\tilde{s} = 4$.

(a) Establish a point estimate of μ.

(b) Establish a .95 confidence interval estimate of μ.

(c) Establish a .99 confidence interval estimate of μ.

Solution: (a) The point estimate of μ is $\overline{x} = 12$.

(b) The .95 confidence interval estimate of the population mean μ is

$$\overline{X} \pm 1.96 \frac{\sigma}{\sqrt{n}}$$

Using $\tilde{s}$ to approximate σ, we have

$$12 \pm 1.96 \frac{4}{\sqrt{36}}$$

or

$$12 \pm 1.3$$

We estimate the average number of days μ of absenteeism to be in the interval such that

$$10.7 < \mu < 13.3 \text{ days}$$

The .95 confidence coefficient implies that in repeated sampling 95% of such confidence intervals will enclose the population mean μ.

(c) The .99 confidence interval estimate of the population mean is

$$12 \pm 2.58 \frac{\sigma}{\sqrt{36}}$$

Again, using $\tilde{s}$ to approximate σ, we have

$$12 \pm 2.58 \frac{4}{\sqrt{36}}$$

or

$$12 \pm 1.7$$

and

$$10.3 < \mu < 13.7$$

The .99 confidence interval, 12 ± 1.7, is longer than the .95 confidence interval, 12 ± 1.3, and will enclose the true mean a higher percentage of the time. Therefore, if we wish to be more confident that the interval will enclose the mean μ, we increase its width by using a larger confident coefficient.

The confidence coefficient to be used in a given situation will depend on the experimenter and the degree of confidence he wishes to place in the estimate. For most practical problems a .95 confidence coefficient is perhaps the most popular. The most commonly used confidence coefficients along with the corresponding Z-values and confidence limits are given in the following table.

Confidence Coefficient	$Z_{\alpha/2}$	LCL	UCL
.90	1.645	$\bar{X} - 1.645 \frac{\sigma}{\sqrt{n}}$	$\bar{X} + 1.645 \frac{\sigma}{\sqrt{n}}$
.95	1.96	$\bar{X} - 1.96 \frac{\sigma}{\sqrt{n}}$	$\bar{X} + 1.96 \frac{\sigma}{\sqrt{n}}$
.99	2.58	$\bar{X} = 2.58 \frac{\sigma}{\sqrt{n}}$	$\bar{X} + 2.58 \frac{\sigma}{\sqrt{n}}$

In using a .95 confidence coefficient, it is a common practice to use $z = 1.96$ when establishing a confidence interval and $z = 2$ when placing bounds on the error of estimate. While $z = 1.96$ is more exact for a .95 confidence coefficient, the calculations using $z = 2$ are much simpler and the error introduced by its use in establishing the bounds is extremely small.

The placing of the bounds $z \dfrac{\sigma}{\sqrt{n}}$ on the point estimate establishes the confidence interval $\bar{X} \pm z \dfrac{\sigma}{\sqrt{n}}$, and $\bar{X} - z \dfrac{\sigma}{\sqrt{n}} < \mu < \bar{X} + z \dfrac{\sigma}{\sqrt{n}}$ is the corresponding confidence interval.

The discussion of the estimation of a population mean opens the door, so to speak, for estimating any population parameter. It will be assumed that the following conditions will hold for all estimation problems in this chapter. Each point estimator of a parameter θ, will be unbiased, and the mean of the distribution of estimates in repeated sampling will be equal to the estimated parameter. That is,

$$E(\tilde{\theta}) = \theta$$

where θ is the unknown parameter, and $\tilde{\theta}$ is an estimator of θ.

7.3 DETERMINING THE SAMPLE SIZE

The size of the sample necessary to ensure that the error in estimating μ is less than some specified amount e must be decided before a sample is selected. The sample size is determined by the degree of accuracy required in the estimation.

The degree of accuracy required depends on the magnitude of the allowable error as well as the degree of confidence that the estimate will not exceed the allowable error. That is, we must choose a sample of size n such that

$$\frac{z_{\alpha/2} \cdot \sigma}{\sqrt{n}} \le e$$

Solving this equation for n,

$$n \ge \left(\frac{z_{\alpha/2} \cdot \sigma}{e} \right)^2$$

Hence, the sample size n is determined by the degree of confidence, the allowable error e, and the standard deviation of the population.

Example 1. How large must a sample be if we want to estimate within \$2 and with .95 confidence the average monthly electric bill of a family living in New Orleans? The 1970 Census showed the average monthly electric bill for a family in the United States to be \$33 with a standard deviation of \$10.

Solution: The standard deviation of the population is \$10.

$$n > \left(\frac{1.96 \cdot 10}{2}\right)^2 > 96.04$$

Hence, we can be confident that random samples of size 97 will provide estimates differing from μ by \$2 or more less than 5% of the time.

Example 2. What size sample is required to establish a .95 confidence interval for the grade point average of college seniors attending a large state university if a random sample of 100 students had a mean grade point average of 2.8 with a standard deviation of .4 and if the length of the interval is to be 1? ($2e$ = length of interval.)

Solution: The sample standard deviation $\tilde{s} = .4$ will be used as an estimate σ. Then

$$n > \left(\frac{1.96 \cdot .4}{.05}\right)^2 = 246.49$$

We can be confident that random samples of size 247 will provide estimates differing from μ by .05 units or more less than 5% of the time.

In determining the sample size the values of e and α are arbitrarily set before the study begins. The value of σ can be estimated from previous studies or census records if they exist. If neither is available, the statistician may be forced to make an estimation of σ on the basis of a preliminary sample, as was done in example 2.

7.4 ESTIMATING THE POPULATION MEAN FROM A SMALL SAMPLE

Frequently, we may be faced with the problem of making an estimation of a population mean when σ is unknown and it is impossible to get a sample of size $n > 30$. Under these circumstances, the t-distribution is used in placing bounds on the point estimate and in determining the interval estimate. As long as the population is approximately normal, the t-distribution can be used; the procedure is the same as for large samples except t-values are used instead of Z-values.

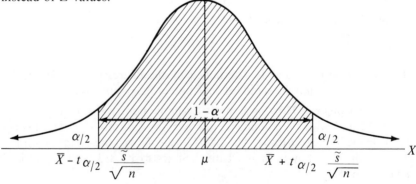

Figure 7.3 A $(1 - \alpha)$ Confidence Interval for μ

When σ is unknown and must be estimated by a small sample standard deviation, the interval estimate of μ is

$$\bar{x} \pm t_{\alpha/2}\frac{\tilde{s}}{\sqrt{n}}$$

and the true mean of the population lies in the interval

$$\bar{x} - t_{\alpha/2}\frac{\tilde{s}}{\sqrt{n}} < \mu < \bar{x} + t_{\alpha/2}\frac{\tilde{s}}{\sqrt{n}}$$

with probability $1 - \alpha$. The appropriate value of t is determined by the number of degrees of freedom and by the degree of confidence required in estimating the population mean.

Example 1. A random sample of 25 cars of the same model were driven in an identical manner using the same brand of 100-octane gasoline. The cars averaged 16 miles per gallon with a standard deviation $\tilde{s}$ of 1.8 miles. Estimate the average miles per gallon for this model of car and establish a .95 confidence interval on the estimate.

Solution: The sample mean, standard deviation, and sample size n are:

$$\bar{x} = 16, \quad \tilde{s} = 1.8, \quad n = 25$$

The point estimate of the population mean μ is 16. If $\alpha = .05$, from table V we find $t_{.025} = 2.064$ for 24 degrees of freedom. The 95% confidence interval estimate for μ is

$$\bar{x} \pm t_{\alpha/2}\frac{\tilde{s}}{\sqrt{n}} = 16 \pm 2.064\,\frac{1.8}{\sqrt{25}}$$

$$= 16 \pm .743$$

We can be 95% confident that the mean of the population lies in the interval, $(15.267 < \mu < 16.743)$.

7.5 ESTIMATING THE DIFFERENCE BETWEEN TWO MEANS

For two populations with means μ_1 and μ_2 and standard deviations of σ_1 and σ_2, the best point estimation of the difference between μ_1 and μ_2 is $(\bar{X}_1 - \bar{X}_2)$. The point estimator $(\bar{X}_1 - \bar{X}_2)$ is obtained by selecting random samples of size n_1 and n_2 from populations 1 and 2 respectively and computing the difference between the two sample means. The mean and standard deviation of the estimator is

$$E(\bar{x}_1 - \bar{x}_2) = \mu_1 - \mu_2$$

and

$$\sigma_{(\bar{x}_1 - \bar{x}_2)} = \sqrt{\frac{\sigma_1^2}{n_1} + \frac{\sigma_2^2}{n_2}}$$

Hence, the interval estimator is

$$(\bar{x}_1 - \bar{x}_2) \pm z_{\alpha/2} \sqrt{\frac{\sigma_1^{\,2}}{n_1} + \frac{\sigma_2^{\,2}}{n_2}}$$

When the parameters $\sigma_1^{\,2}$ and $\sigma_2^{\,2}$ are unknown, they may be estimated by the sample variances $\tilde{s}_1^{\,2}$ and $\tilde{s}_2^{\,2}$. The approximation will be reasonably good when the sample sizes n_1 and n_2 are greater than 30.

Example 1. The grade-point average of a random sample of 50 girls at a state university was 3.0 with a standard deviation of .2, while a random sample of 100 boys had a grade-point average of 2.5 with a standard deviation of .5.

(a) Make a point estimate of the difference between μ_1 and μ_2, where μ_1 is the grade-point average of all girls at the university and μ_2 is the grade-point average of all boys.

(b) Place a .99 confidence interval on the difference between μ_1 and μ_2.

Solution: (a) The point estimate of $(\mu_1 - \mu_2)$ is $\bar{x}_1 - \bar{x}_2 = 3.0 - 2.5 = .5$.

(b) The .99 confidence interval is

$$(\bar{x}_1 - \bar{x}_2) \pm 2.58 \sqrt{\frac{\sigma_1^{\,2}}{n_1} + \frac{\sigma_2^{\,2}}{n_2}}$$

or

$$(3.0 - 2.5) \pm 2.58 \sqrt{\frac{.2^2}{50} + \frac{.5^2}{100}}$$

$$.5 \pm 2.58 \sqrt{.0033}$$

$$.5 \pm .47$$

We can be .99 confident that the difference between μ_1 and μ_2 is in the interval $.353 < \mu_1 - \mu_2 < .647$.

When σ_1 and σ_2 are unknown and it is not possible to get random samples of size $n > 30$, the t-distribution will provide confidence intervals that are valid when the populations are approximately normally distributed with equal variances. The small sample confidence interval for $(\mu_1 - \mu_2)$ has limits

$$(\bar{x}_1 - \bar{x}_2) \pm t_{\alpha/2} s \sqrt{\frac{1}{n_1} + \frac{1}{n_2}}$$

where s is the pooled estimate of σ and the degrees of freedom associated with t is $n_1 + n_2 - 2$.

Example 2. A test was made of the nicotine content of two brands of cigarettes. A random sample of 10 cigarettes from brand A had a mean nicotine content of 22.6 with a standard deviation of 2. A random sample of 12 cigarettes from sample B had a mean of 19.8 with a standard deviation of 1.6.

(*a*) Establish a point estimate between the mean nicotine content of brand *A* and brand *B*.

(*b*) Find a 90% confidence interval estimate for the difference between the population means.

Solution: Let μ_1 represent the average nicotine content of brand *A* and μ_2 that of brand *B*. The point estimate is

$$(\bar{x}_1 - \bar{x}_2) = 22.6 - 19.8 = 2.8$$

(*a*) The .90 confidence interval estimate has limits

$$(\bar{x}_1 - \bar{x}_2) \pm t_{\alpha/2} s \sqrt{\frac{1}{n_2} + \frac{1}{n_2}} \quad \begin{aligned} &= (22.6 - 19.8) \pm 1.725(1.4) \\ &= 2.8 \pm 2.42 \end{aligned}$$

We are 90% confident that the difference between μ_1 and μ_2 lies in the interval

$$.40 < (\mu_1 - \mu_2) < 5.22$$

The interval width is considerable, especially considering the relatively low confidence level, and it would be advisable to increase the sample sizes and reestimate.

Our discussion of the interval estimate of $\mu_1 - \mu_2$ has assumed that the populations from which the samples were selected were approximately normal with equal variances. In using the pooled variance, one assumes equal population variances, but the samples may be of different sizes. Even if the population variances differ, the estimate is good if the populations are normal and n_1 is equal or very close to n_2. However, it is a good practice to always select samples that are approximately equal in size.

7.6 ESTIMATING THE MEAN OF A PROPORTION

An unbiased point estimator of a proportion *P* of a binomial population is the sample proportion

$$\tilde{p} = \frac{x}{n}$$

where *x* represents the number of successes and *n* represents the number of elements in the sample. Moreover, when *n* is large, we know by the Central Limit Theorem that the distribution of *X* is approximately normal and we have every reason to expect that the distribution of $\tilde{P}$ is also normal.

The expected value and standard deviation of $\tilde{P}$ are

$$E(\tilde{P}) = P$$

and

$$\sigma_p = \sqrt{\frac{\tilde{p}\tilde{q}}{n}}$$

where $\tilde{q} = 1 - \tilde{p}$. The bounds on the error of a point estimate are

$$2\sqrt{\frac{\overline{p}\overline{q}}{n}}$$

and for any confidence interval, with confidence coefficient $(1 - \alpha)$, when n is large, the interval estimate of P is

$$\overline{p} \pm z_{\alpha/2}\sqrt{\frac{\tilde{p}\tilde{q}}{n}}$$

where $\tilde{q} = 1 - \overline{p}$.

The true proportion will lie in the interval

$$\tilde{p} - z_{\alpha/2}\sqrt{\frac{\tilde{p}\tilde{q}}{n}} < P < \tilde{p} + z_{\alpha/2}\sqrt{\frac{\tilde{p}\tilde{q}}{n}}$$

with probability $1 - \alpha$.

Example 1. A random sample of 100 students at a community college was polled, and 90 were in favor of not having final examinations.

(a) Estimate the proportion of the entire student body who favor no final exams and place a bound on the error of estimation.

(b) Find a 95% confidence interval for the true proportion of the student body who favor no final exams.

Solution: (a) The point estimate is

$$\tilde{p} = \frac{x}{n} = \frac{90}{100} = .90$$

The bound on the error of estimate is

$$2\sqrt{\frac{\overline{p}\overline{q}}{n}} = 2\sqrt{\frac{(.90)(.10)}{100}} = .06$$

(b) A .95 confidence for P is

$$\tilde{p} \pm 1.96\sqrt{\frac{\tilde{p}\tilde{q}}{n}}$$

or

$$.90 \pm .0588$$

The true proportion lies in the interval

$$.8412 < P < .9588$$

with probability .90.

7.7 ESTIMATING THE DIFFERENCE BETWEEN TWO PROPORTIONS

The point estimator for the difference between two proportions (P_1 and P_2) is ($\tilde{p}_1 - \tilde{p}_2$). That is,

$$E(\tilde{P}_1 - \tilde{P}_2) = (P_1 - P_2)$$

The standard deviation of the estimator is

$$\sigma_{(\tilde{P}_1 - \tilde{P}_2)} = \sqrt{\frac{\tilde{p}_1 \tilde{q}_1}{n_1} + \frac{\tilde{p}_2 \tilde{q}_2}{n_2}}$$

and the bound on the error is

$$2\sqrt{\frac{\tilde{p}_1 \tilde{q}_1}{n_1} + \frac{\tilde{p}_2 \tilde{q}_2}{n_2}}$$

Hence, the interval estimator when both n_1 and n_2 are large is

$$(\tilde{P}_1 - \tilde{P}_2) \pm z_{\alpha/2} \sqrt{\frac{\tilde{p}_1 \tilde{q}_1}{n_1} + \frac{\tilde{p}_2 \tilde{q}_2}{n_2}}$$

Thus,

$$(\tilde{P}_1 - \tilde{P}_2) - z_{\alpha/2} \sqrt{\frac{\tilde{p}_1 \tilde{q}_1}{n_1} + \frac{\tilde{p}_2 \tilde{q}_2}{n_2}} < (P_1 - P_2) < (\tilde{P}_1 - \tilde{P}_2)$$

$$+ z_{\alpha/2} \sqrt{\frac{\tilde{p}_1 \tilde{q}_1}{n_1} + \frac{\tilde{p}_2 \tilde{q}_2}{n_2}}$$

is a $1 - \alpha$ confidence interval for the difference.

Example. A national research institute asked a random sample of 1,000 men and 1,000 women if they were in favor of or against the president's policies in combating inflation. The results showed 60% of the men and 52% of the women were in favor.

(a) Estimate the difference in the true proportion between the men and women who are in favor and place a bound on the error.

(b) Estimate a .90 confidence interval for the difference in the proportion of men and women who are in favor.

Solution: (a) The point estimate of $(P_1 - P_2)$ is

$$(\tilde{P}_1 - \tilde{P}_2) = .60 - .52 = .08$$

The bound on the error of estimate is

$$2\sqrt{\frac{\tilde{p}_1 \tilde{q}_1}{n_1} + \frac{\tilde{p}_2 \tilde{q}_2}{n_2}} = 2\sqrt{\frac{(.60)(.40)}{1000} + \frac{(.52)(.48)}{1000}}$$

$$= .2(.022)$$

$$= .044$$

(b) The .90 confidence interval is

$$(\tilde{P}_1 - \tilde{P}_2) \pm 1.645 \sqrt{\frac{\tilde{p}_1 \tilde{q}_1}{n_1} + \frac{\tilde{p}_2 \tilde{q}_2}{n_2}}$$

or

$$.08 \pm 1.645(.022)$$

Hence, the true difference between the two proportions lies in the interval

$$.024 < (P_1 - P_2) < .116$$

with probability .90.

EXERCISE 7.1

1. A random sample of 100 light bulbs produced by Company A had a mean lifetime of 1,280 hours and a standard deviation of 140 hours.

    (*a*) Estimate the mean lifetime of the population of bulbs from which the sample is selected and place a bound on the error of estimation.

    (*b*) Estimate a .95 confidence interval estimate of the mean lifetime of the population.

2. Suppose that the mean and standard deviation of the population in problem 1 really are 1,280 and 140. If an additional random sample of 100 bulbs are selected from the population, what is the probability that the mean lifetime will be over 1,315 hours?

3. A coffee machine is regulated so that the amount of coffee dispensed is normally distributed with a standard deviation of .5 ounce per cup. If a random sample of 50 cups had an average of 5 ounces per cup

    (*a*) Estimate the average amount of coffee in each cup dispensed by the machine and place a bound on the error of the estimate.

    (*b*) Find a .95 confidence interval for the mean of all cups dispensed.

4. How large a sample is required in problem 3 if we wish to be .95 confident that the sample mean will be within .4 ounce of the true mean?

5. The management of a resort hotel wished to know the average number of days that guests stayed. A random sample of 400 guests who had registered previously produced a mean and standard deviation of 5.4 and 2 days, respectively.

    (*a*) Estimate the mean length of stay for all of the guests and place a bound on the error of estimation.

    (*b*) Find a .90 confidence interval for the mean stay of all guests.

6. Suppose that the weights of all toy fox terrier dogs are normally distributed with a standard deviation of 2.5 pounds. How large a sample should be taken in order to be .95 confident that the sample mean does not differ from the population mean by more than .5 pounds?

7. A comparison of the yield of two different varieties of corn was obtained by planting and growing 100 acres of each variety under similar conditions. Variety A yielded 84 bushels per acre with a standard deviation of 5 bushels. Variety B yielded 80 bushels per acre with a standard deviation of 6 bushels per acre.

    (*a*) Estimate the mean difference in yield between the two varieties.

    (*b*) Make a .90 confidence interval estimate for the mean difference in yield between the two varieties.

8. A random sample of size 16 taken from a normal population has a mean and standard deviation of $\overline{X} = 40$ and $\tilde{s} = 4$. Make a .90 confidence interval estimate for the population mean.

9. A random sample of 10 measurements of the diameter of a ball bearing had a mean of .04 inches and a standard deviation of .005 inches.
   (*a*) Make a .90 confidence interval estimate of the true diameter.
   (*b*) Make a .99 confidence interval estimate of the true diameter.

10. A random sample of 10 washers produced by a machine has a mean thickness of .05 inch and standard deviation of .003 inch. Make a .95 confidence interval estimate of the mean of all washers produced by the machine.

11. The intelligence quotients of 15 students from one ethnic group showed a mean of 107 and a standard deviation of 10. Another ethnic group of 12 students from a similar neighborhood in the same city showed a mean of 112 and a standard deviation of 8. Make a .95 confidence interval estimate of the difference of the mean IQ between the two ethnic populations.

12. In comparing the wearing quality of two types of tires, random samples of size 100 are selected from each of the two types and road-tested on similar cars under similar conditions. A tire was judged to be worn out when its tread showed a specific amount of wear. The results showed that the mean and standard deviation of type *A* to be 30,000 miles and 1,500 miles. The mean and standard deviation of type *B* were 25,000 miles and 2,000 miles.
    (*a*) Estimate the difference in mean miles to wear out between the two types of tires.
    (*b*) Make a .90 confidence interval estimate of the difference of mean miles to wear out between the two types of tires.

13. A random sample of 225 voters in a city showed that 135 are in favor of a citywide tax for civic improvement.
    (*a*) Make a point estimate of the proportion of voters in the city who are in favor of the tax.
    (*b*) Make a .95 confidence interval estimate of the exact proportion who favor the bill.

14. How many voters must be in the sample collected to estimate the proportion of voters favorable to a senatorial candidate in an election if the estimate is to be within .015 with probability equal to .90? Assume that the true proportion to be about 60% of the vote.

15. In Atlanta, a random sample of 400 families contacted by a local TV station showed that 275 owned color TV sets. Make a .90 confidence interval estimate of the proportion of all families living in Atlanta who own color TV sets.

16. A government testing agency wishes to compare the effectiveness of two insecticides in controlling mosquitoes. Two rooms of equal size, each

containing 1,000 mosquitoes, were sprayed with equal amounts of the insecticides. The results of the experiment showed that in the room where insecticide *A* was used, 900 mosquitoes were killed, while in the room where insecticide *B* was used, 820 mosquitoes were killed. Construct a .95 confidence interval estimate of the difference in the rate of kill for the two insecticides.

17. Hospital records show that of 500 men who were admitted for treatment, 60 were admitted because of high blood pressure. Of 500 women who were admitted for treatment, 50 were admitted for high blood pressure. Construct a .95 confidence interval estimate of the difference between the proportion of men and women who have high blood pressure.

7.8 ESTIMATING THE POPULATION VARIANCE

The most efficient point estimator of the variance of a population is the variance $\tilde{s}^2$ of a random sample drawn from the population, i.e., $E(\tilde{s}^2) = \sigma^2$.

A confidence interval estimate of the population variance for normal populations is established by using the test statistic

$$\chi^2 = \frac{(n-1)\tilde{s}^2}{\sigma^2}$$

For a sample of size n and variance $\tilde{s}^2$, a $(1 - \alpha)$ confidence interval is

$$\frac{(n-1)\tilde{s}^2}{\chi_{\alpha/2}^{2}} < \sigma^2 < \frac{(n-1)\tilde{s}^2}{\chi_{(1-\alpha/2)}^{2}}$$

where $\chi_{\alpha/2}^{2}$ and $\chi_{(1-\alpha/2)}^{2}$ are the values of the chi-square distribution with $(n-1)$ *df* (see figure 7.4).

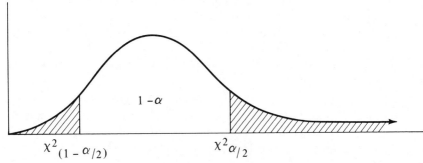

Figure 7.4 Chi-square Distribution Showing Regions Under the Curve Greater than $\chi_{\alpha/2}^{2}$ and Less than $\chi_{(1-\alpha/2)}^{2}$

Example. A random sample of 10 college students who attended summer school produced a mean of 8 credit hours and a variance $\tilde{s}^2$ of .25 credit hour. Establish a .95 confidence interval estimate of the variance of all college students attending summer school (assume normal population).

Solution: A .95 confidence interval implies that $\alpha = .05$. Using table VII with $\alpha = .05$ and 9 df, we find $\chi_{\alpha/2}^2 = 19.0229$ and $\chi_{(1-\alpha/2)}^2 = 2.70039$. Substituting in the formula,

$$\frac{(n-1)s^2}{\chi_{\alpha/2}^2} < \sigma < \frac{(n-1)s^2}{\chi_{(1-\alpha/2)}^2}$$

we have

$$\frac{9(.25)}{19.0228} < \sigma^2 < \frac{9(.25)}{2.70039}$$

which simplifies to

$$.118 < \sigma^2 < .883$$

We are 95% confident that the true variance is within this interval.

7.9 ESTIMATING THE RATIO OF TWO VARIANCES

A point estimate of the ratio of two population variances, σ_1^2/σ_2^2 is the ratio of two sample variances $\tilde{s}_1^2/\tilde{s}_2^2$.

An interval estimate of σ_1^2/σ_2^2 can be established by the use of a calculated value of the test statistic, i.e.,

$$f = \frac{\tilde{s}_1^2}{\tilde{s}_2^2}$$

For two independent random samples of size n_1 and n_2 drawn from two normal populations, it can be shown that a $(1 - \alpha)$ confidence interval is equal to

$$\frac{\tilde{s}_1^2}{\tilde{s}_2^2} \cdot \frac{1}{f_{\alpha/2}(v_1, v_2)} < \frac{\sigma_1^2}{\sigma_1^2} < \frac{\tilde{s}_1^2}{\tilde{s}_2^2} \cdot f_{\alpha/2}(v_2, v_1)$$

where $v_1 = (n_1 - 1)$ degrees of freedom in the numerator and $v_2 = (n_2 - 1)$ degrees of freedom in the denominator.

Example. A random sample of 10 men attending college showed a variance $\tilde{s}^2$ in age of 7.2 years, while a random sample of 8 women attending the same college were observed to have a variance $\tilde{s}^2$ in age of 3.6 years. Find a .90 confidence interval for the ratio between the two variances σ_1^2/σ_2^2. Assume normal populations.

Solution: A .90 confidence interval implies $\alpha = .10$. From table VIII, $f_{.05}(9.7) = 3.68$ and $f_{.05}(7, 9) = 3.29$. Hence,

$$.90 = \frac{s_1^2}{s_2^2} \cdot \frac{1}{f_{\alpha/2}(v_1, v_2)} < \frac{\sigma_1^2}{\sigma_2^2} < \frac{\tilde{s}_1^2}{\tilde{s}_2^2} \cdot f_{\alpha/2}(v_2, v_1)$$

$$= \frac{7.2}{3.6} \cdot \frac{1}{3.68} < \frac{\sigma_1^2}{\sigma_2^2} < \frac{7.2}{3.6} \cdot 3.29$$

$$= .5434 < \frac{\sigma_1^2}{\sigma_2^2} < 6.58$$

We are confident that the true ratio is within the interval .5434, 6.58.

EXERCISE 7.2

1. A random sample of size $n = 10$ and with variance $\tilde{s}^2 = .32$ is taken from a normal population. Find a .95 confidence interval estimate for the variance of all such samples taken from the population.

2. A random sample of size $n = 20$ and with variance $\tilde{s}_1 = 5$ is taken from a normal population. Find a .99 confidence interval estimate for the variance of all such samples taken from the population.

3. Two random samples of size $n_1 = 20$ with variance $\tilde{s}_1{}^2 = 6$ and $n_2 = 15$ with variance $\tilde{s}_2{}^2 = 4$ are taken from two normal populations. Find a .98 confidence interval estimate of $\sigma_1{}^2/\sigma_2{}^2$, where $\sigma_1{}^2$ and $\sigma_2{}^2$ are the respective population variances.

4. A random sample of 16 boys attending college produced a standard deviation in age of 3 years. At the same time, a random sample of 12 girls produced a standard deviation of 2 years. Find a .90 confidence interval estimate for $\sigma_1{}^2/\sigma_2{}^2$ and σ_1/σ_2, where $\sigma_1{}^2$ and $\sigma_2{}^2$ are the variances respectively for the boys and girls. Assume normal distributions.

5. The contents of eight bottles of carbonate of soda were measured and found to be 7.9, 7.8, 8, 8.1, 8.2, 7.9, 7.7, and 8.3 ounces. Find a .95 confidence interval estimate for the variance of all such 8 bottle cartons of this soda produced by the company.

6. A random sample of 12 faculty members showed the following years of teaching experience each had accumulated: 25, 8, 12, 15, 1, 0, 3, 7, 15, 19, 21, and 16. Find a .99 confidence interval estimate for the variance of all such samples. Assume that the population is normal.

7. The records of a random sample of 25 workers in a large factory were checked for the number of days each worker was absent during the previous year. It was observed that the variance of the sample was $\tilde{s}^2 = 4$. Find a .98 confidence interval estimate for the variance for all workers in the factory. Assume normal distribution.

8. Two varieties of corn are being tested to determine which variety is best. Five acres of variety A produced 80, 84, 100, 84, and 82 bushels per acre respectively, while 8 acres of variety B produced 78, 81, 83, 90, 78, 85, 90, and 88 bushels per acre. Find a .98 confidence interval estimate for the ratio of the two variances $\sigma_1{}^2/\sigma_2{}^2$, where $\sigma_1{}^2$ and $\sigma_2{}^2$ are the variances of the two normal populations.

9. A random sample of size $n_1 = 5$ men and $n_2 = 6$ women were tested to

determine their reaction time to a stimulus. The results, recorded in hundreths of seconds, were

Men   .10 .11 .09 .12 .08
Women   .12 .11 .10 .09 .12 .09

Find a .98 confidence interval estimate for the ratio $\sigma_1{}^2/\sigma_2{}^2$, where $\sigma_1{}^2$ and $\sigma_2{}^2$ are the variances of two normal populations.

10. The closing price of two common stocks for a five-day period were

Stock 1   8.5   8.8   8.4   8.3   8.5
Stock 2   10.4   8.6   9.5   10   10.5

Find a .90 confidence interval estimate of the ratio $\sigma_1{}^2/\sigma_2{}^2$.

7.10 STATISTICAL TEST OF AN HYPOTHESIS

The testing of an hypothesis is one of the most important areas of a statistical study. An hypothesis is an assumption about one or more population parameters. It is impossible for us to know if the assumptions that we make are true or false unless we examine the entire population. As we have seen, this is often impractical or impossible. Our objective in this section is to study methods which enable us to decide if our hypotheses are likely to be true or false. The decision made will be based on the statistics of a random sample taken from the population.

In many practical problems, we may formulate an hypothesis for the purpose of rejecting or nullifying it. Such hypotheses are called *null hypotheses* and are denoted H_0. To illustrate: if we want to decide which of two brands of air conditioners has a longer lifetime, we then form the null hypothesis that the two brands have equal lifetimes and any observed difference is due to sampling.

Any hypotheses which differ from the null hypotheses are called *alternate hypotheses*, and are denoted H_1, H_2, etc. In the illustration above, the null hypothesis concerns the means of two populations and is written,

$$H_0 : \mu_1 = \mu_2$$

Some alternate hypotheses are

$$H_1 : \mu_1 > \mu_2$$
$$H_2 : \mu_1 < \mu_2$$
$$H_3 : \mu_1 \neq \mu_2$$

If, in testing a null hypothesis, we find that the results are greater or less than some established value, then we say that the difference is *significant*. When the difference is significant, we reject the null hypothesis on the basis of the evidence obtained. Tests which enable us to decide whether to reject or accept an hypothesis about a population parameter or parameters are called *statistical tests of hypotheses* or *statistical tests of significance*.

A statistical test involves the following steps.

(1) State the null hypothesis which specifies values for a population parameter or parameters.

(2) State the alternate hypothesis which asserts the parameter or parameters is some value other than the one given in the null hypothesis.

(3) State the level of significance, denoted by α, that has been chosen.

(4) State the value or values of the standard random variable for which the null hypothesis is to be rejected. These values are called *critical values*, since they separate the "rejection" region from the "acceptance" region (see figure 7.5).

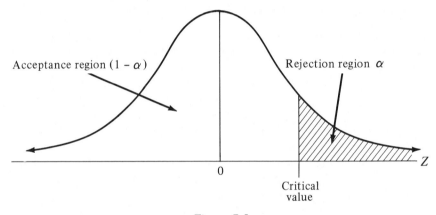

Acceptance region $(1 - \alpha)$ Rejection region α

0

Critical
value

Figure 7.5

(5) State the test statistic to be used and compute its value.

(6) State the rejection or acceptance of the null hypothesis, based on the comparison of the computed value and critical value of the test statistic.

The null hypothesis can never be proved; it is either rejected or accepted. When we reject the null hypothesis, we indirectly assert the truth of its alternate, i.e., the parameter is some value other than the one specified in the null hypothesis.

The decision to reject or not reject the null hypothesis is based on the calculated value of a test statistic. The value of a test statistic is computed from a random sample drawn from the population of interest. If the computed value assumes a value in the rejection region, the null hypothesis is rejected. If the computed value assumes a value in the acceptance region, the null hypothesis is accepted, or at least not rejected.

If we reject the null hypothesis when it should not be rejected, then we say that we have committed a *Type I error*. If we accept the null hypothesis when it should be rejected, then we say we have committed a *Type II error*. In either case, we have made a wrong decision.

The goodness of a statistical test of an hypothesis is judged by how well it minimizes the probability of making either a Type I or a Type II error. This presents quite a dilemma, because the relationship between the two types of errors is such that a decrease in the probability of making one type is often accompanied by an increase in the probability of making the other. In a practical problem, one type of error may be more serious than the other, and we should place the limitations on the more serious error. However, if the sample size is increased, there is more evidence available upon which to base our decision, and the probabilities of both types of errors are reduced.

The maximum probability with which we are willing to accept a Type I error in testing an hypothesis is called the *level of significance*. The level of significance is arbitrarily assigned before the sample is selected so that the results obtained will not influence the choice.

If, in designing a test for an hypothesis, a 5% level of significance is selected, then the probability of rejecting the null hypothesis when it is true (Type I error) is .05. Thus, we would make the wrong decision 5% of the time, but we would make the right decision 95% of the time.

Often an hypothesis states that one process is better than another or that one parameter is greater than another. In testing such hypotheses, we are interested only in the extreme values on one side of the mean, i.e., one tail of the distribution. Such tests are called *one-sided tests* or *one-tailed tests*. In a one-tailed test, the critical region lies to one side of the mean and the probability of making a wrong decision is equal to the level of significance, α (see figure 7.6).

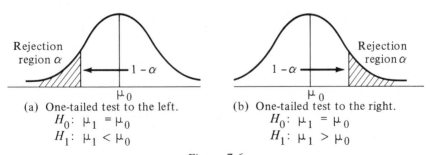

Rejection region α $1 - \alpha$ $1 - \alpha$ Rejection region α

μ_0 μ_0

(a) One-tailed test to the left.   (b) One-tailed test to the right.

$$H_0: \mu_1 = \mu_0 \qquad\qquad H_0: \mu_1 = \mu_0$$
$$H_1: \mu_1 < \mu_0 \qquad\qquad H_1: \mu_1 > \mu_0$$

Figure 7.6

When the nature of the hypothesis is such that we are interested in the extreme values on both sides of the mean, i.e., in both tails of the distribution, the test is referred to as a *two-sided test* or *two-tailed test*. In a two-tailed test, one-half of the rejection region lies to the left of the mean and one-half to the right. The probability of making a wrong decision is evenly divided between the two tails of the distribution (see figure 7.7).

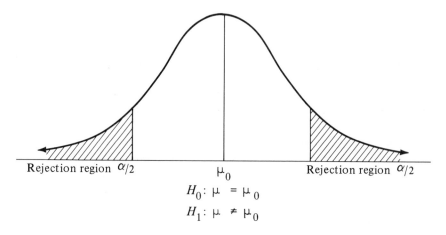

$$H_0 : \mu = \mu_0$$
$$H_1 : \mu \neq \mu_0$$

Figure 7.7 Two-tailed Test

    A large sample test of an hypothesis concerning a population parameter is often based on a normally distributed test statistic. As we have seen, the statistics—mean, difference between two means, proportions, and difference between two proportions—are normally distributed when n is large and can be approximated by the normal curve. The procedure for testing an hypothesis is the same regardless of the test statistic employed. The procedure will be demonstrated in the following examples.

    Example 1. A manufacturer of electrical fuses claims that his product has a mean breaking strength of 15 amps, with a standard deviation of 1.2 amps. A random sample of 36 fuses is tested and found to have a mean breaking strength of 14 amps. Test the manufacturer's claim of the performance of his product at the .05 level of significance.

    Solution: The nature of the manufacturer's claim is such that a one-tailed test to the left is indicated. The null hypothesis and alternate hypothesis are:

$$H_0 : \mu = 15$$
$$H_1 : \mu < 15$$

The critical value at the .05 level of significance is

$$z < -1.645$$

The test statistic to test H_0, is

$$z = \frac{\bar{x} - \mu}{\dfrac{\sigma}{\sqrt{n}}}$$

Computing $\bar{x}$ from the sample and substituting the values in the test statistic,

$$z = \frac{14.5 - 15}{\frac{1.2}{6}} = -2.5$$

The calculated value -2.5 is less than the critical value -1.645. We reject the null hypothesis and conclude that the mean breaking point is less than 15 amps (see figure 7.8).

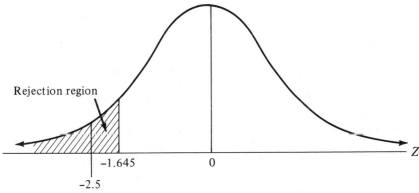

Rejection region

-1.645 0

-2.5

Figure 7.8

The probability of a Type I error in example 1 is .05. The probability of a Type II error is more complicated to calculate. To illustrate, suppose that in example 1 the actual mean of the population was 14.5 amps. To find the probability of a Type II error, we proceed as follows. We first calculate the value of $\bar{x}$ which corresponds to a Z-score of -1.645. Using the formula

$$z = \frac{\bar{x} - \mu}{\frac{\sigma}{\sqrt{n}}}$$

and solving for $\bar{x}$,

$$\bar{x} = (.2)(-1.645) + 15 = 14.67$$

That is, the null hypothesis is rejected if $\bar{x} < 14.67$ and accepted if $\bar{x} > 14.67$. The value $\bar{x} = 14.67$ is said to be the critical value of $\bar{x}$. Since we have assumed that $\mu = 14.5$ amps, the probability of a Type II error is equal to the area under the curve (with mean 14.5) that lies to the right of 14.67. Transforming $x = 14.67$ into a standard Z-score,

$$z = \frac{14.67 - 14.5}{\frac{1.2}{6}} = .85$$

Thus, $P(\bar{x} > 14.67) = P(Z > .85) = .5000 - .3023 = .1977$. The probability of a Type II error is .1977 when the actual mean is 14.5 amps (see figure 7.9).

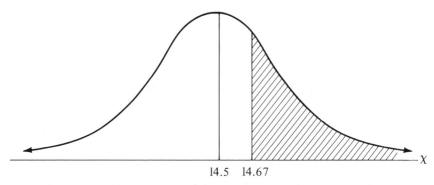

14.5   14.67

Figure 7.9   Probability of Type II Error

As stated previously, the relationship between Type I and Type II errors is such that as the probability of one increases, the probability of the other often decreases. To illustrate, if the level of significance in example 1 is decreased to .01, the probability of a Type II error increases to .7881. If the level of significance is increased to .10, the probability of a Type II error decreases to .1112. The student should verify these statements. These values for the probability of a Type II error pertain only to example 1. For most practical problems we are satisfied with specifying the probability of a Type I error and "hoping" that the probability of a Type II error is within reason. The null hypothesis may be stated in such a way that the error with the more important consequence becomes the Type I error.

Example 2. An official of a trade union reports that the mean yearly wage is $8,000. A random sample of 100 employees in the union produced a mean of $7,875 with a standard deviation of $1,000. Test the null hypothesis at the .05 level of significance that the mean wage is $8,000 against the alternate hypothesis that the wage is greater than or less than $8,000.

       Solution: $H_0 : \mu = \$8,000$
                 $H_1 : \mu \neq \$8,000$

The critical values of the test statistic when $\alpha = .05$ is $Z > 1.96$ or $Z < -1.96$. The test statistic to test the H_0 is

$$z = \frac{\bar{x} - \mu}{\frac{\tilde{s}}{\sqrt{n}}}$$

We are given the values of $\bar{x}$ and $\tilde{s}$. Hence,

$$z = \frac{7,875 - 8,000}{\frac{1,000}{\sqrt{100}}} = \frac{-125}{100} = -1.25$$

when H_0 is true. Since the calculated value lies between -1.96 and 1.96, we do not reject the null hypothesis (see figure 7.10).

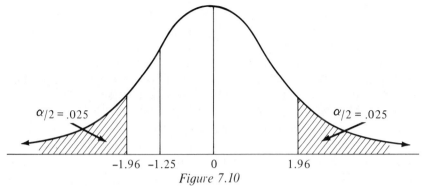

$\alpha/2 = .025$ $\alpha/2 = .025$

-1.96   -1.25   0   1.96

Figure 7.10

Example 3. A lathe is adjusted so that the mean of a certain dimension of the parts is 20 cm. A random sample of 10 of the parts produced a mean of 20.3 cm and a standard deviation of .2 cm. Do the results indicate that the machine is out of adjustment? Test at the .05 level of significance.

Solution: The nature of the test is such that a two-tailed test is appropriate. We shall test the null hypothesis that the mean of the population is 20 cm against the alternate hypothesis that the mean is not equal to 20 cm. Thus

$$H_0 : \mu = 20$$
$$H_1 : \mu \neq 20$$

The critical values of the test statistic t with 9 df and at a .05 level of significance are $t > 2.306$ and $t < -2.306$. The test statistic is

$$t = \frac{\bar{x} - \mu}{\frac{\tilde{s}}{\sqrt{n}}}$$

We are given the value of $\bar{x}$ and $\tilde{s}$. Hence,

$$t = \frac{20.3 - 20.0}{\frac{.2}{\sqrt{10}}} = 4.743$$

when H_0 is true. The calculated value is greater than either of the critical values. We reject the null hypothesis and conclude that the mean is not equal to 20 cm. Hence, the machine is in need of adjustment (see figure 7.11).

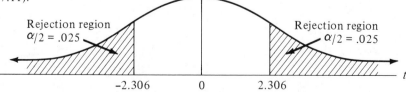

Rejection region   Rejection region
$\alpha/2 = .025$ $\alpha/2 = .025$

-2.306   0   2.306 t

Figure 7.11 t-Distribution with 9 df

Example 4. A recent report claims that college nongraduates get married at an earlier age than college graduates. To support the claim, random samples of size 100 were selected from each group, and the mean age at time of marriage was recorded. The mean and standard deviation of the college nongraduates were 22.5 years and 1.4 years respectively, while the mean and standard deviation of the college graduates were 23 years and 1.8 years. Test the claims of the report at the .05 level of significance.

Solution: The nature of the claim is such that a one tail-test is indicated. We shall test the null hypothesis that there is no difference in ages against the alternate hypothesis that college nongraduates are married at an earlier age. Thus

$$H_0 : \mu_1 = \mu_2$$
$$H_1 : \mu_1 < \mu_2$$

where μ_1 is the mean age at marriage of all nongraduates and μ_2 is the mean age of graduates.

The critical value of the test statistic for $\alpha = .05$ is

$$z < -1.645$$

The test statistic is

$$z = \frac{\bar{x}_1 - \bar{x}_2}{\sqrt{\dfrac{s_1^2}{n_2} + \dfrac{s_2^2}{n_2}}}$$

We are given the values $\bar{x}_1$, $\tilde{s}_1$, $\bar{x}_2$ and $\tilde{s}_2$. Substituting these values in the test statistic,

$$z = \frac{22.5 - 23.0}{\sqrt{\dfrac{(1.4)^2}{100} + \dfrac{(1.8)^2}{100}}} = \frac{-.5}{\dfrac{5.2}{100}} = -2.19$$

The calculated value of z is less than the critical value. We should reject the null hypothesis and accept the alternate hypothesis that the nongrads marry at a younger age than the grads (see figure 7.12).

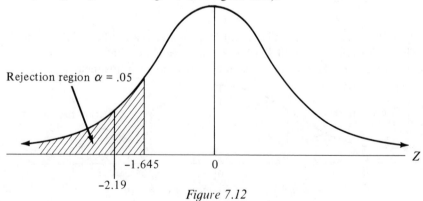

Rejection region $\alpha = .05$

−1.645   0

−2.19

Z

Figure 7.12

Example 5. An electrical repair service claims that 10% of the service calls made resulted from the appliances not having been properly plugged into the receptacle. A random sample of 200 work invoices produced 15 in which the only "repairs" were the plugging in of the appliance. Do the results indicate that the repair service claims are justified? Test at the .01 level of significance.

Solution: The null hypothesis to be tested is the proportion of unnecessary calls is .10. The alternate hypothesis is the proportion of unnecessary calls is not .10. The nature of the claim is such that a two-tailed test is indicated. Thus,

$$H_0 : \mu_p = .10$$
$$H_1 : \mu_p \neq .10$$

The critical value for $\alpha = .01$ is $z < -1.96$ or $z > 1.96$. The test statistic is

$$z = \frac{\tilde{p} - \mu_p}{\sqrt{\dfrac{pq}{n}}}$$

Substituting $\tilde{p} = .075$ and $\mu_p = .10$,

$$z = \frac{.075 - .10}{\sqrt{\dfrac{(.1)(.9)}{200}}} = \frac{-.025}{\sqrt{\dfrac{.09}{200}}} = -1.18$$

The calculated value lies between -1.96 and 1.96, so we accept the null hypothesis and conclude that 10% of the service calls are unnecessary (see figure 7.13).

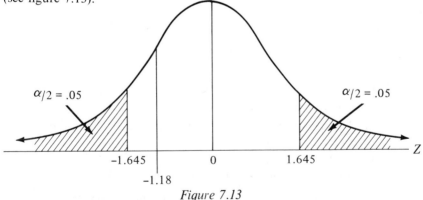

Figure 7.13

Example 6. The student government of a large college polled a random sample of 325 male students and found that 221 were in favor of a new grading system. At the same time, 120 out of a random sample of 200 female students were in favor of the new system. Do the results indicate a significant difference in the proportion of male and female students who favor the new system? Test at the .05 level of significance.

Solution: The nature of the test indicates that a two-tailed test is appropriate. Thus,

$$H_0 : \mu_{p_1} = \mu_{p_2}$$
$$H_1 : \mu_{p_1} \neq \mu_{p_2}$$

The level of significance $\alpha = .05$. The critical value is $z < -1.96$ or $z > 1.96$. Since both $\tilde{p}_1$ and $\tilde{p}_2$ are estimates of the proportion of students who prefer the new grading system, the pooled estimate is

$$\tilde{p} = \frac{x_1 + x_2}{n_1 + n_2} = \frac{221 + 120}{325 + 200} = \frac{341}{525} = .65$$

The test statistic is

$$z = \frac{\tilde{p}_1 - \tilde{p}_2}{\sqrt{pq(\frac{1}{n_1} + \frac{1}{n_2})}} = \frac{.68 - .60}{\sqrt{(1.65)(.35)(\frac{1}{325} + \frac{1}{200})}} = \frac{.08}{.021} = 3.8$$

The computed value is greater than 1.96, and the null hypothesis is rejected (see figure 7.14).

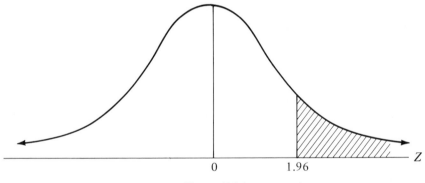

Figure 7.14

EXERCISE 7.3

1. The manufacturer of a certain brand of television sets claims that the average life of the picture tube is 50 months, with a standard deviation of 12 months. If a random sample of 36 television sets has a mean life of 46 months for the picture tube, what can we conclude about the manufacturer's claim if we test at a .05 level of significance?

2. Transistors manufactured by a certain company are claimed to have a mean life of 600 hours and a standard deviation of 49 hours. A random sample of 100 transistors produced a mean life of 615 hours. Test the hypothesis $H_0 : \mu = 600$ hours against the hypothesis $H_1 : \mu \neq 600$. Use a .05 level of significance.

3. If the true mean of the population in problem (2) is 44 months, what is the probability of making a Type II error?

4. The Association of School Superintendents claims that the average yearly salary for teachers is $7,200. In a random sample of 400 teachers, the Teachers' Association finds the average salary to be $6,900 with a standard deviation of $2,000. Should the latter group refute the claim of the first if the decision is to be based on a .01 level of significance.

5. What can we conclude in problem (4) if a .01 level of significance is used?

6. The manufacturer of a certain economy car claims that the car will average 30 miles per gallon of regular gasoline. A random sample of 9 cars was selected and driven under ordinary highway conditions. The sample produced a mean of 29 miles per gallon and a standard deviation of 1.8 miles. What conclusions can we make about the manufacturer's claim if we test at the .05 level of significance?

7 A certain brand of cigarettes is advertised by the manufacturer as having a mean nicotine content of 15 milligrams per cigarette. A sample of 200 cigarettes is tested by an independent research laboratory and found to have an average of 16.2 milligrams of nicotine content and a standard deviation of 3.6. Using a .01 level of significance, what can the laboratory say about the manufacturer's advertisement?

8. A brand of dog food is advertised as containing no more than 40% cereal. A sample of 36 cans was tested, showing a mean content of 42% cereal and a standard deviation of .04. Using a .05 level of significance, should the advertisement be accepted as true?

9. A random sample of 120 students attending Florida State University has a mean age of 20.2 years and a standard deviation of 1.2 years, while a random sample of 100 students attending the University of Florida has a mean age of 21 years and a standard deviation of 1.5 years. At a .05 level of significance, can we conclude that the average age of the students at the two universities are not the same?

10. Two methods of teaching a course in general mathematics were compared. Of 100 randomly selected students in the programed study method, 64 made a grade of C or better, while 84 of 120 randomly selected students using a student-teacher oriented method made a grade of C or better. Does the data present sufficient evidence to indicate a difference in the proportion of students who make C's or better between the two methods? Test at the .05 level of significance.

11. A consumer report shows that in testing 8 tires of brand A the mean life of the tires was 20,000 miles with a standard deviation of 2,500 miles. Twelve tires of brand B were tested under similar conditions with a mean life of 22,000 miles and a standard deviation of 2,800 miles. If a

.05 level of significance is used, does the data present sufficient evidence to indicate a difference in the average life of the two brands of tires?

12. At SP College, the students are required to take an entrance examination. A random sample of 400 girls produced a mean score on the test of 78 and a standard deviation of 6. A random sample of 225 boys produced a mean score of 74 and a standard deviation of 5. Use a .10 level of significance and test the hypothesis that girls and boys perform at the same level.

13. The grade-point average of 64 college freshmen produced a mean of 2.2 and a standard deviation of .4. How large a sample is required if we want to be 95% sure that our estimate of μ is off by less than .05?

14. A random sample of high school students was given a test involving a certain manual skill. The group was composed of 12 girls and 15 boys. The average time for the girls to complete the test was 12.4 minutes with a standard deviation of 1.2 minutes, while the mean time for the boys was 11.8 minutes with a standard deviation of 1.4 minutes. Test the hypothesis, at the .05 level of significance, that the girls have skill equal to the boys.

15. A sports magazine reports that the people who watch Monday night football games on television are evenly divided between men and women. Out of a random sample of 400 people who regularly watch the Monday night game, 220 are men. Using a .10 level of significance, can we conclude the report is false?

16. A pharmaceutical company has developed a new drug for the treatment of a certain allergy and asserts that it is effective 80% of the time. If 400 people who suffer from the allergy are administered the drug and 304 show improvement, what can be concluded about the company's assertion? Use a .05 level of significance.

17. In problem (16), what can be concluded about the company's assertion if a .01 level of significance is used?

18. A public opinion poll reports that 70% of a random sample of 400 women and 75% of 600 men favor stronger pollution control laws. At a .05 level of significance, can we conclude that the observed difference is significant?

19. The marketing department of a company that makes brand X laundry detergent found in a random sample of 200 housewives that 20% favored brand X over all others. After an intensive advertising campaign, another random sample of 300 housewives showed that 25% favored brand X. If the president of the company is willing to accept a

.05 Type I error, should he reject the hypothesis that the advertising campaign was effective?

20. The net contents in four cups of coffee dispensed by vending machine A are 6, 6.1, 5.9, and 6.4 ounces. Five cups of coffee dispensed from machine B produced net contents per cup of 6.2, 5.8, 6, 6.1, and 5.7 ounces. Testing at a .05 level of significance, can we conclude that one machine dispenses more coffee per cup than the other?

21. A political candidate for state office has predicted upon the basis of a poll of the registered voters that he will receive 60% of the vote in the upcoming election. To be 95% confident that he is within 2% of the vote he will actually receive, how many voters should have been polled?

22. The mean lifetime of a random sample of 64 flashlight batteries produced by company A is 60 hours with a standard deviation of 5 hours. A sample of 100 similar batteries from company B produced a mean of 62 hours and a standard deviation of 6 hours. At the .05 level of significance, does the data indicate a significant difference in the lifetimes of the batteries produced by the two companies?

23. An electrical company claimed that at least 95% of the parts which they supplied on a government contract conformed to specifications. A sample of 400 parts was tested, and 45 did not meet specifications. Test the company's claim at a .05 level of significance.

24. In deciding which of two brands, A and B, of tires to purchase for a fleet of cars, a company makes a road test of 16 tires of each brand. The tires were designated as worn out when they showed a specified amount of tire wear. The test results showed the mean wear of brand A to be 24,600 miles with a standard deviation of 1,250 miles. The mean and standard deviation of brand B were 22,400 miles and 1,400 miles, respectively. Test at a .05 level of significance the hypothesis that there is no difference in the mean life of the two brands of tires.

25. A manufacturer of a certain brand of thermostats advertises that the thermostat will open when the temperature reaches 180°. A sample of 15 thermostats was tested and the average temperature at which they opened was 182° with a standard deviation of 2°. Use a .01 level of significance and test the manufacturer's claim.

26. A certain brand of washing machines is claimed by its manufacturer to be free of defects for a three-year period. Five housewives who purchased a machine found that their machines needed repairs before three years. The times before failure were recorded as 2.5, 1.9, 2.9, 2.6, and 2.8 years. At a .05 level of significance, is the data sufficient evidence to contradict the manufacturer's claim?

7.11 TESTS CONCERNING A POPULATION VARIANCE

Many practical problems involve testing the hypothesis that the variance σ^2 of a normal population is equal to some specified value which we call σ_0^2 against an alternate hypothesis that σ^2 is less than σ_0^2. That is, we test

$$H_0 : \sigma^2 = \sigma_0^2$$

against

$$H_1 : \sigma^2 < \sigma_2^2$$

Suppose that a random sample of size n is selected from a normal population and the sample variance

$$\tilde{s}^2 = \frac{\sum\limits_{i=1}^{n} (x_i - \bar{x})^2}{n - 1}$$

is computed. Then

$$\chi^2 = \frac{(n - 1)\tilde{s}^2}{\sigma_0^2}$$

is a value of the chi-square distribution with $n - 1$ degrees of freedom of the random variable χ^2 when σ_0^2 is true. If σ^2 is larger than σ_0^2, then $\tilde{s}^2$, the estimate of σ^2 is usually larger than σ_0^2, and the χ^2 value will lie in the upper tail of the chi-square distribution. On the other hand, if σ^2 is less than σ_0^2, then $\tilde{s}^2$ tends to be less than σ_0^2, and the χ^2 value will lie in the lower tail of the distribution. For testing $\sigma^2 > \sigma_0^2$ at a level of significance α, we find the critical value χ_α^2 such that $\chi^2 > \chi_\alpha^2$ forms the rejection region and $\chi^2 < \chi_\alpha^2$ forms the acceptance region. Similarly, for testing $\sigma^2 < \sigma_0^2$, we find the critical value $\chi_{1-\alpha}^2$ such that $\chi^2 < \chi_{1-\alpha}^2$ forms the critical region and $\chi^2 > \chi_{1-\alpha}^2$ forms the acceptance region (see figure 7.15).

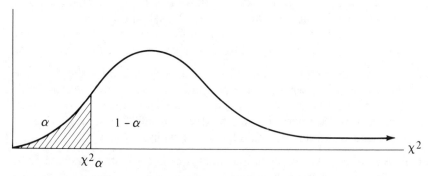

Figure 7.15 Critical Region for the Alternate Hypothesis $\sigma^2 < \sigma_0^2$

For a two-tailed test with a level of significance α, we find two critical values $\chi_{1-\alpha/2}^2$ and $\chi_{\alpha/2}^2$ such that $\chi^2 < \chi_{1-\alpha/2}^2$ and $\chi^2 > \chi_{\alpha/2}^2$ comprise the critical regions.

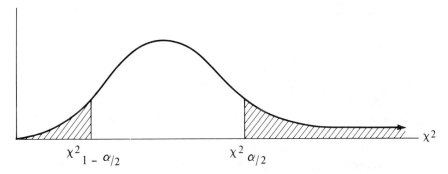

Figure 7.16 Critical Regions for the Alternate Hypothesis $\sigma^2 \neq \sigma_0^2$

The statistical test for testing an hypothesis about a population variance is similar to the previous tests that we have employed.

Example. The makers of a certain brand of car mufflers claim that the life of the mufflers has a variance of .8 year. A random sample of 16 mufflers produced a variance of 1 year. Using a .05 level of significance, test the hypothesis that $\sigma^2 = .8$ year against the alternate hypothesis that $\sigma^2 > .8$ year.

Solution:

$$H_0 : \sigma^2 = .8$$
$$H_1 : \sigma^2 < .8$$

The level of significance is $\alpha = .05$. The critical value is $\chi^2 > 26.2962$, and substituting $\sigma^2 = .8$ for $\tilde{s}$ in the test,

$$\chi^2 = \frac{15(1)}{.8} = 18.75$$

Since 18.75 is less than 24.9958, we accept the null hypothesis.

So far in this chapter, our tests of hypotheses have involved population parameters such as the mean or variance. Sometimes we need to test if a population has a specified theoretical distribution. Thes test for this theoretical distribution is based on the frequency of occurrence of observations in an observed sample and the expected frequency of occurrence from the hypothetical distribution.

To illustrate, suppose that a large college claims that it has an equal number of students enrolled in each of the four classes, freshman, sophomore, junior, and senior. A random sample of 100 students is selected, and the class of each student is recorded. If there is an equal number of each of the four classes, then we would expect that the sample would contain 25 students from each class. The results of the sample along with the expected frequency for each class are given in table 7.1.

Table 7.1 Observed and Expected Frequency of 100 Students

	Classes			
	Freshman	Sophomore	Junior	Senior
Observed	30	25	23	22
Expected	25	25	25	25

We must decide, by comparing the observed frequency of each class with the corresponding expected frequency, if the discrepancies are due to chance or if there really is a difference in the number of students enrolled in each class. A common practice is to refer to each possible outcome of an experiment as a *cell*; thus, the above experiment has four cells. The statistic upon which to base our decision for an experiment involving k cells is

$$\chi^2 = \frac{\sum_{i=1}^{k} (\theta - e_i)^2}{e_i}$$

where χ^2 is a value of the random variable χ^2 and χ^2 is a sampling distribution that can be closely approximated by a chi-square distribution.

If the observed and expected frequencies are close, then the χ^2 value will be small. On the other hand, if observed and expected frequencies are not close, then the χ^2 value will be large. A small value of χ^2 indicates acceptance of the null hypothesis, whereas a large value indicates that the null hypothesis should be rejected. Since a χ^2 value can never be negative, the critical region will always be in the right tail of the chi-square distribution. The criteria described here should not be used for making a decision unless each of the expected frequencies is at least 5 or more.

The number of degrees of freedom associated with the chi-square distribution used here depends on two factors; (1) the number of cells in the experiment and (2) the number of quantities from the observed data that are necessary in the calculation of the expected frequencies. For our problem, the only quantity provided by the observed data was the total frequency. Therefore the computed χ^2 value has $4 - 1 = 3$ degrees of freedom. Hence,

$$\chi^2 = \frac{\sum_{i=1}^{n} (0 - e_i)^2}{e_i}$$
$$= \frac{(30 - 25)^2}{25} + \frac{(25 - 25)^2}{25} + \frac{(23 - 25)^2}{25} + \frac{(22 - 25)^2}{25}$$
$$= \frac{38}{25}$$
$$= 1.52$$

We find from table VII that $\chi_{.05}^2 = 7.815$ for 3 degrees of freedom. Since

1.52 is less than the critical value, we accept the null hypothesis and conclude that there is an equal number of students in each class.

The chi-square test discussed above can also be used to test the hypothesis of independence of two variables. To illustrate, suppose that we wish to know if there is a relationship between grades received in high school and grades received in college. A random sample of 400 college students selected from various state colleges was selected, each person classified as doing good, fair, or poor work. The observed frequencies are presented in table 7.2, an example of what is sometimes called a *contingency table*.

Table 7.2 Contingency Table

| High
School | | College Work | | |
	Good	Fair	Poorly	Total
Good	40	20	15	75
Fair	70	60	25	155
Poorly	50	60	60	170
Total	160	140	100	400

It is common practice to describe contingency tables by giving their rows first and columns second. Table 7.2 has 3 rows and 3 columns, and is called a 3 by 3 table. To test the null hypothesis of independence between high school work and college work, we must find the expected frequency of each cell. The expected frequency of each cell, assuming H_0 is true, is the probability of the event multiplied by the total number of observations. Thus the expected number of students who did well in high school and who are doing well in college is $\left(\frac{75}{400}\right)\left(\frac{160}{400}\right)400 = 30$. In general, the expected frequency of any cell of an r-by-c table is the product of the totals of the row and column to which the cell belongs divided by the total number of all observed frequencies. The expected frequency of each cell is enclosed in parenthesis in table 7.3.

Table 7.3 Observed and Expected Frequencies

| High
School | | College | | |
	Good	Fair	Poorly	Total
Good	40 (30)	20 (26)	15 (19)	75
Fair	70 (62)	60 (54)	25 (39)	155
Poorly	50 (68)	60 (59)	60 (42)	170
Total	160	140	100	400

The number of degrees of freedom for an r-by-c contingency table is given by $V = (r - 1)(c - 1)$. Therefore, we have $(3 - 1)(3 - 1) = 4$ degrees of freedom.

To test the null hypothesis that the quality of work in college is independent of the quality of work done in high school,

$$\chi^2 = \frac{\sum_{i=1}^{n} (0_i - e_i)^2}{e_i} = \frac{(40 - 30)^2}{30} + \frac{(70 - 62)^2}{62} + \frac{(50 - 68)^2}{68}$$

$$+ \frac{(20 - 26)^2}{26} + \frac{(60 - 54)^2}{54} + \frac{(60 - 59)^2}{59} + \frac{(15 - 19)^2}{19}$$

$$+ \frac{(23 - 39)^2}{39} + \frac{(60 - 42)^2}{42}$$

$$= 26.3$$

We find that $\chi^2_{.05} = 9.488$ for $V = 4$ degrees of freedom. We reject the null hypothesis at this level and conclude that the college record is not independent of the high school record.

A program to compute χ^2 is given in program 7.1.

Program 7.1

```
  5 READ R,C
 10 DATA (ENTER NUMBER OF ROWS AND NUMBER OF
    COLUMNS)
 20 FOR I = 1 TO R
 30 FOR J = 1 TO C
 40 READ O (I,J)
 45 DATA (ENTER DATA BY ROWS)
 50 LET Z = Z + O(I,J)
 60 LET S(I) = S(I) + O(I,J)
 70 LET T(J) = T(J) + O(I,J)
 80 NEXT I
 90 NEXT J
100 FOR I = 1 TO R
110 FOR J = 1 TO C
120 LET E = (T(J)*S(I))/Z
130 LET Q = Q +((O ((I,J)-E)*(O(I,J)-E))/E
140 NEXT J
150 NEXT I
160 PRINT "CHI-SQUARE IS"; Q
990 END
```

EXERCISE 7.4

1. Test the null hypothesis

$$H_0 : \sigma^2 = 25$$

against the alternate hypothesis

$$H_1 : \sigma^2 > 725$$

(a) Should H_0 be rejected when $n = 14$, $\tilde{s}^2 = 5$, and $\sigma^2 = 3.2$, with a .05 level of significance?

(b) Should H_0 be rejected when $n = 6$, $\tilde{s}^2 = 8$, and $\sigma^2 = 2.2$ with a .01 level of significance?

2. Test the null hypothesis

$$H_0 : \sigma^2 = 225$$

against the alternate hypothesis

$$H_1 : \sigma^2 < 225$$

(a) Should H_0 be rejected when $n = 25$, $\tilde{s}^2 = 64$, and $\sigma^2 = 42$ with a .05 level of significance?

(b) Should H_0 be rejected when $n = 25$, $\tilde{s}^2 = 64$, and $\sigma^2 = 42$ with a .01 level of significance?

3. A sample of size 10 produced a variance of 14. Is this sufficient to reject the null hypothesis that $\sigma^2 = 6$ when tested using a .05 level of significance? Using a .01 level of significance?

4. A manufacturer of car batteries claims that the life of the batteries has a standard deviation equal to .8 year. The lives of a random sample of 5 batteries were recorded as 2.8, 3.1, 3.6, 2.5, and 3.0 years. Using a .10 level of significance, test the null hypothesis that $\sigma^2 = .8$.

5. To test the hypothesis that 75% of the people favored President Nixon's trip to China, a random sample of 100 people in each of the four geographical sections of the country were asked "Do you favor summit diplomacy?" The number of affirmative replies, along with the expected, was

	North	East	South	West
Observed	65	60	85	80
Expected	75	75	75	75

Does the data indicate that the hypothesis should be rejected at a .05 level of significance?

6. A random sample of 500 on-the-job trainees was conducted with the results tabulated as follows.

Intelligence	Good Work	Fair Work	Poor Work	Total
Above average	45	25	10	80
Average	75	50	40	165
Below average	80	120	55	255
Total	200	195	105	500

Use a .05 level of significance and test the null hypothesis that the performance on-the-job is independent of the intelligence of the trainees.

7. A random sample of 400 people living in Atlanta, 300 living in Memphis, and 300 living in New Orleans were asked the question: "Which network evening news program do you prefer, *A*, *B*, or *C*?" The responses are given in the following table.

Network	Number of People in Atlanta	Number of People in Memphis	Number of People in New Orleans	Totals
A	164	135	131	430
B	137	99	94	330
C	99	66	75	240
Totals	400	300	300	1000

Test the null hypothesis that there is no difference in the proportion of people who watch the three networks in the three cities. Use a .025 level of significance.

8. In a recent survey, 1,000 students in Pinellas County were asked: "How do you rate the way the school system meets the needs of today's youth: good, fair, or poor?" The responses, according to educational level of those responding, are given in the table below.

	Actual Responses		
Rating	Jr. High	Sr. High	College
good	82	427	191
fair	10	110	60
poor	8	63	49
Total	100	600	300

Using a .05 level of significance, can we conclude that the rating is independent of the educational level of those responding?

9. The following data pertains to the color of hair and the average number of dates per week of a sample of 600 unmarried women.

Number of dates Per week	Blonde	Redhead	Brunette
3	150	80	175
2	50	20	75
1	25	5	30
Total	225	105	280

At a .01 level of significance, test the hypothesis that blondes really have more fun.

10. A study is made to determine if there is a relationship between religious

affiliation and political affiliation. The results of the study are given below.

Party affiliation	Catholic	Protestant	Jewish	All others
Democrat	220	280	130	70
Republican	195	320	90	65
Independent	60	225	40	35
All Others	25	175	40	30
Totals	500	1000	300	200

Using a .01 level of significance, test the hypothesis that religious affiliation is independent of political affiliation.

7.12 TESTS CONCERNING THE EQUALITY OF POPULATION VARIANCES

Often we may wish to make comparisons between such things as the precision of two different measuring devices, the average yield per acre of two varieties of corn, or the effectiveness of two teaching methods.

To illustrate, to determine which of two teaching methods is best we might compare the two population variances σ_1^2 and σ_2^2. If σ_1^2 and σ_2^2 are not known, which is usually the case, then independent random samples of size n_1 and n_2 are selected from the two populations and the sample variances $\tilde{s}_1^2$ and $\tilde{s}_2^2$ are computed. To test the hypothesis that the two population variances are equal, i.e.,

$$H_0 : \sigma_1^2 = \sigma_2^2$$

against the alternate hypothesis,

$$H_1 : \sigma_1^2 \neq \sigma_2^2$$

we use the ratio of the two sample variances as the test statistic. Thus,

$$f = \tilde{s}_1^2 / \tilde{s}_2^2$$

is a value of the random variable F which has the F-distribution with $v_1 = n_1 - 1$ and $v_2 = n_2 - 1$ degrees of freedom.

If H_0 is true, the f-value computed from the ratio $\tilde{s}_1^2 / \tilde{s}_2^2$ should be very close to 1. A large value of f indicates that $\tilde{s}_1^2$ is larger than $\tilde{s}_2^2$ and $\sigma_1^2 > \sigma_2^2$. A value of f that is close to zero indicates that $\tilde{s}_1^2$ is less than $\tilde{s}_2^2$ and $\sigma_1^2 < \sigma_2^2$.

To test the null hypothesis

$$H_0 : \sigma_1^2 = \sigma_2^2$$

against the alternate hypothesis

$$H_1 : \sigma_1^2 \neq \sigma_2^2$$

with a level of significance α, the two critical values $f_{(1-\alpha/2)}(v_1, v_2)$ and

$f_{\alpha/2}(v_1, v_2)$ are found such that the critical regions are $F < f_{(1-\alpha)}(v_1, v_2)$ and $F > f_{\alpha/2}(v_1, v_2)$. The critical regions are shown in figure 7.17.

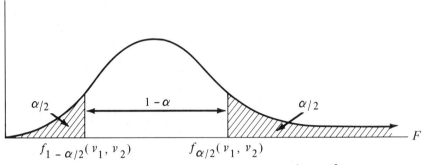

$$Figure\ 7.17\ Critical\ Region\ for\ H_1 : \sigma_2^1 \neq \sigma_2^2$$

The f-value $f_{1-\alpha/2}(v_1, v_2)$ is found by using table VIII, and the relation

$$f_{(1-\alpha/2)}(v_1, v_2) = \frac{1}{f_{\alpha/2}(v_2, v_1)}.$$

If the computed value of

$$f = \tilde{s}_1^2 / \tilde{s}_2^2$$

falls in the critical region, then H_0 is rejected. To test

$$H_0 : \sigma_1^2 = \sigma_2^2$$

against the alternate hypothesis

$$H_1 : \sigma_1^2 < \sigma_2^2$$

the entire critical region lies to the left of $F < f_{1-\alpha}(v_1, v_2)$, or $F < \dfrac{1}{f_\alpha(v_2, v_1)}.$

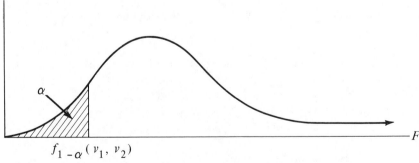

$$Figure\ 7.18\ Critical\ Region\ for\ H_1 : \sigma_1^2 < \sigma_2^2$$

If the null hypothesis

$$H_0 : \sigma_1^2 = \sigma_2^2$$

is to be tested against the alternate hypothesis

$$H_2 : \sigma_1^2 > \sigma_2^2$$

then the entire rejection lies to the right of $F > f_\alpha(v_1, v_2)$, as shown in figure 7.19.

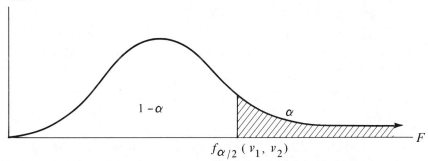

$$f_{\alpha/2}(v_1, v_2)$$

Figure 7.19 Critical Region for $H_2 : \sigma_1^2 > \sigma_2^2$

Example. Two independent random samples of size $n_1 = 10$ and $n_2 = 7$ were observed to have sample variances of $\tilde{s}_1^2 = 16$ and $\tilde{s}_2^2 = 3$.
   (*a*) Using a .10 level of significance, test

$$H_0 : \sigma_1^2 = \sigma_2^2$$

against

$$H_1 : \sigma_1^2 \neq \sigma_2^2$$

   (*b*) Using a .05 level of significance, test

$$H_0 : \sigma_1^2 = \sigma_2^2$$

against

$$H_2 : \sigma_1^2 > \sigma_2^2$$

   (*c*) Using a .05 level of significance, test H_0 against

$$H_3 : \sigma_1^2 < \sigma_2^2$$

Solutions: (*a*) $H_0 : \sigma_1^2 = \sigma_2^2$
$$H_1 : \sigma_1^2 \neq \sigma_2^2$$

The level of significance α is .10; thus

$$\alpha/2 = .05$$

The critical region is $F < .244$ or $F > 4.10$. We are given $\tilde{s}_1^2$ and $\tilde{s}_2^2$; thus

$$f = \frac{16}{3} = 5.33$$

Reject H_0.

$$(b)\ H_0 : \sigma_1^2 = \sigma_2^2$$
$$H_1 : \sigma_1^2 > \sigma_2^2$$

The level of significance α is .05. The critical region is $F > 4.10$. We are given $\tilde{s}_1^2$ and $\tilde{s}_2^2$; thus

$$f = \frac{16}{3} = 5.33$$

Reject H_0.

(c) $H_0 : \sigma_1{}^2 = \sigma_2{}^2$

$H_3 : \sigma_1{}^2 < \sigma_2{}^2$

The level of significance α is .05. The critical region is $F < .297$. We are given $\tilde{s}_1{}^2$ and $\tilde{s}_2{}^2$; thus

$$f = \frac{16}{3} = 5.33$$

Accept H_0.

The discussion in the previous section can be generalized to test the equality of more than two variances. That is, we may want to decide on the basis of sample data if there is a difference between three or more sample variances. To illustrate, we may want to compare the effectiveness of three different remedies for the common cold. Suppose that random samples were taken of four adults who were suffering from colds and were administered a remedy. The time to the nearest one-tenth hour that elapsed before effects were felt was recorded for each.

Remedy 1	Remedy 2	Remedy 3
2.0	2.3	3.4
1.5	2.6	4.0
2.5	3.0	4.6
2.0	2.5	4.4

The means of each of the samples are $\bar{x}_1 = 2$, $\bar{x}_2 = 2.6$, and $\bar{x}_3 = 4.1$. If we let $\sigma_1{}^2$, $\sigma_2{}^2$, and $\sigma_3{}^2$ denote the variance of all people who have or who will take each of the three remedies, we want to decide on the basis of the given data whether or not it is reasonable to say that these variances are equal. That is, we want to test the null hypothesis

$$H_0 : \sigma_1{}^2 = \sigma_2{}^2 = \sigma_3{}^2$$

against the alternate hypothesis

$$H_1 : \sigma_1{}^2 \neq \sigma_2{}^2 \neq \sigma_3{}^2$$

The test we shall employ is the ratio of two estimates of σ^2. That is, we find a value of the F-statistic such that

$$f = \frac{\text{the estimate of } \sigma^2 \text{ based on the variation among sample means}}{\text{the estimate of } \sigma^2 \text{ based on the variation within the samples}}$$

The estimate of σ^2 is based on the variation within the samples. For this test, it must be assumed that the populations from which we are sampling are approximately normal and have the same standard deviation σ.

where The estimate of σ^2 based on the variation of the sample means

$$\bar{x} = \frac{\sum\limits_{i=1}^{n} \bar{x}_i}{n} = \frac{2 + 2.6 + 4.1}{3} = 2.9$$

is

$$\tilde{s}_{\bar{x}}^2 = \frac{(2 - 2.9)^2 + (2.6 - 2.9)^2 + (4.1 - 2.9)^2}{3 - 1} = .78$$

Hence $\tilde{s}_{\bar{x}}^2 = .78$ is an estimate of $\sigma_{\bar{x}}^2$. Using the relation

$$\sigma_{\bar{x}}^2 = \frac{\sigma^2}{n}$$

we solve

$$\sigma^2 = n\sigma_{\bar{x}}^2$$

Substituting $\tilde{s}_{\bar{x}}^2 = .78$ for $\sigma_{\bar{x}}^2$ we have an estimate of σ^2 based on the variance of the sample means.

$$\sigma^2 = 4(.78) = 3.12$$

However, since $\tilde{s}_1^2$, $\tilde{s}_2^2$, and $\tilde{s}_3^2$ are each estimates of σ^2, we can use their mean as an estimate based on the variation within the samples.

$$\sigma^2 = \frac{\tilde{s}_1^2 + \tilde{s}_2^2 + \tilde{s}_2^2}{3}$$

$$= \frac{1}{3}\left[\left(\frac{(2 - 2)^2 + (1.5 - 2)^2 + (2.5 - 2)^2 + (2 - 2)^2}{4 - 1} \right) \right.$$

$$+ \left(\frac{(2.3 - 2.6)^2 + (1.6 - 2.6)^2 + (3 - 2.6)^2 + (2.5 - 2.6)^2}{4 - 1} \right)$$

$$+ \left. \left(\frac{(3.4 - 4.1)^2 + (4 - 4.1)^2 + (4.6 - 4.1)^2 + (4.4 - 4.1)^2}{4 - 1} \right) \right]$$

$$= .18$$

The ratio of the two estimates of σ^2

$$f = \frac{3.12}{.18} = 17.44$$

is a value of the F-statistic, if the null hypothesis is true. The sampling distribution of the F-statistic is called the F-distribution.

The null hypothesis will be rejected only when the computed f-value is large, i.e., when the ratio of the two estimates of σ^2 is too large to be attributed to chance.

The critical F_{α}-value depends on the degrees of freedom of both the numerator and denominator. When we compare k samples of size n, the number of degrees of freedom for the numerator is $v_1 = k - 1$ and the number of degrees of freedom of the denominator is $v_2 = k(n - 1)$.

   Returning to our problem, we find the critical value $f_{.05}(2, 9) = 4.26$. Since

$$f = \frac{3.12}{.18} = 17.44$$

we reject the null hypothesis and conclude that there is a difference in the effectiveness of the three cold remedies.

   A program to compute the F-ratio is given in program 7.2.

Program 7.2

```
 10 READ K,N
 15 DATA (NUMBER OF ROWS, NUMBER OF COLUMNS)
 25 FOR J = 1 TO K
 40 FOR I = 1 TO N
 50 READ X(I)
 51 DATA (BY COLUMNS)
 60 LET M(J) = M(J) + X(I)/N
 70 NEXT I
 80 FOR I = 1 TO N
 90 LET V(J) = V(J) + ((X(I) - M(J)) * (X(I)
    - (M(J)))/(N - 1)
100 NEXT I
110 LET P = P + V(J)
120 LET S = S + M(J)
130 NEXT J
140 LET R = P/K
150 LET U = S/K
160 FOR J = 1 TO K
170 LET E = E + ((M(J) - U) * (M(J) - U))/
    (K - 1)
190 NEXT J
210 LET G = N * E
220 IF G < R THEN 250
230 LET F = G/R
240 GO TO 260
250 LET F = R/G
211 PRINT "G =" G
153 PRINT "R =" R
260 PRINT "F =" F
999 END
```

EXERCISE 7.5

1. Two independent samples of size $n_1 = 12$ and $n_2 = 8$ were observed to have sample variances of $\tilde{s}_1^2 = 7$ and $\tilde{s}_2^2 = 5$. Test the null hypothesis

$$H_0 : \sigma_1^2 = \sigma_2^2$$

against the alternate hypothesis

$$H_1 : \sigma_1{}^2 \neq \sigma_2{}^2$$

using a .02 level of significance.

2. In problem 1, test the null hypothesis against the alternate hypothesis

$$H_2 : \sigma_1{}^2 > \sigma_2{}^2$$

using a .05 level of significance.

3. A random sample of 20 boys and 15 girls were given a standardized test. The average grade of the boys was 78 with a standard deviation of 6, while the girls made an average grade of 84 with a standard deviation of 8. Test the hypothesis that $\sigma_1{}^2 = \sigma_2{}^2$ against the alternate hypothesis $\sigma_1{}^2 < \sigma_2{}^2$ where $\sigma_1{}^2$ and $\sigma_2{}^2$ are the variances of the population of boys and girls. Use a .05 level of significance.

4. A homogeneous group of 12 third-grade students was divided into three subgroups, and each subgroup was taught reading by one of three different teaching methods, A, B, or C. At the end of the experiment, the students were given the same test and the scores were as follows.

Method A	Method B	Method C
78	74	76
80	75	79
83	77	80
85	82	81

Assume that the attributes of the teachers played no part in the experiment. Test, at a .05 level of significance, whether the difference between the three groups is significant.

5. Mr. X, Mr. Y, and Mr. Z are used-car salesmen employed by a given firm. The weekly earnings of each of five consecutive weeks were as follows.

Mr. X: 175, 225, 200, 150, 220
Mr. Y: 190, 210, 180, 230, 215
Mr. Z: 215, 185, 175, 205, 200

Test, at the .05 level of significance, the hypothesis that there is no difference in the true weekly earnings of the three salesmen.

6. There are four different routes leading from St. Petersburg to Tampa. Mr. Brown, who commutes between the two cities, recorded the following times (in minutes) that it took him to make the trip on four occasions for each route. The results were:

Route 1: 20, 22, 19, 21
Route 2: 23, 18, 19, 21
Route 3: 17, 19, 21, 24
Route 4: 18, 23, 19, 22

Using a .05 level of significance, test the hypothesis that there is no difference in the time it takes to make the trip over the four routes.

7. The final grades earned by five students in music, art and literature are as follows.

Music	Art	Literature
75	78	70
83	72	68
70	84	78
92	90	84
65	82	95

Using a .01 level of significance, test the hypothesis that the students are equally proficient in each subject.

8. Mr. Brown plans to buy a new economy car. Three cars from each of four different automobile companies A, B, C, and D were driven in the same manner and the average miles per gallon of each car was recorded. The results were as follows.

Company A	Company B	Company C	Company D
28	27	26	25
26	29	32	28
30	31	29	29

At a .05 level of significance, test the null hypothesis that there is no difference in the gas consumption in the cars.

CHAPTER 8

Linear Regression and Correlation

8.1 INTRODUCTION

Our objective in this chapter is to introduce the concepts of regression and correlation between two random variables. *Regression* may be regarded as a relationship that exists between paired observations of two variables, and *correlation* may be regarded as an indicator of the strength of that relationship. The concept of regression has wide use in statistics in making predictions about the unknown value of one variable on the basis of a known value of another variable. To illustrate, consider the following.

Example 1. The scores on a high school senior placement test may be used to predict the grade point average of the student as a college freshman.

Example 2. The age of a used car may be used to predict the cost.

If the known values of any variable X provides information about another variable Y, then X and Y are related. Our concern in regression is to make the best estimate possible in predicting a value of the variable Y from a known value of an associated variable X.

8.2 LINEAR REGRESSION BY THE GRAPHICAL METHOD

When two variables are related, it may be possible to express this relationship by means of a mathematical equation. The kind of equation is dependent upon the type of relationship that exists. The simplest equation of the
relationship between two variables is known as a linear equation, i.e.,

$$Y = A + BX$$

Our discussion will be limited to relationships of this type.

Actually, we assume that X and Y are two random variables such
that for any given value of X, say x_i, $E(y) = A + Bx_i$. Hence, $A + Bx_i$ is
an unbiased estimator of the value of y_i for the given value x_i of X.

The line showing this relationship between the two variables,
represented by $Y = A + BX$, is called the *regression line*. The regression
line provides a method of predicting the value of one variable Y associated
with a designated value of the other variable X; that is, given a specific
value of X we can predict the associated value of Y.

The geometric representation of the equation,

$$Y = A + BX$$

is the line shown in figure 8.1.

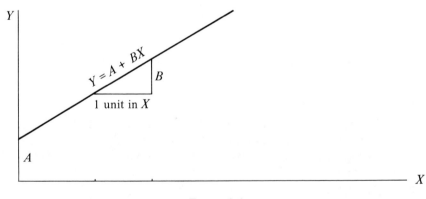

Figure 8.1

For any specified value of X, the predicted value of Y is given by the height
of the line at that point. When $X = 0$, the predicted value of Y is A. The
line crosses the Y-axis at the point $(0, A)$; therefore A is called the Y-
intercept. The other constant B denotes the change in Y resulting from a unit
change in X and is termed the *slope* of the line. If the sign before B is positive,
as in the above equation, the average value of Y increases with each increase
in X. However, if the sign before B is negative, then the value of Y decreases
with each increase in X.

Any straight line is determined by its intercept and slope. The problem of finding the simple regression line showing the relationship between two variables reduces to estimating the intercept and slope, i.e., the parameters A and B of the population.

The quantitative relationship between the two variables can be determined once the sample data has been obtained. The data to establish the relationship consists of paired observations of X and Y, and each of the pairs indicates a particular observation in the sample. Determination of the quantitative relationship is illustrated in the following example which will be often referred to in the remainder of the chapter.

Example. Five people are on a diet reducing plan. Estimate the regression line for the relationship between the number of pounds of weight lost and the number of weeks each of the five people were on the plan. Accumulated data consists of five paired observations; the first element of each pair indicates the number of pounds of weight lost and the second element indicates the number of weeks the person was on the diet. These five paired observations are given in table 8.1, where X represents the number of weeks on the diet and Y represents the number of pounds lost.

Table 8.1 Quantitative Relationship between Two Variables

X	Y
3	6
2	5
1	4
4	9
5	11

The first pair of observations ($X = 3, Y = 6$) indicates that the first person lost 6 pounds in 3 weeks; the second pair ($X = 2, Y = 5$) indicates the second person lost 5 pounds in 2 weeks. In like manner, the third pair ($X = 1, Y = 4$) indicates that the third person lost 4 pounds in 1 week; the fourth pair ($X = 4, Y = 9$) indicates the person lost 9 pounds in 4 weeks; and the fifth pair ($X = 5, Y = 11$) indicates the fifth person lost 11 pounds in 5 weeks.

Solution: We begin by constructing a graph of the paired observations on a horizontal and vertical axis. The "predicting" variable, in this case X, is measured along the horizontal axis, and the dependent variable Y is measured along the vertical axis. The pairs (X, Y) are then plotted on the graph in the usual way. The points representing the pairs in table 8.1 are shown in figure 8.2. Such a graph is called a *scattergram*.

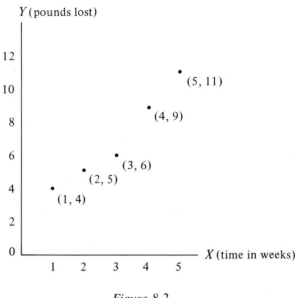

Figure 8.2

After the points are plotted, a straight line that represents the relationship between the two variables can be drawn. This line, called an *estimated regression line*, is shown in figure 8.3.

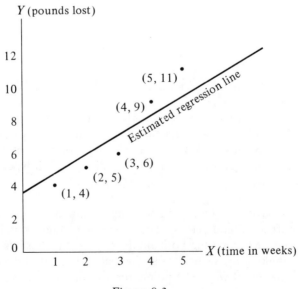

Figure 8.3

The estimated regression line enables us to predict the value of Y for any specified value of X. For instance, if a value of X is known, say 6, then the predicted value of Y is approximately 10.

The estimated regression line, as drawn in figure 8.3, is easily constructed. However, the points in the scattergram may not fall exactly on any one straight line, and other lines may be constructed that seem to fit the data as well as the one shown. This is the difficulty encountered in constructing the estimated regression line by visual examination of the data. Since visual examination is subjective, each person viewing the scattergram could conceivably construct a different regression line to "fit" the data. To illustrate we reproduce the scattergram of the five paired observations and construct different regression lines that seem to fit the data.

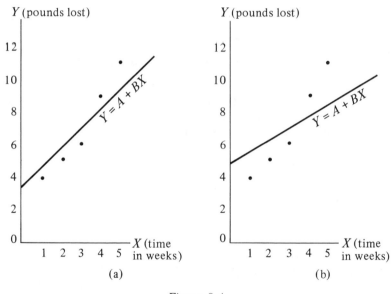

Figure 8.4

The subjective nature of the graphical method for determining the relationship between two variables is apparent. Obviously, more accurate methods for determining this relationship are needed. Such a method, known as the *least squares method*, is covered in the next section.

8.3 REGRESSION BY THE LEAST SQUARES METHOD

The least squares method always yields the same estimated regression line for showing the relationship between the two variables. In the least squares method, the vertical distance of each point in the scattergram from any proposed line is squared; the average of these squares is used as the criterion of *goodness of fit* of the regression line to the data. The smaller the average of the squared deviations, the better the fit. The line to use according to the least squares criterion is the one for which the mean square deviation is the least.

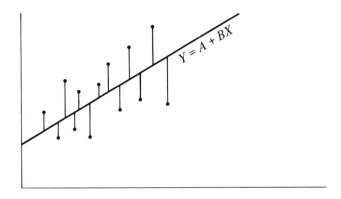

Figure 8.5 Deviations from a Regression Line

Let us return to the diet problem and estimate the regression line, $Y = A + BX$, by the least squares method. The set of five paired observations is reproduced below for ready reference.

X	Y
3	6
2	5
1	4
4	9
5	11

The least squares method provides a means for finding estimates for the Y-intercept A and the slope B of the line. The formulas we shall use for finding a, the estimate of A, and b, the estimate of B, involve $\sum X, \sum Y, \sum X^2$, $\sum Y^2$, and $\sum XY$. Where the summation is over all ordered pairs of observation, the calculations for finding these sums from our data are shown in table 8.2.

Table 8.2 Estimating a Regression Line

X	Y	X^2	Y^2	XY
3	6	9	36	18
2	5	4	25	10
1	4	1	16	4
4	9	16	81	36
5	11	25	121	55
$\sum X = 15$	$\sum Y = 35$	$\sum X^2 = 55$	$\sum Y^2 = 279$	$\sum XY = 123$

The derivation of the formulas for the least squares estimator b of the slope B of the regression equation utilizes calculus and is beyond our purpose in this text. The formula we shall use for determining the slope is,

$$b = \frac{\sum\limits_{i=1}^{n}(x_i - \bar{x})(y_i - \bar{y})}{\sum\limits_{i=1}^{n}(x_i - \bar{x})^2}$$

By algebraic manipulation it can be shown that

$$\sum_{i=1}^{n}(x_i - \bar{x})(y_i - \bar{y}) = \sum_{i=1}^{n}x_i y_i - \frac{\left(\sum\limits_{i=1}^{n}x_i\right)\left(\sum\limits_{i-1}^{n}y_i\right)}{n}$$

$$= \frac{n\left(\sum\limits_{i=1}^{n}x_i y_i\right) - \left(\sum\limits_{i=1}^{n}x_i\right)\left(\sum\limits_{i=1}^{n}y_i\right)}{n}$$

and

$$\sum_{i=1}^{n}(x_i - \bar{x})^2 = \sum_{i=1}^{n}x_i^2 - \left(\frac{\sum\limits_{i=1}^{n}x_i^2}{n}\right) = \frac{\left(n\sum\limits_{i=1}^{n}x_i^2\right) - \left(\sum\limits_{i=1}^{n}x_i\right)^2}{n}$$

Therefore, the formula can be written in a more convenient form when the computation is to be done manually as

$$b = \frac{\left(n\sum\limits_{i=1}^{n}x_i y_i\right) - \left(\sum\limits_{i=1}^{n}x_i\right)\left(\sum\limits_{i=1}^{n}y_i\right)}{\left(n\sum\limits_{i=1}^{n}x_i^2\right) - \left(\sum\limits_{i=1}^{n}x_i\right)^2}$$

Substituting the values from table 8.2 into the formula, we have

$$b = \frac{5(123) - (15)(35)}{5(55) - 225} = \frac{90}{50}$$

$$= 1.8 \text{ pounds per week}$$

That is, an average of 1.8 pounds is lost for each week the person is on the diet.

Once the estimated slope b is known, the estimated intercept a is easily determined. It can be shown that the least squares line will always pass through the point $(\bar{X}, \bar{Y})$; thus we can find the Y-intercept of the line by solving the equation,

$$\bar{y} = a + b\bar{x}$$

for a. Thus

$$a = \bar{y} - b\bar{x}, \quad \text{where} \quad \bar{y} = \frac{\sum\limits_{i=1}^{n}y_i}{n} \quad \text{and} \quad \bar{x} = \frac{\sum\limits_{i=1}^{n}x_i}{n}$$

Substituting these values, the equation for finding a is,

$$a = \frac{\sum\limits_{i=1}^{n} y_i}{n} - \left(b \frac{\sum\limits_{i=1}^{n} x_i}{n} \right)$$

For our problem involving the pounds of weight lost and the number of weeks on the diet, we have,

$$a = \frac{35}{5} - 1.8 \cdot \frac{15}{5} = 7 - 5.4 = 1.6$$

The equation of the estimated least squares regression line, also called *the equation of the best fit line*, is

$$\tilde{Y} = 1.6 + 1.8X$$

The estimated values of the constants a and b of the least squares regression line can also be found by a simultaneous solution to what are called two *normal* equations. These two normal equations are

$$\sum_{i=1}^{n} y_i = na + b \sum_{i=1}^{n} x_i$$

and

$$\sum_{i=1}^{n} x_i y_i = a \left(\sum_{i=1}^{n} x_i \right) + b \left(\sum_{i=1}^{n} x_i^2 \right)$$

where n denotes the number of paired observations in the set. Substituting values from table 8.2 in the equations, we have

$$35 = 5a + 15b$$
$$123 = 15a + 55b$$

The solution to the equations yields

$$a = 1.6 \quad \text{and} \quad b = 1.8$$

which are the values found previously.

A program to derive the regression equation where a is the estimated Y-intercept and b is the estimated slope is given in program 8.1.

Program 8.1

```
10 READ N
20 DATA 5,3,6,2,5,1,4,4,9,5,11
30 FOR I = I TO N
40 READ X,Y
50 LET E = E + X
60 LET F = F + Y
70 LET G = G + X * X
80 LET D = D + X * Y
90 NEXT I
100 LET B = (N * D - E * F)/(N * G - E * E)
```

```
110 LET A = (F/N) - B * (E/N)
120 PRINT "SLOPE IS"; B
130 PRINT "Y INT IS"; A
140 PRINT "REG LINE IS Y ="; A; +";
    B; "X"
999 END
```

```
SLOPE IS 1.8
Y INT IS 1.6
REG LINE IS Y = 1.6 + 1.8X
```

The least squares regression line enables us to predict the value of the dependent variable Y for a value of the independent variable X. For our least squares regression line,

$$\tilde{Y} = 1.6 + 1.8X$$

each 1-unit change in X will produce a 1.8 unit change in the predicted value of Y.

A clear distinction must be made between the *observed value* and the *estimated value* of the dependent variable Y. The observed value refers to actual value, while the estimated value is the predicted value using the least squares regression line as a basis for making the prediction. The observed value and the estimated value of Y can be the same, but in most cases the values are different. Table 8.3 lists the values of X, the observed values y_i of Y, and the estimated values $\tilde{Y}$.

Table 8.3 Observed Values and Estimated Values

x_i	y_i	$\tilde{Y}_i$
3	6	7.0
2	5	5.2
1	4	3.4
4	9	8.8
5	11	10.6

In each case the observed and estimated values of Y differ. That a difference exists is to be expected, since the estimated value of Y is the value associated with a value of X as computed from the equation of the least squares regression line.

8.4 STANDARD ERROR OF THE ESTIMATE

The *standard error of the estimate* of Y from X, denoted by *SEE*, is the standard deviation of the difference between the observed and estimated values of Y. That is, it measures the average disparity between the two values. In computing the standard error of estimate, $n - 2$ is used in the denominator instead of $n - 1$; this is because the deviations of the squares we are averaging are based on two quantities instead of one, as was the case in simple standard deviation. The standard error of estimate, as estimated from a sample of size n, is

$$SEE = \sqrt{\frac{\sum_{i=1}^{n}(y_i - \bar{Y}_i)^2}{n - 2}}$$

where y_i is the observed value of a given X and $\bar{Y}_i$ is the estimated value of Y. If the computation is to be done manually, a more convenient form of the formula to use is

$$SEE = \sqrt{\frac{\sum_{i=1}^{n}(y_i - \bar{y})^2 - b\sum_{i=1}^{n}(x_i - \bar{x})(y_i - \bar{y})}{n - 2}}$$

Returning to the problem of pounds of weight lost and the number of weeks on the diet, we apply the formula to compute the estimate of the standard error of estimate. The value of b has been calculated as

$$b = 1.8$$

and

$$\sum(x_i - \bar{x}_i)(y_i - \bar{y}) = \sum x_i y_i - \frac{(\sum x_i)(\sum y_i)}{n} = 18$$

Furthermore,

$$\sum(y_i - y_i)^2 = \sum y_i^2 - \frac{(\sum y_i)^2}{n} = 279 - \frac{1225}{5} = 34$$

Substituting these values in the formula, we find the standard error of estimate to be

$$SEE = \sqrt{\frac{\sum y_i^2 - \frac{(y_i)^2}{n} - B\left[\sum x_i y_i - \frac{(x_i)(y_i)}{n}\right]}{n - 2}} = \sqrt{\frac{34 - 1.8(18)}{5 - 2}}$$

$$= \frac{1.6}{3} = .73$$

A program to compute the SEE using the formula

$$SEE = \sqrt{\frac{\sum_{i=1}^{n}(y_i - \bar{Y}_i)^2}{n - 2}}$$

where y_i represents the observed value of the dependent variable and $\bar{Y}_i$ the estimated value, is given in program 8.2.

Program 8.2

```
 10 READ N,A,B
 30 DATA
 40 FOR I = 1 TO N
 50 READ X,Y1
 60 LET Y = A + B * X
 70 LET Z = Z + (Y1 - Y) * (Y1 - Y)
 80 NEXT I
 90 LET S = (Z/(N - 2)) ↑ .5
100 PRINT "SEE =";  S
999 END
    SEE = .730296
```

The standard error of estimate "measures" the disparity between the observed and estimated values of Y. The goodness of fit of the regression equation is indicated by the value of the standard error of estimate. A small value of SEE indicates that the observed and estimated values of Y are very close and that the regression equation is a good description of the relationship between the two variables as based on the data. If the value of SEE is 0, then the regression equation is an exact description of the relationship. On the other hand, a large value of SEE indicates a wide disparity between the observed and estimated values of Y. In such cases, the regression equation does not give a good description of the relationship between the two variables.

The value of SEE is only a sample estimate of the true population standard error of estimate σEE. If the true population standard error of estimate were known to be some value, say 2, then 95% of the Y-values, assuming Y is normally distributed for each value of X, would be within four pounds of the true regression line. Thus, the weight lost cannot be exactly predicted from the time on the diet, because of the inherent variability of other factors involved, such as emotional stress and body chemistry.

There are two sources of error in predicting the weight lost from the number of weeks on the diet: (1) A sample does not show the exact location of the true regression line and (2) the inherent variability of each individual causes uncertainty of prediction. A larger sample may reduce the error in locating the true regression line, but it will not significantly affect the inherent variability nor reduce SEE.

A comparison of SEE by s_y, the standard deviation in weight lost when time is disregarded, indicates the strength of the inherent variability.

$$SEE = \sqrt{\frac{\sum_{i=1}^{n} (y_i - \bar{Y}_i)^2}{n - 1}} = 2.91$$

$$SEE = .73$$

The standard deviation is reduced from 2.91 for weight lost per person regardless of time to .73 for persons on the diet for the same number of weeks. This large reduction indicates that the amount of time on the diet is a great help in predicting the loss in weight and shows a strong relationship between the two variables.

8.5 THE COEFFICIENT OF CORRELATION

The standard error of estimate is a measure of the average discrepancy between the observed values of Y and the fitted line; that is, it measures the goodness of fit of the line to the data. This measure is given in the same units as those in which the dependent variable is measured. As a result, the value of SEE is affected by a change in units of measure of Y. If the weight lost in the preceding problem had been given in ounces instead of pounds, the value of SEE would have been sixteen times as great as the value that was calculated. Since the value of SEE will change according to the units in which Y is measured, it is not suitable for testing hypotheses. What is needed is a measure that is unaffected by a change in units for the dependent variable.

One such measure is called the *coefficient of correlation*. This measure, which is independent of the scales of measure of X and Y, is an indication of the linear relationship between the two variables. The coefficient of correlation, denoted by r, is computed as follows.

$$r = \frac{\sum_{i=1}^{n} (x_i - \bar{x})(y_i - \bar{y})}{\sqrt{\sum_{i=1}^{n} (x_i - \bar{x})^2 \sum_{i=1}^{n} (y_i - \bar{y})^2}}$$

$$= \frac{n\left(\sum_{i=1}^{n} x_i y_i\right) - \left(\sum_{i=1}^{n} x_i\right)\left(\sum_{i=1}^{n} y_i\right)}{\sqrt{n\left(\sum_{i=1}^{n} x_i^2\right) - \left(\sum_{i=1}^{n} x_i\right)^2} \sqrt{n\left(\sum_{i=1}^{n} y_i^2\right) - \left(\sum_{i=1}^{n} y_i\right)^2}}$$

The coefficient of correlation for the weight loss and the number of weeks on the diet may be found by using the formula and the data in table 8.2. Since the quantities

$$n\left(\sum_{i=1}^{n} x_i y_i\right) - \sum_{i=1}^{n} x_i \sum_{i=1}^{n} y_i$$

and

$$n\left(\sum_{i=1}^{n} x_i^2\right) - \left(\sum_{i=1}^{n} x_i\right)^2$$

have previously been computed as 90 and 50 respectively, we need to compute the value of

$$n\left(\sum_{i=1}^{n} y_i^2\right) - \left(\sum_{i=1}^{n} y_i\right)^2$$

Using the data in table 8.2, we have

$$5(279) - (35)^2 = 1395 - 1225 = 170$$

Thus,

$$r = \frac{n\left(\sum_{i=1}^{n} x_i y_i\right) = \left(\sum_{i=1}^{n} x_i\right)\left(\sum_{i=1}^{n} y_i\right)}{\sqrt{n\left(\sum_{i=1}^{n} x_i^2\right) - \left(\sum_{i=1}^{n} x_i\right)^2} \sqrt{n\left(\sum_{i=1}^{n} y_i\right) - \left(\sum_{i=1}^{n} y_i\right)^2}} = \frac{90}{\sqrt{50}\sqrt{170}} = .976$$

Program 8.3 derives the regression equation and computes the correlation coefficient.

Program 8.3

```
10 READ N
20 DATA 5,3,6,2,5,1,4,4,9,5,11
30 FOR I = 1 TO N
40 READ X,Y
50 LET E = E + X
60 LET F = F + Y
70 LET G = G + X * X
80 LET H = H + Y * Y
90 LET D = D + X * Y
100 NEXT I
110 LET B = (N * D - E * F)/(N * G - E * E)
120 LET A = (F/N) - B * (E/N)
125 LET C = (N * D - E * F)/(((N * G - E * E)
    *(N * H - F * F)) ↑ .5)
130 PRINT "SLOPE IS"; B
140 PRINT "Y INT IS"; A
150 PRINT "REG LINE IS Y ="; A; "+"; B;
    "X"
160 PRINT "THE COR COEF IS" C
999 END
```

```
SLOPE IS 1.8
Y INT IS 1.6
REG LINE IS Y = 1.6 + 1.8X
THE COR COEF IS .976191
```

If r is positive, X and Y are said to be positively correlated; if r is negative, X and Y are said to be negatively correlated; if r is zero, X and Y are said to be uncorrelated. A value of r that is near $+1$ or -1 indicates that the estimated value of the variation of the dependent variable is nearly as great as the observed value. In such cases, we say that the independent variable is capable of explaining nearly all of the variation in the dependent variable and there is a strong relationship between the two. On the other hand, a value of r that is near zero indicates that the independent variable is capable of explaining very little of the variation in the dependent variable, and we have a weak relationship. A positive value of r indicates that the two are directly related, while a negative value indicates that the two are inversely related.

The denominator used in calculating r is the product of two positive numbers and is always positive. The numerator is the same as that used in calculating b the slope of the regression line. Thus, r will always assume the same sign as the slope b.

The correlation coefficient depends not only on how well the regression line fits the data, but also upon the amount of dispersion. Since it is a relative measure and is unaffected by the scale in which the observations are measured, it is widely used in showing the relationship between two variables.

For any nonzero value of r there are always two hypotheses to explore. First, it must be determined that there is a *cause-effect* relationship between the two variables. To illustrate, during the depression of the 1930's the number of red-headed woodpeckers being sighted showed a remarkable increase over the number sighted during the boom times of the 1920's. This led to the assumption that the number of such birds observed was an economic barometer. The reason more red-headed woodpeckers were sighted was that more people were unemployed and out in the woodlands which was the habitat of the birds. The relationship is not a cause-effect one, but one in which both variables are the result of a common cause. Consequently, any correlation coefficient, regardless of size, cannot be used as a cause-effect relationship.

The second hypothesis to be explored, once the cause-effect relationship has been established, is that the value of the correlation coefficient is significant. That is, we must determine if the value of r is such that it cannot be explained by chance alone.

To test the null hypothesis that there is no correlation between the two variables, we refer to table VII in the back of the book. The table is based on the assumption that X and Y are approximately normally distributed independent variables and, hence, have no correlation. The table is constructed so that a value of r which we compute for a set of paired data is significant at a $(1 - \alpha)$ level of significance if it exceeds $r_{\alpha/2}$ or is less than $-r_{\alpha/2}$. If the value we get for r falls between $-r_{\alpha/2}$ and $r_{\alpha/2}$, we say that there is no significant correlation, or that the value of r is not statistically significant.

Applying this test to our problem concerning the weight loss to the number of weeks the person was on the diet; we find that $r = .976$ is significant, since when $n = 5$ it exceeds both $r_{.025} = .878$ and $r_{.005} = .959$. Therefore, we are justified in concluding that there is a linear relationship between the loss in weight and the number of weeks on the diet.

Our discussion has been restricted to simple linear regression and correlation. Other types of regression may be explored in subsequent courses. Our purpose has been to discuss some of the basic concepts and to give the student an idea of what regression and correlation are about.

EXERCISE 8.1

1. In each of the following pairs of random variables, which would you expect to find (a) positive correlation, (b) negative correlation, or (c) no correlation?
   (a) The average miles per gallon of gasoline and speed of the automobile.
   (b) The amount of your electric bill and the amount of electricity used.
   (c) The size of a person's head and his IQ.
   (d) Hours spent on homework and grade point average.
   (e) Hours spent watching TV and grade point average.
   (f) Advertising budget of a firm and sales.
   (g) Cigarette smoking and occurrence of lung cancer.
   (h) Air pollution and respiratory disease.
   (i) Drinking of alcohol and the automobile accident rate.
   (j) Success in life and grade point average in school.

2. List three pairs of variables between which you would expect the correlation to be positive. Do the same for negative correlation and for no correlation.

3. Given the following pairs of measurements for the two variables

X	5	8	3	9	10	12
Y	9	12	5	15	18	20

   (a) Construct a scattergram and draw an estimated regression line.
   (b) Using the regression line in part (a) estimate the values of Y when:
       (1) $X = 4$, (2) $X = 1$, and (3) $X = 15$.

4. Using the pairs of measurements in problem 3, find:
   (a) the equation of the least squares regression line.
   (b) the standard error of estimate.
   (c) the correlation coefficient r.
   (d) Using the least squares regression line of part (a), estimate the values of Y when (1) $X = 4$, (2) $X = 1$, and (3) $X = 15$.

5. The heights of fathers, X, and the heights of their oldest sons when grown, Y, are given as measurements to the nearest inch),

X	68	64	70	72	69	74
Y	67	68	69	73	66	70

(a) Construct a scattergram.
(b) Find the equation of the least squares regression line.
(c) Compute the standard error of estimate.
(d) Compute the coefficient of correlation r.

5. A small business keeps account of its weekly expenditure for advertising X and weekly sales Y. Over a ten-week period the records showed

X	55	40	50	60	70	80	90	60	100	55
Y	130	125	140	155	160	200	210	150	200	140

(a) Find the equation of the least squares regression line.
(b) Find the standard error of estimate.
(c) Find the correlation coefficient r.
(d) Does the value of r indicate a significant correlation when $\alpha = .05$?

6. The ages X and the systolic blood pressures Y of 10 men are

X	35	40	45	47	50	55	60	50	40	45
Y	115	120	125	130	140	135	140	130	140	150

(a) Find the equation of the best fitting line.
(b) Find the standard error of estimate.
(c) Compute the correlation coefficient, r.
(d) Does the value of r indicate a significant correlation when $\alpha = .01$?

7. A group of 20 students enrolled in first year algebra course was administered both a pretest and a posttest with the following results.

Pretest X 10 19 17 8   5 4 8 16 21 26   5 9 12   8   9 26 19 20 2   3
Posttest Y 12 15 12 8 10 7 5 20 19 20 15 5 25 20 12 15 19 24 8 15

(a) Find the equation of the least squares regression equation.
(b) Construct a scattergram of the data and plot the graph of the estimated regression line.
(c) Compute the correlation coefficient r.
(d) Compute the standard error of estimate and compare it with the correlation coefficient as an indicator of the relationship.
(e) Should the instructor consider the results of the two tests to be significant at a .95 level of significance?

Answers to
Odd-Numbered
Exercises

CHAPTER 1

Exercise 1.1

1. (a) Statement 4 is incorrect. The line should read:

    4 PRINT X, "IS THE SUM OF", A, "AND", B

  (b) All statements except 50 are incorrect. The program should read as follows:

```
10   READ  X,Y
20   DATA  2,4,6,8
30   LET  Z = X+Y
40   PRINT  Z
50   GO TO  10
60   END
```

  (c) Statements 7, 8, and 9 are incorrect.

```
7   LET  Y = X↑3
8   PRINT "THE CUBE OF", X, "IS", Y
9   GO TO  6
```

3. (a) LET A = B*(C+D)
   (b) LET B2=X1+X2+X3
   (c) LET X=2*Z−Y
   (d) LET Z5=2*(5+.03*X)
   (e) LET W7=X2*X7

5. 10   READ N1,C1,N2,C2,N3,C3
   20   DATA 3000,.035,5150,.022,10310,.048
   30   PRINT "JOHN OWES", N1*C1
   40   PRINT "MARY OWES", N2*C2
   50   PRINT "JIM OWES", N3*C3
   70   END

Exercise 1.2

1.

QUANTITY	UNIT COST	TOTAL COST
10000	.01	100.
12000	.012	144.
16000	.025	400.

3. The program is:
    5   PRINT "EMP", "GROSS", "TAX", "SS", "NET"
   10   READ E,G
   20   DATA 1,500, 2,100, 3,700, 4,900, 5,400
   30   LET T = .1 * G
   40   LET S = .05 * G
   50   LET N = G − (T+S)
   60   PRINT E,G,T,S,N
   70   GO TO 10
   999 END

The printout is:

EMP	GROSS	TAX	SS	NET
1	500	50.	25.	425.
2	1000	100.	50.	850.
3	700	70.	35.	595.
4	900	90.	45.	765.
5	400	40.	20.	340.

5.   10   PRINT "ITEM", "QUAN", "UNIT COST", "TOTAL COST"
   15   READ I,Q,U
   20   DATA
   30   LET T = Q * U
   40   PRINT I,Q,U,T
   50   GO TO 15
   999 END

Exercise 1.3

1.

TABLE OF POWERS OF 2

EXPONENT	2↑E
0	1
1	2
2	4
3	8
4	16
5	32
6	64
7	128
8	256
9	512
10	1024

3.
```
10   LET S = 0
20   FOR I = 1 TO 100
30   LET S = S+I
40   NEXT I
50   PRINT S
999  END
```

5.
```
10   FOR I = 1 TO 10
20   LET R = I↑.5
30   PRINT I,R
40   NEXT I
999  END
```

CHAPTER 2

Exercise 2.1

1. (a) $\{5,6,7,8,9,10\}$
  (b) $\{a,e,i,o,u,y\}$
  (c) ϕ
  (d) $\{(1,1),(1,2),(1,3),(2,1),(2,2),(2,3),(3,1),(3,2),(3,3)\}$

3. $\{(s,r),(r,s)\} = \{(r,s),(s,r)\}$

5. (a) ϕ, {Kansas City}, {Dallas}, {Kansas City,Dallas}
  (b) ϕ, {Nixon}, {Johnson}, {Kennedy}, {Nixon,Johnson},
    {Nixon,Kennedy}, {Johnson,Kennedy}, {Nixon,Johnson,Kennedy}
  (c) ϕ {1} {3} {5}, **{7}**, {9} {1,3}, {1,5}, {1,7} {1,9} {3,5},
    {3,7}, {3,9}, {5,7}, {5,9}, {7,9}, {1,3,5}, {1,3,7},
    {1,3,9}, {1,5,7}, {1,5,9}, {1,7,9}, {3,5,7}, {3,5,9},
    {3,7,9}, {5,7,9},
    {1,3,5,7}, {1,3,5,9}, {1,3,7,9}, {1,5,7,9}, {3,5,7,9},
    {1,3,5,7,9}

7. (a) 8

   (b) 4

   (c) 16

   (d) 8

9.

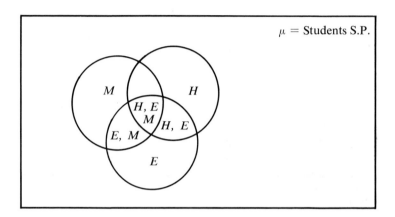

Exercise 2.2

1. (a) $A \cup B = \{1,2,3,4,5,6,7,8,9,10,12,14\}$

   (b) $B \cup C = \{1,2,3,4,5,6,7,8,9,10,12,14\}$

   (c) $A \cup C = A$

   (d) $(A \cup B) \cup C = A \cup B$

   (e) $A \cup (B \cup C) = A \cup B$

   (f) $A \cup (B \cap C) = A$

   (g) $A' = \{11,12,13,14\}$

   (h) $B' = \{1,3,5,7,9,11,13\}$

   (i) $C' = \{2,4,6,8,10,11,12,13,14\}$

   (j) $A' \cap (B' \cup C') = A' \cap U = A'$

3. (a) 10   (b) 5

5. A is the set $\{(s,f),(s,s)\}$

   B is the set $\{(f,f),(s,f)\}$

   (a) $A \cup B = \{(s,s),(s,f),(f,f)\}$

   (b) $A \cap B = \{(s,f)\}$

   (c) $A' = \{(f,s),(f,f)\}$

   (d) $B' = \{(f,s),(s,s)\}$

7. (a) All Caucasians 21 years of age or older.
   (b) All human beings, including Caucasians, 21 years of age or older.
   (c) All Caucasians and all Negros.
   (d) All Negros 21 years of age or older.
   (e) All human beings except Caucasians and Negros.

9. (a) f and g
   (b) e and h
   (c) all
   (d) a,e,f,g,h

Exercise 2.3

1. (a) $A \times B = \{(1,x),(1,y),(1,z),(2,x),(2,y),(2,z),(3,x),(3,y),(3,z)\}$
   (b) $B \times A = \{(x,1),(x,2),(x,3),(y,1),(y,2),(y,3),(z,1),(z,2),(z,3)\}$
   (c) $A \times A = \{(1,1),(1,2),(1,3),(2,1),(2,2),(2,3),(3,1),(3,2),(3,3)\}$
   (d) $B \times B = \{(x,x),(x,y),(x,z),(y,x),(y,y),(y,z),(z,x),(z,y),(z,z)\}$

3. (a) $A \times B - \{(a,1),(a,5),(a,7),(a,9),(b,1),(b,5),(b,7),(b,9),(c,1),$
                 $(c,5),(c,7),(c,9),(d,1),(d,5),(d,7),(d,9)\}$
   (b) $A \times C = \{(a,a),(a,2),(a,b),(a,3),(b,a),(b,2),(b,b),(b,3),(c,a),$
                 $(c,2),(c,b),(c,3),(d,a),(d,2),(d,b),(d,3)\}$
   (c) $B \times C = \{(1,a),(1,2),(1,b),(1,3),(5,a),(5,2),(5,b),(5,3),(7,a),$
                 $(7,2),(7,b),(7,3),(9,a),(9,2),(9,b),(9,3)\}$
   (d) $A \times B \times C = \{(a,1,a),(a,1,2),(a,1,b),(a,1,3), \ldots ,(d,9,3)\}$

5. The Cartesian product is not commutative; however, the number of elements in $A \times B \times C$ is unchanged by commuting.

Exercise 2.4

1. $3! = 3 \cdot 2 \cdot 1 = 6$
     $6! = 6 \cdot 5 \cdot 4 \cdot 3 \cdot 2 \cdot 1 = 720$
     $11! = 39,916,800$

3. (a) $5!$
   (b) $4!$

5. $5 \cdot 4 = 20$ ways.

7. $(n - 1)! = (8 - 1)! = 7!$

9. $6 \cdot 4 \cdot 3 \cdot 5 = 360$ ways.

11. (a) $8!$
    (b) $4!4!$
    (c) $4!4! \cdot 2$

13. (a) $P\left(\begin{matrix} 5 \\ 3,2 \end{matrix}\right) = \dfrac{5!}{3!2!} = \dfrac{120}{6 \cdot 2} = 10$

    (b) $P\left(\begin{matrix} 5 \\ 4,1 \end{matrix}\right) = \dfrac{5!}{4!1!} = \dfrac{120}{24} = 5$

    (c) $P\left(\begin{matrix} 4 \\ 4 \end{matrix}\right) = 4! = 24$

(d) $P\left(\begin{array}{c} 9 \\ 3,3,3 \end{array}\right) = \dfrac{9!}{3!3!3!} = \dfrac{362,880}{6 \cdot 6 \cdot 6} = 1,680$

15. 3^{10}, since each game has three possible choices.

Exercise 2.5

1. (a) $C\left(\begin{array}{c} 8 \\ 4 \end{array}\right) = \dfrac{8!}{4!4!}$ (d) $C\left(\begin{array}{c} 18 \\ 2 \end{array}\right) = \dfrac{18!}{2!16!}$

(b) $C\left(\begin{array}{c} 12 \\ 0 \end{array}\right) = \dfrac{12!}{0!(12-0)!} = 1$

(c) $C\left(\begin{array}{c} n \\ n-2 \end{array}\right) = \dfrac{n!}{(n-2)!(n-(n-2))!}$

3. $\dfrac{4!}{4!} + \dfrac{4!}{1!3!} + \dfrac{4!}{2!2!} + \dfrac{4!}{1!3!} + \dfrac{4!}{4!0!} = 1 + 4 + 6 + 4 + 1$
$= 16 = 2^4$ (problem 2).

5. $C\left(\begin{array}{c} 10 \\ 2 \end{array}\right) \cdot C\left(\begin{array}{c} 25 \\ 3 \end{array}\right) \cdot C\left(\begin{array}{c} 6 \\ 2 \end{array}\right)$

7. Disregarding limitations, $C\left(\begin{array}{c} 8 \\ 6 \end{array}\right)$ groups of 6 people may be chosen. With the restrictions imposed, we must deduct those groups in which A is included and B is not included. Hence,

$C\left(\begin{array}{c} 8 \\ 6 \end{array}\right) = 28$

$28 - C\left(\begin{array}{c} 6 \\ 5 \end{array}\right) = 22$

9. $C\left(\begin{array}{c} 52 \\ 5 \end{array}\right)$

11. (a) $C\left(\begin{array}{c} 6 \\ 4 \end{array}\right)$

(b) $C\left(\begin{array}{c} 6 \\ 2 \end{array}\right) \cdot C\left(\begin{array}{c} 9 \\ 2 \end{array}\right)$

(c) $C\left(\begin{array}{c} 9 \\ 4 \end{array}\right) + C\left(\begin{array}{c} 9 \\ 3 \end{array}\right) C\left(\begin{array}{c} 6 \\ 1 \end{array}\right) + C\left(\begin{array}{c} 9 \\ 2 \end{array}\right) C\left(\begin{array}{c} 6 \\ 2 \end{array}\right)$

(d) $C\left(\begin{array}{c} 6 \\ 0 \end{array}\right) C\left(\begin{array}{c} 9 \\ 4 \end{array}\right) + C\left(\begin{array}{c} 6 \\ 1 \end{array}\right) C\left(\begin{array}{c} 9 \\ 3 \end{array}\right) + C\left(\begin{array}{c} 6 \\ 2 \end{array}\right) C\left(\begin{array}{c} 9 \\ 2 \end{array}\right)$

Exercise 2.6

1. (a) $x^5 + 5x^4y + 10x^3y^2 + 10x^2y^3 + 5xy^4 + y^5$

(b) $\left(\dfrac{x}{2}\right)^7 + 7\left(\dfrac{x}{2}\right)^6 \dfrac{y}{3} + 21\left(\dfrac{x}{2}\right)^5 \left(\dfrac{x}{3}\right)^2 + 35\left(\dfrac{x}{2}\right)^4 \left(\dfrac{y}{3}\right)^3 + 35\left(\dfrac{x}{2}\right)^3 \left(\dfrac{y}{3}\right)^4$
$+ 21\left(\dfrac{x}{2}\right)^2 \left(\dfrac{y}{3}\right)^5 + 7\left(\dfrac{x}{2}\right) \left(\dfrac{y}{3}\right)^6 + \left(\dfrac{y}{3}\right)^7$

$$= \frac{x^7}{2^7} + \frac{7}{2^6 3} x^6 y + \frac{21}{2^5 3^2} x^5 y^2 + \frac{35}{2^4 3^3} x^4 y^3 + \frac{35}{2^3 3^4} x^3 y^4 + \frac{21}{2^2 3^5} x^2 y^5$$

$$+ \frac{7}{2^2 3^6} xy^6 + \frac{y^7}{3^7}$$

(c) $(S + F)^9 = C\binom{9}{0} S^9 + C\binom{9}{1} S^8 F + C\binom{9}{2} S^7 F^2 + C\binom{9}{3} S^6 F^3$

$$+ C\binom{9}{4} S^5 F^4 + C\binom{9}{5} S^4 F^5 + C\binom{9}{6} S^3 F^6$$

$$+ C\binom{9}{7} S^2 F^7 + C\binom{9}{8} SF^8 + C\binom{9}{9} F^9$$

(d) $(2a - 7)^4 = C\binom{4}{0} (2a)^4 + C\binom{4}{1} (2a)^3 (-7)$

$$+ C\binom{4}{2} (2a)^2 (-7)^2 + C\binom{4}{3} (2a)(-7)^3 + C\binom{4}{4} (-7)^4$$

3. (a) $C\binom{5}{0}\left(\frac{1}{2}\right)^5 + C\binom{5}{1}\left(\frac{1}{2}\right)^4 \frac{1}{2} + C\binom{5}{2}\left(\frac{1}{2}\right)^3 \left(\frac{1}{2}\right)^2 + C\binom{5}{3}$

$$\left(\frac{1}{2}\right)^2 \left(\frac{1}{2}\right)^3 + C\binom{5}{4}\left(\frac{1}{2}\right)\left(\frac{1}{2}\right)^4 + C\binom{5}{5}\left(\frac{1}{2}\right)^5$$

$$= \frac{1}{2^5} + \frac{5}{2^5} + \frac{10}{2^5}$$

$$+ \frac{10}{2^5} + \frac{5}{2^5} + \frac{1}{2^5} = 1$$

(b) $\frac{1}{4^7} + \frac{7 \cdot 3}{4^7} + \frac{21 \cdot 3^2}{4^7} + \frac{35 \cdot 3^3}{4^7} + \frac{35 \cdot 3^4}{4^7} + \frac{21 \cdot 3^5}{4^7} + \frac{7 \cdot 3^6}{4^7} + \frac{3^7}{4^7}$

(c) $\frac{1}{10^9} + \frac{9 \cdot 9}{10^9} + \frac{9^2 \cdot 36}{10^9} + \frac{9^3 \cdot 84}{10^9} + \frac{9^4 \cdot 126}{10^9} + \frac{9^5 \cdot 126}{10^9} + \frac{9^6 \cdot 84}{10^9}$

$$+ \frac{9^7 \cdot 36}{10^9} + \frac{9^8 \cdot 9}{10^9} + \frac{9^9 \cdot 1}{10^9}$$

5. (a) $P\binom{9}{4,3,2} = \frac{9!}{4!3!2!} = \frac{9 \cdot 8 \cdot 7 \cdot 6 \cdot 5}{3 \cdot 2 \cdot 2 \cdot} = \frac{9 \cdot 8 \cdot 7 \cdot 5}{2} = 9 \cdot 4 \cdot 7 \cdot 5$

$$= 36 \cdot 35 = 1,260$$

(b) $P\left(\frac{30}{10,10,5,5}\right) = \frac{30!}{10!10!5!5!} = 29 \cdot 3 \cdot 13 \cdot 5 \cdot 23 \cdot 11 \cdot 21$

$$= 19 \cdot 3 \cdot 17 \cdot 14 \cdot 13 \cdot 12 \cdot 11$$

7. $3^n = (1 + 1 + 1)^n = P\binom{n}{n,0,0} + P\binom{n}{n-1,1,0} + P\binom{n}{n-1,0,1}$

$$+ P\binom{n}{n-2,2,0} + P\binom{n}{n-2,1,1} + P\binom{n}{n-2,0,2} + \cdots$$

$$+ P\binom{n}{0,0,n}$$

CHAPTER 3

Exercise 3.1

1. $\{(s,s,),(s,f),(f,s),(f,f)\}$

3. $C\left(\begin{array}{c}5\\2\end{array}\right) = \dfrac{5!}{2!3!} = 10$

$S = \{(P_1,P_2),(P_1,P_3),(P_1,P_4),(P_1,P_5),(P_2,P_3),(P_2,P_4),(P_2,P_5),(P_3,P_4),$
$(P_3,P_5),(P_4,P_5)\}$

5. $\{((s,s),(s,s)),((s,s),(s,f)),((s,s),(f,s)),((s,f),(s,s)),((f,s),(s,s)),$
$((s,s),(f,f)),((s,f),(f,s)),((s,f),(s,f)),((f,s),(f,s)),((f,s),(s,f)),$
$((f,f),(s,s)),((f,f),(f,s)),((f,f),(s,f)),((f,s),(f,f)),((s,f),(f,f)),$
$((f,f),(f,f))\}$

The number of points in this space is identical to those for the experiment of calling on four customers to sell one product.

7. $C\left(\begin{array}{c}10\\4\end{array}\right) = \dfrac{10!}{4!6!} = \dfrac{10 \cdot 9 \cdot 8 \cdot 7}{4 \cdot 3 \cdot 2 \cdot 1} = 210$ points in the space.

$C\left(\begin{array}{c}9\\3\end{array}\right) = \dfrac{9!}{3!6!} = \dfrac{9 \cdot 8 \cdot 7}{3 \cdot 2} = 84$ points in which a given order appears.

9. If $(F + H + T)^{10}$ is expanded, a total of 3^{10} sample points is found. The number of terms indicating five hospitalizations is found by the sum

$$P\left(\begin{array}{c}10\\5,5,0\end{array}\right) + P\left(\begin{array}{c}10\\4,5,1\end{array}\right) + P\left(\begin{array}{c}10\\3,5,2\end{array}\right) + P\left(\begin{array}{c}10\\2,5,3\end{array}\right) + P\left(\begin{array}{c}10\\1,5,4\end{array}\right)$$
$$+ P\left(\begin{array}{c}10\\0,5,5\end{array}\right)$$

Exercise 3.2

1. $E_1 = \{(s,s,f,f),(s,f,s,f),(s,f,f,s),(f,s,s,f),(f,s,f,s),(f,f,s,s)\}$
$E_2 = E_1 \cup \{(s,s,s,f),(s,s,f,s),(s,f,s,s),(f,s,s,s),(s,s,s,s)\}$
$E_3 = \{(f,f,f)\}$
$E_4 = \{(s,s,f,f)\}$
$E_1 \cup E_2 = \{(s,s,f,f),(s,f,s,f),(s,f,f,s),(f,s,s,f),(f,s,f,s),(f,f,s,s),$
$(s,s,s,f),(s,s,f,s),(s,f,s,s),(f,s,s,s),(s,s,s,s)\}$
$E_2 \cap E_4 = \phi$
$E_1' = \{(s,s,s,s),(s,s,s,f),(s,s,f,s),(s,f,s,s),(f,s,s,s),(f,f,f,s),$
$(f,f,s,f),(f,s,f,f),(s,f,f,f),(f,f,f,f)\}$

3. (a) $2^{10} =$ number of points in the sample space.

(b) $E = P\left(\begin{array}{c}10\\5,5\end{array}\right) = 252$

Exercise 3.3

1. $P\begin{pmatrix} 4 \\ 4 \end{pmatrix} = 4!$

$E_1 = P_1$ and P_2 are seated side by side.

$$n(E_1) = 2P\begin{pmatrix} 3 \\ 3 \end{pmatrix}$$

$$n(S) = P\begin{pmatrix} 4 \\ 4 \end{pmatrix}$$

$$P(E_1) = \frac{2P\begin{pmatrix} 3 \\ 3 \end{pmatrix}}{P\begin{pmatrix} 4 \\ 4 \end{pmatrix}} = \frac{2 \cdot 3 \cdot 2}{4 \cdot 3 \cdot 2} = \frac{1}{2}$$

$E_2 = P_1$ and P_2 or P_1 and P_3

$E_3 = P_1$ and P_3

$$P(E_1 \cup E_3) = P(E_2)$$
$$= P(E_1) + P(E_2) - P(E_1 \cap F_2)$$
$$= \frac{1}{2} + \frac{1}{2} - \frac{1}{6}$$
$$= \frac{5}{6}$$

3. $n(S) = C\begin{pmatrix} 30 \\ 2 \end{pmatrix}$

$E_1 = A_1$ and A_2 are both selected.

$E_2 = A_1$ is selected and A_{15} is not selected.

$$n(E_1) = C\begin{pmatrix} 2 \\ 2 \end{pmatrix}$$

$$P(E_1) = \frac{C\begin{pmatrix} 2 \\ 2 \end{pmatrix}}{C\begin{pmatrix} 30 \\ 2 \end{pmatrix}} = \frac{1}{\dfrac{30 \cdot 29}{2}} = \frac{2}{30 \cdot 29}$$

$$n(E_2) = C\begin{pmatrix} 1 \\ 1 \end{pmatrix} \cdot C\begin{pmatrix} 28 \\ 1 \end{pmatrix}$$

$$P(E_2) = \frac{C\begin{pmatrix} 1 \\ 1 \end{pmatrix} \cdot C\begin{pmatrix} 28 \\ 1 \end{pmatrix}}{C\begin{pmatrix} 30 \\ 2 \end{pmatrix}} = \frac{2 \cdot 28}{30 \cdot 29}$$

5. $n(s) = C\begin{pmatrix} 100 \\ 10 \end{pmatrix}$

$E_1 = $ first and last of 100 items are selected.

$$n(E_1) = C\begin{pmatrix} 98 \\ 8 \end{pmatrix} \cdot C\begin{pmatrix} 2 \\ 2 \end{pmatrix}$$

$$P(E_1) = \frac{C\left(\begin{array}{c}98\\8\end{array}\right) \cdot C\left(\begin{array}{c}2\\2\end{array}\right)}{C\left(\begin{array}{c}100\\10\end{array}\right)}$$

E_2 = item 49 is selected.

$$n(E_2) = C\left(\begin{array}{c}99\\9\end{array}\right) \cdot C\left(\begin{array}{c}1\\1\end{array}\right)$$

$$P(E_2) = \frac{C\left(\begin{array}{c}99\\9\end{array}\right) \cdot C\left(\begin{array}{c}1\\1\end{array}\right)}{C\left(\begin{array}{c}100\\10\end{array}\right)}.$$

Exercise 3.4

1. (a) $\dfrac{115}{402}$ or $\dfrac{195}{402}$ (assuming all college graduates are also high-school graduates).

(b) $\dfrac{17}{402}$

(c) $\dfrac{20}{402} = \dfrac{10}{201}$

3.

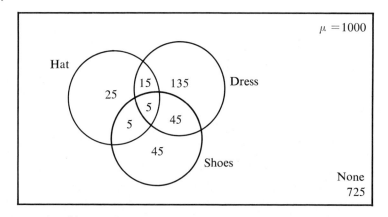

$$P(\text{hat}) = \frac{50}{1,000} = \frac{1}{20}$$

$$P(\text{dress}) = \frac{200}{1,000} = \frac{1}{5}$$

$$P(\text{shoes and hats}) = \frac{10}{1,000} = \frac{1}{100}$$

$$P(\text{shoes, hats, and dresses}) = \frac{5}{1,000} = \frac{1}{200}$$

$$P(\text{no purchase}) = \frac{725}{1,000}$$

Exercise 3.5

1. The sample space is $\{(s,s,s),(s,s,f),(s,f,s),(f,s,s),(f,f,s),(f,s,f),(s,f,f),(f,f,f)\}$

$$P\{(s,s)\} = \frac{8}{12} \cdot \frac{7}{11}$$

$$P\{(s,f,s)\} = \frac{8}{12} \cdot \frac{4}{11} \cdot \frac{7}{10}$$

$$P\{(f,f,s)\} = \frac{4}{12} \cdot \frac{3}{11} \cdot \frac{8}{10}$$

3. $S = \{(m,m,m),(m,m,w),(m,w,m),(w,m,m),(w,w,m),(w,m,w),(m,w,w),$
   $(w,w,w)\}$

$$P\{(m,w,m)\} = \frac{1,800}{3,000} \cdot \frac{1,200}{2,999} \cdot \frac{1,799}{2,998}$$

$$P\{(w,w,w)\} = \frac{1,200}{3,000} \cdot \frac{1,199}{2,999} \cdot \frac{1,198}{2,998}$$

$$P\{(m,m,w)\} = \frac{1,800}{3,000} \cdot \frac{1,799}{2,999} \cdot \frac{1,200}{2,998}$$

5. $S = \{(c,c,c),(c,c,n),(c,n,c),(n,c,c),(n,n,c),(n,c,n),(c,n,n),(n,n,n)\}$

$$P\{(c,n,c)\} = \frac{1}{5} \cdot \frac{4}{5} \cdot \frac{1}{5}$$

$$P\{(n,n,n)\} = \frac{4}{5} \cdot \frac{4}{5} \cdot \frac{4}{5}$$

$$P\{(n,c,n)\} = \frac{4}{5} \cdot \frac{1}{5} \cdot \frac{4}{5}$$

7. $C\left(\begin{smallmatrix} 5 & 2 \\ & 5 \end{smallmatrix}\right)$ is the number of points in the space.

$$P\{(As,Ks,Qs,Js,10s)\} = \frac{1}{52} \cdot \frac{1}{51} \cdot \frac{1}{50} \cdot \frac{1}{49} \cdot \frac{1}{48} \text{ if the 5 cards are ordered as}$$

shown; since order is to be disregarded, this product must be multiplied by

$$P\binom{5}{5}.$$

$$P\binom{5}{5} \cdot \frac{1}{52} \cdot \frac{1}{51} \cdot \frac{1}{50} \cdot \frac{1}{49} \cdot \frac{1}{48} = \frac{P\binom{5}{5}}{P\left(\begin{smallmatrix}5 & 2\\ & 5\end{smallmatrix}\right)}$$

$$P\{(H,H,H,H,H)\} = \frac{13}{52} \cdot \frac{12}{51} \cdot \frac{11}{50} \cdot \frac{10}{49} \cdot \frac{9}{48} = \frac{P\binom{13}{5}}{P\binom{52}{5}}$$

$$P\{(As,Ah,Ad,Ac,2c)\} = P\binom{5}{5} \cdot \frac{1}{52} \cdot \frac{1}{51} \cdot \frac{1}{50} \cdot \frac{1}{49} \cdot \frac{1}{48}$$

Exercise 3.6

1. $S = \{(s,s,s),(s,s,f),(s,f,s),(s,f,f),(f,s,s),(f,s,f),(f,f,s),(f,f,f)\}$

$$P(E_1) = \frac{9}{10} \cdot \frac{9}{10} \cdot \frac{9}{10}$$

$$P(E_2) = \frac{9}{10} \cdot \frac{9}{10} \cdot \frac{1}{10}$$

$$P(E_3) = \frac{9}{10} \cdot \frac{9}{10} \cdot \frac{1}{10}$$

3. There are 2^6 points in the sample space:

$$P(E_1) = \left(\frac{1}{2}\right)$$

The number of permutations $P\left(\begin{array}{c}6\\4,2\end{array}\right)$ yields the number of ways four boys and two girls may be born; only one of these points satisfys E_2:

$$P(E_2) = \frac{1}{2^6}$$

5. $E_1 = $ the next ten prospects will make purchases.

$$P(E_1) = \left(\frac{1}{5}\right)^{10}$$

$E_2 = $ the next two will make purchases.

$$P(E_2) = \left(\frac{1}{5}\right)^2$$

$E_3 = $ the next three will fail to purchase.

$$P(E_3) = \frac{4}{5} \cdot \frac{4}{5} \cdot \frac{4}{5}$$

Exercise 3.7

1. $(P + T)^5 = C\left(\begin{array}{c}5\\0\end{array}\right)P^5 + C\left(\begin{array}{c}5\\1\end{array}\right)P^4T + C\left(\begin{array}{c}5\\2\end{array}\right)P^3T^2 + C\left(\begin{array}{c}5\\3\end{array}\right)P^2T^3$

$$+ C\left(\begin{array}{c}5\\4\end{array}\right)PT^4 + C\left(\begin{array}{c}5\\5\end{array}\right)T^5$$

$$P(E_1) = C\left(\begin{array}{c}5\\0\end{array}\right)P^5 = \left(\frac{100}{120}\right)^5 = \left(\frac{5}{6}\right)^5$$

$$P(E_2) = C\left(\begin{array}{c}5\\0\end{array}\right)P^5 + C\left(\begin{array}{c}5\\1\end{array}\right)P^4T + C\left(\begin{array}{c}5\\2\end{array}\right)P^3T^2 = \left(\frac{100}{120}\right)^5$$

$$+ 5\left(\frac{100}{120}\right)^4\left(\frac{20}{120}\right) + 10\left(\frac{100}{120}\right)^3\left(\frac{20}{120}\right)^2$$

$$= 2\left(\frac{5}{6}\right)^5 + 10\left(\frac{5}{6}\right)^3\left(\frac{1}{6}\right)^2$$

$$P(E_3) = C\binom{5}{2} P^3 T^2 = 10\left(\frac{100}{120}\right)^3 \left(\frac{20}{120}\right)^2 = 10\left(\frac{5}{6}\right)^3 \left(\frac{1}{6}\right)^2$$

$$P(E_4) = P(E_2 \cup E_3) = P(E_2) + P(E_3) - P(E_2 \cap E_3)$$

$$P(E_5) = P(E_1 \cup E_3) = P(E_1) + P(E_3) - P(E_1 \cap E_3)$$

3. The number of points in $S = C\binom{5}{3} = 10$; the space is equally probable.

E_1 = both m_1 and m_2 are selected.

$$n(E_1) = C\binom{2}{2} \cdot C\binom{3}{1}$$

$$P(E_1) = \frac{n(E_1)}{n(s)} = \frac{3}{10}$$

E_2 = neither m_1 nor m_2 is selected.

$$n(E_2) = C\binom{3}{3} = 1$$

$$P(E_2) = \frac{n(E_2)}{n(s)} = \frac{1}{10}$$

E_3 = m_1 is selected, but m_2 is not selected.

$$n(E_3) = C\binom{1}{1} C\binom{3}{2} = 3$$

$$P(E_3) = \frac{n(E_3)}{n(s)} = \frac{3}{10}$$

E_4 = m_1 and m_2 are both selected, or neither m_1 nor m_2 is selected.

$$P(E_4) = P(E_1 \cup E_2) = P(E_1) + P(E_2) - P(E_1 \cap E_2) = \frac{3}{10} + \frac{1}{10} - 0 = \frac{4}{10}$$

5. P(newspaper subscriber) $= \dfrac{1}{4} + \dfrac{1}{2} + \dfrac{1}{10} = \dfrac{17}{20}$

P(both papers or *Times*) $= P$(both papers) $+ P(Times)$

$$- P(\text{both papers} \cap Times) = \frac{1}{4} + \frac{1}{2} = \frac{3}{4}$$

P(both papers or *Independent*) $= P$(both papers) $+ P(Independent)$

$$- P(\text{both papers} \cap Independent)$$

$$= \frac{1}{4} + \frac{1}{10} = \frac{7}{20}$$

Exercise 3.8

1. E_1: The card is red.

E_2: The card is an ace.

E_3: The card is a king.

E_4: The card is a spade.

$$P(E_1 \mid E_2) = \frac{P(E_1 \cap E_2)}{P(E_2)}$$

$$= \frac{\frac{2}{52}}{\frac{1}{2}} = \frac{1}{13}$$

$$P(E_3 \mid E_4) = \frac{\frac{1}{52}}{\frac{13}{13}} = \frac{1}{13}$$

3.

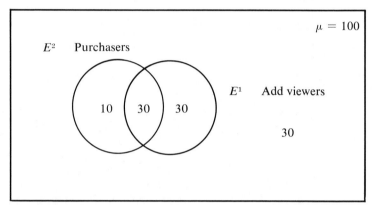

E_1: Ad readers

E_2: Purchasers

$$P(E_2 \mid \sim E_1) = \frac{P(E_2 \cap \sim E_1)}{P(\sim E_1)}$$

$$= \frac{10}{100} \left| \frac{40}{100} = \frac{1}{4} \right.$$

$$P(E_2 \mid E_1) = \frac{P(E_2 \cap E_1)}{P(E_1)}$$

$$= \frac{30}{100} \left| \frac{60}{100} = \frac{1}{2} \right.$$

5. $S = \{(B,B,B),(B,B,G),(B,G,B),(G,B,B),(G,G,B),(G,B,G),(B,G,G),$
$(G,G,G)\}$

$P(\text{all boys}) = \dfrac{1}{7}$

$P(\text{two girls}) = \dfrac{3}{7}$

$P(\text{two boys, one girl}) = \dfrac{3}{7}$

7. E_1: A man is chosen.

E_2: The man is Rep.

$$P(E_2 \mid E_1) = \frac{P(E_1 \cap E_2)}{P(E_1)}$$

$$= \frac{\dfrac{3}{11}}{\dfrac{6}{11}} = \frac{1}{2}$$

Exercise 3.9

1. E: The person selected is a supervisor.

E_1: The person is a college graduate.

E_2: The person is not a college graduate.

We are seeking $P(E_1 \mid E)$.

$$P(E_1 \mid E) = \frac{P(E_1)\,P(E \mid E_1)}{P(E_1)P(E \mid E_1) + P(E_2)P(E \mid E_2)}$$

$$= \frac{.2 \cdot .75}{.2 \cdot .75 + .8 \cdot .2}$$

$$= \frac{.15}{.15 + .16} = \frac{.15}{.31}$$

$$= \frac{15}{31}$$

3. E: The item is defective.

E_1: The item is produced at A.

E_2: The item is produced at B.

E_3: The item is produced at C.

E_4: The item is produced at D.

$P(E_1 \mid E) =$

$$\frac{P(E_1)P(E \mid E_1)}{P(E_1)P(E \mid E_1) + P(E_2) + (E \mid E_2) + P(E_3) + (E \mid E_3) + P(E_4)P(E \mid E_4)}$$

$$= \frac{.0001}{.0001 + .0001 + .0015 + .008} = \frac{.0001}{.0025} = \frac{1}{25}$$

$$P(E_2 \mid E) = \frac{.0001}{.0025} = \frac{1}{25}$$

$$P(E_3 \mid E) = \frac{.0015}{.0025} = \frac{3}{5}$$

$$P(E_4 \mid E) = \frac{.0008}{.0025} = \frac{8}{25}$$

Check: $\dfrac{1}{25} + \dfrac{1}{25} + \dfrac{3}{5} + \dfrac{8}{25} = 1$

5. E: The student is studying mathematics.

E_1:   The student is a woman.

E_2:   The student is not a woman.

$$P(E_1 \mid E) = \frac{P(E_1)P(E \mid E_1)}{P(E_1)P(E \mid E_1) + P(E_2)P(E \mid E_2)}$$

$$= \frac{.45 \cdot .2}{.45 \cdot .2 + .55 \cdot .45} = \frac{.09}{.09 + .2475} = \frac{.09}{.3375} = \frac{.03}{.1125}$$

$$= \frac{12}{45}$$

Exercise 3.10

1. $(A + R)^3 = A^3 + 3A^2R + 3AR^2 + R^3$

3. $(F + N)^{30}$

(a) $C\begin{pmatrix} 30 \\ 0 \end{pmatrix} \cdot \left(\dfrac{3}{1000}\right)^0 \left(\dfrac{997}{1000}\right)^{30}$

(b) $C\begin{pmatrix} 20 \\ 4 \end{pmatrix} \cdot \left(\dfrac{3}{1000}\right)^4 \left(\dfrac{997}{1000}\right)^{16}$

5. $C\left(\dfrac{100}{80}\right) \cdot \left(\dfrac{6}{10}\right)^{80} \left(\dfrac{4}{10}\right)^{20}$

7. $(A + R + D)^3$

(a) $P\begin{pmatrix} 3 \\ 1,1,1 \end{pmatrix} D \cdot R \cdot A = 6\,DRA$

(b) $P\begin{pmatrix} 3 \\ 2,0,1 \end{pmatrix}\left(\dfrac{7}{10}\right)^2 \left(\dfrac{1}{10}\right)^1 = \dfrac{3!}{2!0!1!}\left(\dfrac{7}{10}\right)^2 \left(\dfrac{1}{10}\right)^1 \quad 3 \cdot \left(\dfrac{7}{10}\right)^2 \dfrac{1}{10}$

9. $(N + S + H + A)^{30}$

(a) (1) $P\begin{pmatrix} 30 \\ 10,10,10 \end{pmatrix} N^{10}A^{10}H^{10}$

$\dfrac{30!}{10!10!10!} \; N^{10}A^{10}H^{10}$

(2) $P\begin{pmatrix} 30 \\ 5,10,10,5 \end{pmatrix} N^5 S^{10}H^{10}A^5$

$\dfrac{30!}{5!10!10!5!} \; N^5 S^{10}H^{10}A^5$

(b) $\dfrac{30!}{10!10!10!}\left(\dfrac{30}{100}\right)^{10}\left(\dfrac{10}{100}\right)^{10}\left(\dfrac{20}{100}\right)^{10}$

CHAPTER 4

Exercise 4.1

1. Reliable data yields approximately the same results each time it is gathered on the same subject. Valid data provides a true measure of the characteristics it is supposed to measure.

3. A population is the total collection of elements under discussion having one or more common characteristics (definition 4.1); a sample is that part of the population that is examined in a statistical investigation (definition 4.2).

5. A sample (definition 4.2, question 3 above) is a random sample when each element in the population has the same chance of being included in it (definition 4.3).

7. Variates are the individual values of quantitative data; attributes are the individual values of qualitative data.

9. The statistician utilizes statistics to make logical decisions based on the obtaining, processing, and analysis of valid and reliable data.

Exercise 4.2

1. (a) The mean number of touchdowns is calculated by the formula

$$\bar{x} = \sum_{i=1}^{n} \frac{x_i}{n} = \frac{2+3+0+3+4+1+3+0}{8} = \frac{16}{8} = 2$$

(b) The data in order of magnitude is 0,0,1,2,3,3,3,4, and the median is given by the formula $\dfrac{x_{\frac{n}{2}} + x_{\frac{n+2}{2}}}{2} = \dfrac{2+3}{2} = 2.5$

(c) The observation 3 appears most often and is the mode.

3. (a) The largest observation is 3 and the smallest is 0; thus the range is $3 - 0 = 3$.

(b) The variance can be calculated by either formula

$$s^2 = \sum_{i=1}^{n} \frac{(x_i - \bar{x})^2}{n} \quad \text{or} \quad s^2 = \frac{\sum_{i=1}^{n} x_i^2 - \dfrac{\left(\sum_{i=1}^{n} x_i\right)^2}{n}}{n}$$

For illustration, s^2 is calculated using each formula.

$$s^2 = \frac{\sum_{i=1}^{n}(x_i - x)^2}{n} =$$

$$\frac{(2-2)^2+(3-2)^2+(0-2)^2+(3-2)^2+(4-2)^2+(1-2)^2+(3-2)^2+(0-2)^2}{8}$$

$$= \frac{(0)^2+(1)^2+(-2)^2+(1)^2+(2)^2+(-1)^2+(1)^2+(-2)^2}{8} = \frac{16}{8} = 2$$

For the formula

$$s^2 = \frac{\sum\limits_{i=1}^{n} x_i^2 - \dfrac{\left(\sum\limits_{i=1}^{n} x_i\right)^2}{n}}{n}$$

we need $\sum\limits_{i=1}^{n} x_i^2$ and $\sum\limits_{i=1}^{n} x_i$. A table, similar to the following, facilitates computation.

x_i	x_i^2
2	4
3	9
0	0
3	9
4	16
1	1
3	9
0	0
$\sum\limits_{i=1}^{8} x_i = 16$	$\sum\limits_{i=1}^{8} x_i^2 = 48$

From the table,

$$s^2 = \frac{48}{8} - \frac{16^2}{8} = \frac{48 - 32}{8} = 2$$

(c) The standard deviation is $s = \sqrt{s^2} = \sqrt{2} = 1.414$.

5. (a) $\bar{x} = \dfrac{\sum\limits_{i=1}^{n} x_i}{n} = \dfrac{100}{8} = 12.5$

The median is $\dfrac{12 + 14}{2} = 13$

The mode is 14.

(b) The range is $17 - 8 = 9$. $\sum\limits_{i=1}^{n} x_i^2 = 1{,}316$

$\sum\limits_{i=1}^{n} x_i = 100$, $\quad s^2 = \dfrac{1{,}316 - \dfrac{100^2}{20}}{20} = 8.25$, and $s = 2.87$

7. (a) $\bar{x} = \dfrac{\sum\limits_{i=1}^{n} x_i}{n} = \dfrac{250}{10} = 25$. The median is $\dfrac{27 + 27}{2} = 27$. The mode is 27.

(b) The range is $29 - 19 = 10$. The variance is

$$s^2 = \frac{6{,}376 - \dfrac{250^2}{10}}{10} = 12.6.$$

The standard deviation is $s = \sqrt{12.6} = 3.55$

9. (a) Vera: $\bar{x} = 83.6$; John: $\bar{x} = 83.6$.

(b) Vera: $s^2 = 12.24$; John: $s^2 = 195.84$; difference $= 183.60$.

(c) This is a subjective question with no absolute answer.

11. The observations are all the same.

Exercise 4.3

1.

	Class interval	Class boundary	Class width	Class mark
(a)	3–10	2.5–10.5	8	6.5
(b)	6.5–12.5	6.45–12.55	6.1	9.5
(c)	1.35–3.24	1.345–3.245	1.9	2.295
(d)	7.312–10.105	7.3115–10.1055	2.794	1.397

3. (a)

Class interval	Class boundaries	Tally	Class mark (x_i)	Frequency (f_i)	x_i^2	$f_i x_i$	$f_i x_i^2$
35–39	34.5–39.5	1	37	1	1,369	37	1,369
40–44	39.5–44.5	11	42	2	1,764	84	3,528
45–49	44.5–49.5	111	47	3	2,209	141	6,627
50–54	49.5–54.5	1111	52	4	2,704	208	10,816
55–59	54.5–59.5	1111	57	4	3,249	228	12,996
60–64	59.5–64.5	ⵏHT 111	62	8	3,844	496	30,752
65–69	64.5–69.5	ⵏHT 111	67	8	4,489	536	35,912
70–74	69.5–74.5	1111 1	72	6	5,184	432	31,104
75–79	74.5–79.5	1111	77	4	5,929	308	23,716
80–84	79.5–84.5	ⵏHT	82	5	6,724	410	33,620
85–89	84.5–89.5	111	87	3	7,569	261	22,707
90–94	89.5–94.5	11	92	2	8,464	184	16,928

(b) Frequency Histograms   (c) Frequency Polygon

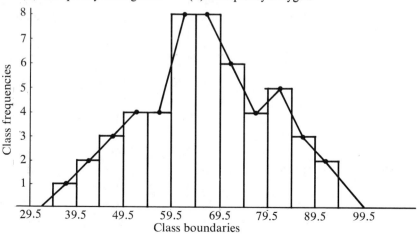

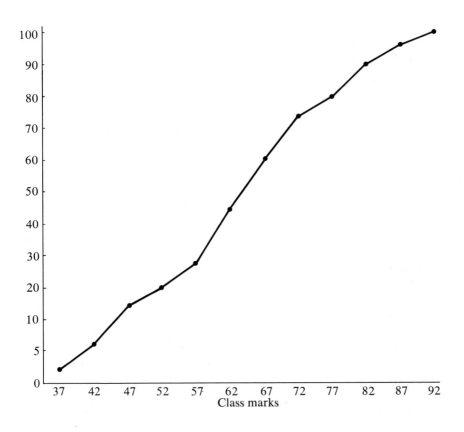

(d)

Class interval	Class mark (x_i)	Cumulative frequency	Frequency (f_i)	Cumulative percentage
35–39	37	1	1	2
40–44	42	2	3	6
45–49	47	3	6	12
50–54	52	4	10	20
55–59	57	4	14	28
60–64	62	8	22	44
65–69	67	8	30	60
70–74	72	6	36	72
75–79	77	4	40	80
80–84	82	5	45	90
85–89	87	3	48	96
90–94	92	2	50	100

5.

Class interval	Class mark	Frequency	Cumulative frequency	Cumulative percentage
96–102	99	2	2	8.34
103–109	106	3	5	20.83
110–116	113	3	8	33.33
117–123	120	4	12	50.00
124–130	127	5	17	71.00
131–137	134	1	18	75.00
138–144	141	4	22	91.33
145–151	148	1	23	96.00
152–158	155	1	24	100.00

(a)

(b) 25th percentile $= L + C \dfrac{\left[N\,\dfrac{n}{100} - S_f \right]}{f_n}$

$= 109.5 + 7 \dfrac{\left[24 \cdot \dfrac{25}{100} - 5 \right]}{8}$

$= 109.5 + .875 = 110.375.$

The scores below the 25th percentile are those scores less than 110.375.

(c) The 75th percentile $= 130.5 + 7 \dfrac{\left[24 \cdot \dfrac{75}{100} - 17 \right]}{1}$

$= 130.5 + 7 = 137.5.$

The scores below the 75th percentile are those scores less than 137.5.

(d) The median $= 116.5 + 7 \dfrac{\left[\dfrac{24}{2} - 8 \right]}{4} = 116.5 + 7 = 123.5.$

7. (a)

Class interval	Class boundary	Class mark (x_i)	Frequency (f_i)	x_i^2	$f_i x_i$	$f_i x_i^2$
40–44	39.5–44.5	42	1	1,764	42	1,764
45–49	44.5–49.5	47	3	2,209	141	6,627
50–54	49.5–59.5	52	6	2,704	312	16,224
55–59	54.5–59.5	57	5	3,249	285	16,245
60–64	59.5–64.5	62	8	3,844	496	30,752
65–69	64.5–69.5	67	15	4,489	1,005	67,335
70–74	69.5–74.5	72	6	5,184	432	31,104
75–79	74.5–79.5	77	4	5,929	308	23,716
80–84	79.5–84.5	82	2	6,424	164	12,848

(b) $\bar{X} = \dfrac{\sum\limits_{i=1}^{n} f_i x_i}{\sum\limits_{i=1}^{n} f_i} = \dfrac{3,185}{50} = 63.7$

(c) $s = \sqrt{\sum\limits_{i=1}^{n} f_i x_i^2 - \dfrac{\left(\sum\limits_{i=1}^{n} f_i \right)^2}{n}} = \sqrt{207,215 - \dfrac{(3,185)^2}{50}}$

$= \sqrt{86.6416} = 9.3$

CHAPTER 5

Exercise 5.1

1. (a) $\bar{x} = np = 100(.5) = 50$, $s = \sqrt{npq} = \sqrt{100(.5)(.5)} = 5$
(b) $\bar{x} = np = 672(.75) = 484$, $s = \sqrt{npq} = \sqrt{672(.75)(.25)} = 11$
(c) $\bar{x} = np = 400(.9) = 360$, $s = \sqrt{npq} = \sqrt{400(.1)(.9)} = 6$

3. This problem is similar to problem 2; $n = 10,000$ and $p = .02$. The expected number of batteries to be replaced is $E(x) = np = 10,000(.02) = 200$.

5. This is a binomial in which the probability that a student will not complete the course is $q = .25$ and the probability that a student will complete the course is $p = .75$. The expected number to complete the course is $E(x) = 24(.75) = 18$ and $s = \sqrt{24(.75)(.25)} = 2.12$.

Exercise 5.2

1. (a) To find the percentage of measurements below 47, change the X-score into a Z-score and use table III in the appendix: $z = \dfrac{47 - 50}{6} = \dfrac{-3}{6} = -.5$.

The percentage less than $z = -.5$ is $.5000 - .1915 = 30.85\%$.

(b) $Z = \dfrac{60 - 50}{6} = \dfrac{10}{6} = 1.67$. The percentage less than $Z = 1.67$ is $.5000 + .4525 = 95.25\%$.

(c) $r_1 = 41$ and $x_2 - 58$

$z_1 = \dfrac{41 - 50}{6} = \dfrac{-9}{6} = -1.5$ and $z_2 = \dfrac{58 - 50}{6} = 1.33$.

The percentage of measurements in the interval is $.4332 + .4082 = 84.14\%$.

(d) The Z-score corresponding to an area less than 30% is $Z = -.525$. The X-score is $x = \sigma z + x = 6(-3.15 + 50) = 46.85$.

(e) The Z-score corresponding to an area greater than 72% is $Z = .585$. The X-score is $x = 6(.585) + 50 = 3.51 + 50 = 53.51$.

3. (a) The Z-score corresponding to $x = 19$ is $z = \dfrac{19 - 16}{2.2} = 1.36 \ P(X > 19)$

$= P(Z > 1.36) = .5000 - .4131 = .0869$.

(b) The Z-scores corresponding to $x_1 = 13$ and $x_2 = 14$ are

$z_1 = \dfrac{13 - 16}{2.2} = -1.36$ and $z_2 = \dfrac{14 - 16}{2.2} = -.91$.

$P(13 < X < 14) = P(-1.36 < Z < -.91) = P(1.36 > Z > .91)$
$= P(Z < 1.36) - P(Z < .91) = .4131 - .3186 = .0945$.

(c) The Z-scores corresponding to $x_1 = 19$ and $x_2 = 17.5$ are

$z_1 = \dfrac{19 - 16}{2.2} = 1.36$ and $z_2 = \dfrac{17.5 - 16}{2.2} = .68$.

$P(19 > X > 17.5) = P(1.36 > Z > .68) = P(Z < 1.36) - P(Z < .68)$
$= .4131 - .2517 = .1614$.

5. $\mu = 7$; $\sigma = 1.5$; $x_1 = 8$; $x_2 = 9$; $z_1 = \dfrac{8 - 7}{1.5} = .67$;

$z_2 = \dfrac{9 - 7}{1.5} = 1.33$; $P(8 < X < 9) = P(.67 < Z < 1.33)$

$= P(0 < Z < 1.33) - P(0 < Z < .67) = .4082 - .2486 = .1596$.

7. $\mu = 7, \sigma = .3$

    (a) The fraction of cups that will contain more than 7.1 ounces is
$$P(X > 7.1) = P(Z > .33) = .5000 - P(0 < Z < .33) = .5000 - 1293$$
$$= .3707.$$

    (b) $P(X > 8) = P(Z > 3.33) = .5000 - P(0 < Z < 3.33) = .5000 - .4988$
$$= .0012.$$

    (c) The problem is to find the setting, X-score, so that the cup will overflow only 1% of the time. The Z-score such that only 1% is to its right is $z = 2.33$. Then $X = 2.33(.3) + 1 = .699 + 7 = 7.699$.

9. (a) The percentage of workers who make between \$3.50 and \$4.90 is equal to $P(3.50 < X < 4.90) = P(-1 < Z < .87) = P(0 < Z < 1)$
$+ P(0 < Z < .87) = .3413 + .3078 = 64.91\%$.

    (b) The hourly wage that represents the 95th percentile is such that 95% of the normal curve is to its left and 5% is to its right. The corresponding Z-score is $z = 1.645$. The hourly rate that represents the 95th percentile is $x = 1.645(.75) + \$4.25 = \$5.48$.

Exercise 5.3

1. (a) The percentage of a binomial distribution that is to the left of 5 when $\bar{x} = 6$ and $s = 1.5$ is the probability to the left of a Z-score corresponding to $x = 5$:
$$z = \frac{5.5 - 6}{1.5} = \frac{-.5}{1.5} = -.33; \quad P(X < 5.5)$$
$$= P(Z < -.33) = .5000 - P(0 < Z < .33) = .5000 - .1293 = .3707$$

    (b) The percentage to the right of 7.25 is the probability to the right of a Z-score corresponding to $x = 6.5$. $P(X > 6.5) = P(Z > .33) = .5000 - P(0 < Z < .33) = .5000 - .293 = .3707$.

3. The probability of a defective switch is .02. If $n = 1,000$ and $p = .02$, then $\bar{x} = 1,000(.02) = 20$ and $s = \sqrt{1,000(.02)(.98)} = 4.43$; $P(X > 29.5) = P(Z > 2.14) = .5000 - .4838 = .0162$.

5. $n = 500$, $p = .6$; hence, $\bar{x} = 500(.6) = 300$ and $s = \sqrt{500(.6)(.4)} = 11$; $P(X > 274.5) = P(Z > -2.32) = .5000 + (.5000 - P(0 < Z < 2.32))$
$= .5000 + .4898 = .9898$.

7. $\bar{x} = 500$ and $s = 50$. If the owner wishes that no more than 1% of the bulbs burn out between replacements, then $P(Z < z) = .01$. From table III, $z = -2.33$; $\bar{x} = 50(-2.33) + 500 = -16.50 + 500 = 483.5$. The owner should replace the bulbs when they have burned 484 hours.

9. $n = 100$, $p = .1$; hence, $\bar{x} = 9$ and $s = \sqrt{(100(.1)(.9)} = 3$. $P(7 < X < 12)$
$= P(6.5 < X < 12.5) = P(-.83 < Z < 1.7) = P(0 < Z < .83)$
$= P(0 < Z < 1.7) = .2969 + .4554 = .7523$.

11. The washers will be unacceptable if the internal diameters are such that $x < .371$ or $x > .379$; $x = .373$, $x_1 = .371$, $x_2 = .379$, $s = .002$. The corresponding Z-scores are $z_1 = \dfrac{.371 - .373}{.002} = -1$ and $z_2 = \dfrac{.379 - .373}{.002} = 3$.
Thus, $P(X < .371 \text{ or } X > .379) = P(Z < -1 \text{ or } Z > 3) = .1887 + .0013 = .1600$.

CHAPTER 6

Exercise 6.1

1. The population is 2,4,6,8.

(a) $\mu = \dfrac{\sum\limits_{i=1}^{4} x_i}{4} = 5$

$\sigma = \sqrt{\sum\limits_{i=1}^{4} \dfrac{(x_i - 5)^2}{4}} = \sqrt{5}$

(b)

	Sample	Mean		Sample	Mean
1.	2,2	2	9.	6,2	4
2.	2,4	3	10.	6,4	5
3.	2,6	4	11.	6,6	6
4.	2,8	5	12.	6,8	7
5.	4,2	3	13.	8,2	5
6.	4,4	4	14.	8,4	6
7.	4,6	5	15.	8,6	7
8.	4,8	6	16.	8,8	8

(c) $\overline{X} = \dfrac{\sum\limits_{i=1}^{n} f_i x_i}{\sum\limits_{i=1}^{n} f_i} = \dfrac{80}{16} = 5$

$\sigma_{\overline{x}} = \sqrt{\sum\limits_{i=1}^{n} f_i(x_i - X)^2 P(X - x_i)} =$

$\sqrt{(1(2-5)^2 + 2(3-5)^2 + 3(4-5)^2 + 4(5-5)^2 + 3(6-5)^2 + 2(7-5)^2 + 1(8-5)^2) \cdot \dfrac{1}{16}}$

$= \sqrt{\dfrac{40}{16}} = \sqrt{\dfrac{5}{2}}$

3. (a) $E(\overline{x}_i - \overline{x}_2) = \mu_1 - \mu_2 = 10 - 8 = 2$

(b) $\sigma_{(\overline{x}_1 - \overline{x}_2)} = \sqrt{\dfrac{\sigma_1^2}{n_1} + \dfrac{\sigma_2^2}{n_2}} = \sqrt{\dfrac{4}{100} + \dfrac{1}{100}} = \dfrac{\sqrt{5}}{10}$

(c) $P < 0 < (x_1 - x_2) < (1.5) = P(0 < (z_1 - z_2) < -2.24)$
$= .5000 - P(0 < z_1 - z_2 < 2.24)$
$= .5000 - 4875 = .0125$

(d) $P(2.5 > (x_1 - x_2) > 1.75) = P(2.24 > Z > -1.12)$
$= P(0 < Z < 2.24) + P(0 < Z < 1.12)$
$= .4875 + .3686 = .8561$

5. The population is 5,8,11,12.
(a) The samples and mean of each sample are:

	Sample	Mean		Sample	Mean		Sample	Mean
1.	5,8	6.5	5.	8,11	9.5	9.	11,12	11.5
2.	5,11	8	6.	8,12	10	10.	12,5	8.5
3.	5,12	8.5	7.	11,5	8	11.	12,8	10
4.	8,5	6.5	8.	11,8	9.5	12.	12,11	11.5

(b) $\bar{X} = \dfrac{\sum\limits_{i=1}^{n} f_i x_i}{\sum\limits_{i=1}^{n} f_i} = 2(6.5) + 2(8) + 2(8.5) + 2(9.5) + 2(10) + 2(11.5) \cdot \dfrac{1}{12} = 9$

$$\sigma_{\bar{x}} = \sqrt{\sum_{i=1}^{n} f_i(\bar{x}_i - \bar{x})^2 P(\bar{x} - \bar{x}_i)} = \sqrt{\dfrac{N-n}{N-1}}$$

$$= \sqrt{2(6.5-9)^2 + 2(8-9)^2 + 2(8.5-9)^2 + 2(9.5-9)^2 + 2(10-9)^2 + 2(11.5-9)^2}$$

$$\cdot \dfrac{1}{12} \sqrt{\dfrac{12-2}{12-1}} = \sqrt{\dfrac{30}{12}} \sqrt{\dfrac{10}{11}} = 1.51$$

7. (a) $P(\bar{X} > 1,825) = P(Z > 1.25) = .5000 - P(0 < Z < 1.25)$
$= .5000 - .3944 = .1056$

(b) $P(1,760 < \bar{X} < 1,775) = P(-2 < Z < -1.25) = P(0 < Z < 2)$
$- P(0 < Z < 1.25) = .4772 - .3944 = .0828$

9. (a) The probability of accepting the sample whose mean is .24 is the probability that the random variable will fall in the interval between .245 and .255. If $x_1 = .255$, $x_2 = .245$, and $n = 36$, using the sample standard deviation to estimate σ,

$$z_1 = \dfrac{.255 - .24}{.015/\sqrt{36}} = 6 \quad \text{and} \quad z_2 = \dfrac{.245 - 24}{.015/\sqrt{36}} = 2$$

$$P(.255 < X < .245) = P(6 < Z < 2) = .5000 - .4772 = .0228$$

(b) Same as part (a), except the sample mean is .2515 and the standard deviation is .005. Thus,

$$z_1 = \dfrac{.255 - .2515}{.005/\sqrt{36}} = 4.2 \quad \text{and} \quad z_2 = \dfrac{.245 - .2515}{.005/\sqrt{36}} = 7.8$$

$$P(.255 > X > .245) = P(4.2 > Z > -7.8)$$
$$= P(0 < Z < 4.2) + P(0 < Z < 7.2)$$
$$= .5000 + .5000 = 1$$

11. $\mu_1 = 54$, $\sigma_1 = 4$, $\mu_2 = 60$, $\sigma_2 = 6$

$E(\bar{x}_1 - \bar{x}_2) = \mu_1 - \mu_2 = 6$

$$\sigma_{(\bar{x}_1 - \bar{x}_2)} = \sqrt{\dfrac{4^2}{400} + \dfrac{6^2}{400}} = .36$$

(a) $Z = \dfrac{5-6}{.36} = -2.78$

$P(\bar{x}_1 - \bar{x}_2 < 5) = P(Z < -2.78) = .5000 - P(0 < Z < 2.78)$
$= .5000 - .4980 = .002$

(b) $Z = \dfrac{0-6}{.36} = -16.67$

$P(\bar{x}_1 - \bar{x}_2 = 0) = P(Z < -16.67) = 0$

Exercise 6.2

1. (a) $t = 1.812$.
   (b) The t-value on the right tail is 1.812 and the t-value on the left tail is -1.812.
   (c) The total shaded area is $1 - .99 = .01$; thus the shaded area in each tail is .005. The t-value in the right tail is 3.169 and the t-value in the left tail is -3.169.
   (d) If the shaded area on the left is .01, then the shaded area on the right is .01. Thus, the t-value for the shaded area on the left is -2.764.
   (e) If the area to the right of $-t$ is .90, then the area to the right of t_1 is .10. The t-value such that .10 is to its right is 1.372, and the t-value for the are to the left of $-t$ is .372.

3. (a) $P(t > 1.740) = .05$ when $n = 18$
   (b) $P(t < -1.323) = .10$ when $n = 22$
   (c) $P(t < -2.201$ or $t > 2.201) = .025$ when $n - 12$

5. The t-scores for $-t_{.025}$ and $t_{.025}$ with 9 degrees of freedom are -2.262 and 2.262. The computed value of t is

$$t = \frac{.053 - .05}{.003/\sqrt{10}} = 3.16$$

The computed t-value is outside the accepted limits and should be adjusted.

7. $\mu_1 = 20, \quad \bar{X}_1 = 20, \quad \tilde{s}_1 = 4, \quad n_1 = 12$
   $\mu_2 = 24, \quad \bar{X}_2 = 21, \quad \tilde{s}_2 = 3.5, \quad n_2 = 15$

   The pooled estimate of the standard deviation is

$$s = \sqrt{\frac{(n_1 - 1)s^2 + (n_2 - 1)s_2{}^2}{n_1 + n_2 - 2}} = 3.73$$

$$t = \frac{(\bar{x}_1 - \bar{x}_2) - (\mu_1 - \mu_2)}{s\sqrt{\dfrac{1}{n_1} + \dfrac{1}{n_2}}}$$

The t-scores for $-t_{.01}$ and $t_{.01}$ with $v = 25$ degrees of freedom are -2.485 and 2.485. The computed t-value for the difference lies within this interval.

Exercise 6.3

1. (a) $E(\tilde{p}) = np = 50(.40) = 20$
   (b) $\sigma_{\tilde{p}} = \sqrt{\dfrac{pq}{n}} = \sqrt{\dfrac{(.40)(.60)}{50}} = .069$
   (c) $P(\tilde{p} > .455) = P(Z > .80) = .5000 - P(0 < Z < .80) = .2119$

3. (a) $E(\tilde{p}) = 36(.6) = 21.6$
   $$\sigma_{\tilde{p}} = \sqrt{\frac{(.6)(.4)}{36}} = .08$$
   $P(\tilde{p} < .495) = P(Z < -1.31) = .5000 - P(0 < Z < 1.31) - .0951$

(b) $P(.485 < p < .715) = P(-1.44 < Z < 1.44) = 2\,[P(0 < Z < 1.44)]$
$= .8502$

5. $P(\tilde{p} > .725) = P(Z > -1.25) = .5000 + P(0 < Z < 1.25) = .8944$

7. (a) .05   (b) .01   (c) .995

CHAPTER 7

Exercise 7.1

1. (a) $\overline{X} = 1,280,\ \tilde{s} = 140,\ n = 100$

Since n is sufficiently large, we can use the sample mean as an estimate of the population mean. That is,

$$E(\overline{X}) = \mu = 1,280$$

The bound on the point estimate of μ can be established by using s to estimate σ; thus, the bound is

$$\overline{X} - 2 \cdot \frac{s}{\sqrt{n}} < \mu < \overline{X} + 2 \cdot \frac{s}{\sqrt{n}} = 1,280 - 2 \cdot \frac{140}{\sqrt{100}} < \mu < 1,280$$

$$+ 2\frac{140}{\sqrt{100}}\ \text{which reduces to}\ 1,252 < \mu < 1,308.$$

(b) A .95 confidence interval estimate is $1,280 - 1.96(14) < \mu < 1,280 + 1.96(14)$, which reduces to $1,252.56 < \mu < 1,307.44$. We estimate with .95 confidence that the mean of the population is in the interval $1,252.56 < \mu < 1,307.44$.

3. (a) The point estimate of the coffee in each cup dispensed is $\overline{X} = \mu = 5$ ounces. A bound on the error of estimate is $\overline{X} \pm 2\frac{\sigma}{n} = 5 \pm 2\frac{.5}{\sqrt{50}}$

$= 5 \pm .14$. Hence, the lower bound is 4.86 and the upper bound is 5.14.

(b) A .95 confidence interval estimate for the mean implies that $Z = \pm 1.96$;

that is, $P(-1.96 < Z < 1.96) = .95$. Thus, $P\left(-1.96 < \frac{\overline{x} - \mu}{\sigma/\sqrt{n}}\right) < 1.96$

$= .95$. The point estimate of μ is 5; hence, the .95 confidence interval is

$$5 - 1.96\frac{.5}{\sqrt{50}} < \mu < 5 + 1.96\frac{.5}{\sqrt{50}}\quad \text{or}\quad 4.86 < \mu < 5.14$$

5. The standard deviation is 2.5. The Z-score corresponding to .95 is 1.96. Thus,

$$n \geqq \left[\frac{(1.96)\,(2.5)}{.5}\right]^2 \geqq 96$$

The sample size should be 96 or greater.

7. (a) The sample from variety A yielded a mean equal to 84 and a standard deviation of 5, while variety B yielded a mean of 80 and a standard deviation of 6. The estimated difference between the population means is $\mu_1 - \mu_2 = E(\overline{x}_1 - \overline{x}_2) = 84 - 80 = 4$.

(b) The point estimation of $\mu_1 - \mu_2$ is 4. Since N is sufficiently large, we substitute the sample standard deviation for the population standard deviation. For $\alpha = .10$, the Z-score for $Z_{\frac{\alpha}{2}}$ is $Z_{.05} = 1.645$. Substituting in the formula,

$$(\bar{X}_1 - \bar{X}_2) - Z_{\frac{\alpha}{2}} \sqrt{\frac{\sigma_1^2}{n_1} + \frac{\sigma_2^2}{n_2}} < \mu_1 - \mu_2 < (\bar{X}_1 - \bar{X}_2) + Z_{\frac{\alpha}{2}} \sqrt{\frac{\sigma_1^2}{n_1} + \frac{\sigma_2^2}{n_2}}$$

we have

$$4 - 1.645 \sqrt{\frac{25}{100} + \frac{36}{100}} < \mu_1 - \mu_2 < 4 + 1.645 \sqrt{\frac{25}{100} + \frac{36}{100}}$$

which simplifies to $2.72 < \mu_1 - \mu_2 < 5.28$.

9. (a) This part is similar to problem 8. The sample size is 10, $\bar{X} = .64$, and $\tilde{s} = .005$. A .90 confidence interval estimate infers that $\alpha = .10$ and $t_{.05} = 1.833$ for $v = 9$ df. The true diameter refers to the population mean; hence, a .90 confidence interval is

$$.04 - 1.833 \cdot \frac{.005}{\sqrt{10}} < \mu < .04 + 1.8333 \cdot \frac{.005}{\sqrt{10}}$$

which reduces to $.0371 < \mu < .0429$.

(b) $\alpha = .01$ and $t_{.005} = 3.250$ for $v = 9$ df. Hence, a .99 confidence interval is

$$.04 - 3.250 \cdot \frac{.005}{\sqrt{10}} < \mu < .04 + 3.250 \cdot \frac{.005}{\sqrt{10}}$$

which reduces to $.0348 < \mu < .0452$.

11. The data for the one group is $n_1 = 12$, $\bar{x}_1 = 112$, $\tilde{s}_1 = 8$. The data for the other group is $n_2 = 15$, $\bar{x}_2 = 107$, $\tilde{s}_2 = 10$. A .90 confidence interval estimate implies $\alpha = .10$ and $t_{.05} = 1.708$ for v 25 df. Since both $\tilde{s}_1$ and $\tilde{s}_2$ are estimates of σ, the pooled estimate is

$$s = \sqrt{\frac{(n_1 - 1)\tilde{s}_1^2}{n_1} + \frac{(n_2 - 1)\tilde{s}_2^2}{n_2}} = \sqrt{\frac{11(8)^2}{12} + \frac{14(10)^2}{15}} = 12.33$$

Hence,

$$(\bar{X}_1 - \bar{X}_2) - t_{\frac{\alpha}{2}} \cdot s \sqrt{\frac{1}{n_1} + \frac{1}{n_2}} < (\mu_1 - \mu_2) < (\bar{X}_1 - \bar{X}_2) + t_{\frac{\alpha}{2}} \cdot s \sqrt{\frac{1}{n_1} + \frac{1}{n_2}}$$

$$= (112 - 107) - (1.708)(12.33) \sqrt{\frac{1}{12} + \frac{1}{15}} < \mu_1 - \mu_2 < (112 - 107)$$

$$+ (1.708)(12.33) \sqrt{\frac{1}{12} + \frac{1}{15}}$$

which reduces to $-3.15 < \mu_1 - \mu_2 < 13.15$.

13. (a) The point estimate of the proportion who favor the tax is

$$\tilde{P} = \frac{135}{225} = .6.$$

(b) A .95 confidence interval estimate implies $\alpha = .05$ and $\alpha/2 = .025$.

The Z-score for $z_{.025}$ is 1.96. Substituting in the formula

$$\widetilde{P} - z_{\frac{\alpha}{2}} \sqrt{\frac{\widetilde{p}\widetilde{q}}{n}} < P < P + z_{\frac{\alpha}{2}} \sqrt{\frac{\widetilde{p}\widetilde{q}}{n}}$$

we have

$$.6 - 1.96 \sqrt{\frac{(.6)(.4)}{225}} < P < .6 + 1.96 \sqrt{\frac{(.6)(.4)}{225}}$$

which reduces to $.536 < P < .664$.

15. The point estimate of the proportion is $\widetilde{P} = \dfrac{225}{400} = .56$. A .90 confidence interval estimate implies $\alpha = .10$ and $\alpha/2 = .05$. The Z-score for $z_{.05}$ is 1.645. Hence,

$$\widetilde{P} - z_{\frac{\alpha}{2}} \sqrt{\frac{\widetilde{p}\widetilde{q}}{n}} < P < \widetilde{P} + z_{\frac{\alpha}{2}} \sqrt{\frac{\widetilde{p}\widetilde{q}}{n}}$$

yields

$$.56 - 1.645 \sqrt{\frac{(.56)(.44)}{400}} < P < .56 + 1.645 \sqrt{\frac{(.56)(.44)}{400}}$$

which reduces to $.519 < P < .601$.

17. The point estimate of the proportion of men is $\widetilde{P}_1 = \dfrac{60}{500} = .12$, while the point estimate of the women is $\widetilde{P}_2 = \dfrac{50}{500} = .10$. A .95 confidence interval estimate is

$$(.12-.10) - 1.645 \sqrt{\frac{(.12)(.88)}{500} + \frac{(.10)(.90)}{500}} < P_1 - P_2 < (.12-.10)$$

$$+ 1.645 \sqrt{\frac{(.12)(.88)}{500} + \frac{(.1)(.9)}{500}}$$

which reduces to $-.01 < P_1 - P_2 < .05$.

Exercise 7.2

1. A .95 confidence interval implies $\alpha.05$. Using the table of Chi-square values with $\alpha = .05$ and 9 df, we find $\chi^2_{.025} = 19.0228$ and $\chi^2_{1-.025} = 2.70039$. Substituting in the formula,

$$\frac{(n-1)s^2}{x^2_{\frac{\alpha}{2}}} < \sigma^2 < \frac{(n-1)s^2}{x^2_{\left(1-\frac{\alpha}{2}\right)}}$$

we have

$$\frac{9(.32)}{19.0228} < \sigma^2 < \frac{9(.32)}{2.70039}$$

which reduces to $.15 < \sigma^2 < 1.07$.

3. The estimated ratio of σ_1^2/σ^2 is $\tilde{s}_1^2/\tilde{s}_2^2 = 6^2/4^2 = 2.25$. For a .98 confidence interval estimate, $\alpha = .02$. From the table of F-values, $f_{.01}(19,14) = 3.51$ and $f_{.01}(14,19) = 3.15$. Hence,

$$.98 = \frac{\tilde{s}_1^{\,2}}{\tilde{s}_2^{\,2}} \cdot \frac{1}{f_{\frac{\alpha}{2}(v_1 v_2)}} < \frac{\sigma_1^{\,2}}{\sigma_2^{\,2}} < \frac{\tilde{s}_1^{\,2}}{\tilde{s}_2^{\,2}} \cdot f_{\frac{\alpha}{2}}(v_2, v_1)$$

$$= \frac{6^2}{4^2} \cdot \frac{1}{3.51} < \frac{\sigma_1^{\,2}}{\sigma_2^{\,2}} < \frac{6^2}{4^2} \cdot (3.15) = .641 < \frac{\sigma_1^{\,2}}{\sigma_2^{\,2}} < 7.088$$

We are .98 confident that the true ratio is within the interval.

5. $\bar{x} = 7.99$, $\tilde{s}^2 = .04$, $\alpha = .05$, df $= 7$, $\chi^2_{.025} = 16.0128$, and $\chi^2_{(1-.025)} = 1.68987$. Hence, by substituting in the formula $\dfrac{(n-1)\tilde{s}^2}{\chi^2 \mu} < \sigma^2 < \dfrac{(n-1)\tilde{s}^2}{\chi^2 L}$, a .95 confidence interval estimate is

$$\frac{7(.2)}{16.0128} < \sigma^2 < \frac{7(.2)}{1.68987}$$

which reduces to $.018 < \sigma^2 < .166$.

7. We are given that $\tilde{s}^2 = 4$, $n = 25$, and $\alpha = (1 - .98) = .02$. Thus, with 24 df, $t_{.01} = 42.9798$ and $t_{91-.01} = 10.8564$. Hence, by substituting in the formula, a .98 confidence interval estimate is

$$\frac{24(4)}{42.9798} < \sigma^2 < \frac{24(4)}{10.8564}$$

which reduces to $2.234 < \sigma^2 < 8.842$.

9. $n_1 = 5$, $\Sigma x_1 = .50$, $\Sigma x_1^2 = .051$, $\tilde{s}_1^2 = .00025$
$n_2 = 6$, $\Sigma x_2 = .63$, $\Sigma x_1^2 = .0668$, $\tilde{s}_2^2 = .00019$

A .98 confidence interval estimate implies $\alpha = .02$. From the table of F-values, $f_{.01}(4.5) = 11.39$ and $f_{.01}(5,4) = 15.52$. Substituting in the formula, a .98 confidence interval is

$$\frac{.00025}{.00019} \cdot \frac{1}{15.52} < \frac{\sigma_1^{\,2}}{\sigma_2^{\,2}} < \frac{.00025}{.00019}(11.39)$$

which reduces to $.085 < \dfrac{\sigma_1^{\,2}}{\sigma_2^{\,2}} < 14.99$.

Exercise 7.3

1. $\mu = 50$, $\sigma = 12$, $\bar{X} = 46$, $n = 36$
The null and alternate hypotheses are

$$H_0: \mu = 50$$
$$H_1: \mu < 50$$

A one-tailed test is appropriate, since we are interested only if the tubes last a minimum of 50 months. Thus $\alpha = .05$, and the critical value for the test statistic is $Z < -1.645$. The calculated value of the test statistic is

$$z = \frac{45.5 - 50}{\frac{12}{\sqrt{36}}} = -2.25$$

The calculated value lies in the rejection region. We reject the null hypothesis and conclude that the tubes do not justify the manufacturer's claim.

3. $\mu = 600$, $\sigma = 49$, $n = 100$, $\overline{X} = 615$

$$H_0: \mu = 600$$
$$H_1: \mu \neq 600$$

A two-tailed test is requested with $\alpha = .05$, hence $\alpha/2 = .025$.
The critical values for the test statistic is $Z > 1.96$ and $Z < 1.96$.
The test statistic is

$$z = \frac{614.5 - 600}{\dfrac{49}{\sqrt{100}}} = \frac{14.5}{4.9} = 2.96$$

The calculated value of Z lies in the rejection region. We should reject the null hypothesis. However, since the calculated value is larger than the critical value, the manufacturer would be justified in increasing the mean hours.

5. $\mu = \$7,200$, $n = 400$, $\overline{X} = 6900$ and $s = 2000$

$$H_0: \mu < 7,200$$
$$H_1: \mu < 7,200$$

A one-tailed test is indicated with $\alpha = .01$.
The critical value is $Z = < -2.33$.
The test statistic where s is used to estimate σ is

$$z = \frac{6900 - 7200}{\dfrac{2000}{\sqrt{400}}} = \frac{-300}{100} = -3$$

The calculated value is less than the critical value for the test statistic. We conclude that the mean is less than $7,200 and reject the null hypothesis.

7. $\mu = 15$, $\overline{X} = 16.2$, $s = 3.6$, $n = 200$

$$H_0: \mu = 15$$
$$H_1: \mu > 15$$

To test the null hypothesis, a one-tailed test is appropriate with $\alpha = .01$. The critical value is $Z = 2.33$. The calculated value of the test statistic is

$$z = \frac{x - \mu}{\dfrac{s}{\sqrt{n}}} = \frac{16.2 - 15}{\dfrac{3.5}{\sqrt{200}}} = 4.85$$

The calculated value is greater than the critical value for the test statistic. The laboratory should reject the null hypothesis and conclude the manufacturer's claim is not justified.

9. $\overline{X}_1 = 20.2$, $s_1 = 1.2$, $n_1 = 120$, $\overline{X}_2 = 21$, $s_2 = 1.5$, $n_2 = 100$

$$H_0: \overline{X}_1 - \overline{X}_2 = 0$$
$$H_1: \overline{X}_1 - \overline{X}_2 \neq 0$$

A two-tailed test is indicated with $\dfrac{\alpha}{2} = .05$. The critical value for rejecting the null hypothesis is $Z \geq 1.645$ or $Z \leq -1.1645$. The calculated value for the test statistic is

$$z = \frac{\bar{X}_1 - \bar{X}_2}{\sqrt{\dfrac{s_1^2}{n_1} + \dfrac{s_2^2}{n_2}}} = \frac{20.2 - 21}{\sqrt{\dfrac{(1.2)^2}{120} + \dfrac{(1.5)^2}{100}}} = \frac{-.8}{.186} = -4.3$$

The calculated value is less than the critical value of the test statistic. We conclude that the means are not the same and reject the null hypothesis.

11. $\bar{X}_1 = 20{,}000$, $s_1 = 2{,}500$, $n_1 = 6$, $\bar{X}_2 = 22{,}000$, $s_2 = 2{,}800$, $n_2 = 12$

$$H_0: \bar{X}_1 = \bar{X}_2$$
$$H_1: \bar{X}_1 \neq \bar{X}_2$$

A two-tailed test is indicated, with $\alpha = .05$; and $\dfrac{\alpha}{2} = .025$. The critical values for the test statistic for rejecting the null hypothesis with $(n_1 + n_2 - 2)$ df are $t \geq 2.12$ and $t \leq -2.12$. The calculated value of the test statistic is

$$t = \frac{\bar{X}_1 - \bar{X}_2}{s\sqrt{\dfrac{1}{n_1} + \dfrac{1}{n_2}}}$$

where

$$s = \sqrt{\frac{(n_1 - 1)s_1{}^2 + (n_2 - 1)s_2{}^2}{n_1 + n_2 - 2}} = \sqrt{\frac{(6 - 1)2{,}500^2 + (12 - 1)2{,}800^2}{6 + 12 - 2}} = 2{,}710$$

$$t = \frac{20{,}000 - 22{,}000}{2{,}710\sqrt{\dfrac{1}{6} + \dfrac{1}{12}}} = \frac{-2{,}000}{2{,}710\left(\dfrac{1}{2}\right)} = -1.47$$

The calculated value lies between $t \leq -2.12$ and $t \geq 2.12$. We accept the null hypothesis and conclude the difference between tire A and tire B is not significant.

13. $\bar{X} = 2.2$, $s = .4$,   maximum error $= .05$, $Z = 1.96$

$$n \geq \left(\frac{(Z)(\sigma)}{e}\right)^2 \text{; using the sample variance } s \text{ to estimate } \sigma \text{ we have,}$$

$$n \geq \left[\frac{(1.96)(.4)}{.05}\right]^2 = 246$$

We can be 95% certain that a random sample of size 246 will produce an estimate of $\bar{X}$ differing from μ by less than .05.

15. $p = \dfrac{220}{400} = .55$, $q = 1 - P = .45$, $\widetilde{P} = .55$, $P = .50$

$$H_0: P = .50$$
$$H_1: P \neq .50$$

A two-tailed test is indicated, with $\alpha = .10$ and $\dfrac{\alpha}{2} = .05$. The critical value for the test statistic for testing the null hypothesis is $Z \geq 1.645$ or $Z \leq -1.645$. The calculated value is

$$Z = \frac{\widetilde{P} - P}{\sqrt{\dfrac{pq}{n}}} = \frac{.55 - .50}{\sqrt{\dfrac{(.55)(.45)}{400}}} = 2.01$$

The calculated value is greater than the critical value. We reject the null hypothesis and conclude that there is a difference in the number of men and women who watch the game.

17. For problem 18 and with $\alpha = .01$, the critical value of the test statistic for testing the null hypothesis is $Z \leq -2.33$. The calculated value is not less than the critical value. We do not reject the null hypothesis, concluding the company's assertion is justified.

19. $\widetilde{P}_1 = .20, \quad n_1 = 200, \quad \widetilde{P}_2 = .25, \quad n_2 = 300$

The null hypothesis to be tested is that the advertising was effective, i.e.,

$$H_0: P_1 < P_2$$
$$H_1: P_1 \geq P_2$$

A one-tailed test is indicated, with $\alpha = .05$. The critical value for rejecting the null hypothesis is $Z < -1.645$. The calculated value is

$$z = \frac{\widetilde{P}_1 - \widetilde{P}_2}{\sqrt{\dfrac{p_1 q_1}{n_1} + \dfrac{p_2 q_2}{n_2}}} = \frac{.20 - .25}{\sqrt{\dfrac{(.20)(.80)}{200} + \dfrac{(.25)(.75)}{300}}} = -1.32$$

The calculated value is greater than the critical value. The president should accept the null hypothesis and conclude that the advertising campaign was successful.

21. Since the candidate expects to receive 60% of the vote, we are provided with an estimate of $\widetilde{P}$. Then, when $\alpha = .05$,

$$n \geq \frac{Z_{\frac{\alpha}{2}}^2 \widetilde{p}\widetilde{q}}{e^2} = \frac{(1.96)^2(.6)(.4)}{(.02)^2} = 2{,}305$$

If the candidate based his prediction on a sample of 2,300 registered voters, he can be 95% certain that the sample proportion will not differ from the population proportion by more than 2%.

23. $n_1 = 400, \quad P = .95, \quad \widetilde{P} = \dfrac{355}{400} = .8875$

$$H_0: P \geq .95$$
$$H_1: P < .95$$

A one-tailed test of the null hypothesis is indicated, with $\alpha = .05$. The critical value of the test statistic for testing the null hypothesis is $Z < -1.645$. The calculated value is

$$z = \frac{\widetilde{P} - P}{\sqrt{\dfrac{pq}{n}}} = \frac{.8875 - .95}{\sqrt{\dfrac{(.8875)(.1125)}{400}}} = \frac{-.0625(20)}{.316} = -.395$$

The calculated value is greater than the critical value. We accept the null hypothesis and conclude that the company's claim is justified.

25. $n = 15, \quad \mu = 180, \quad \overline{X} = 182, \quad s = 2$

$$H_0: \overline{X} = \mu$$
$$H_1: X \neq \mu$$

A two-tailed test of the null hypothesis is indicated, with $\alpha = .01$ and 14 df. The critical value for the test statistic is $t < -2,650$ or $t > 2.650$. The calculated value is

$$t = \frac{\overline{X} - \mu}{\dfrac{s}{\sqrt{n}}} = \frac{182 - 180}{\dfrac{2}{\sqrt{15}}} = \frac{2(3.87)}{2} = 3.87$$

The calculated value is greater than the critical value. We reject the null hypothesis and conclude that the manufacturer's claim is not justified.

Exercise 7.4

1. (a) $n = 14$, $\overline{s}^2 = 5$, $\sigma^2 = 3.2$, $\alpha = .05$

The null and alternate hypotheses are

H_0: $\sigma^2 = 25$
H_1: $\sigma^2 > 25$

The alternate hypothesis indicates a one-tailed test. Since $\alpha = .05$, the critical value for the test statistic is $\chi^0 = 22.326$. The test statistic to be used is

$$\chi^2 = \frac{(n-1)\overline{s}^2}{\sigma^2} = \frac{13(5)}{3.2} = 20.3125.$$

$20.3125 < 22.362$; therefore accept H_0.

(b) $n = b$, $s^2 = 8$, $\sigma^2 = 2.2$, $\alpha = .01$

The null and alternate hypothesis are

H_0: $\sigma^2 = 25$
H_1: $\sigma^2 > 25$

A one-tailed test is indicated. Since $\alpha = .01$, the critical value for the test statistic is $\chi^2 = 15.086$. The test statistic to be used is

$$\chi^2 = \frac{(n-1)\overline{s}^2}{\sigma^2} = \frac{5(8)}{2.2} = \frac{40}{2.2} = 18.1818$$

$18.1818 > 15.086$; therefore reject H_0.

3. $n = 10$, $\overline{s}^2 = 14$, $\sigma^2 = 6$, $\alpha = .05$

H_0: $\sigma^2 = 6$
H_1: $\sigma^2 \neq 6$

A two-tailed test indicated. Since $\alpha = .05$, the critical values for the test statistic are $\chi^2_{.025} = 19.023$ and $\chi^2_{(1-.025)} = 2.700$. The test statistic is

$$\chi^2 = \frac{(n-1)s^2}{2} = \frac{9(14)}{6} = 21$$

$21 > 19.023$; therefore reject H_0.

If a .01 level of significance is used, the critical values for the test statistic are $\chi^2_{.005} = 23.589$ and $\chi^2_{.995} = 1.735$. The test statistic is
$1.735 < 21 < 23.589$; therefore accept H_0.

5. $n = 100$, the number of degrees of freedom is $4 - 1 = 3$, and $\alpha = .05$.

H_0: $P = 75\%$
H_1: $P > 75\%$

At a .05 level of significance and 3 degrees of freedom, the critical value of the test statistic is $\chi^2_{.05} = 7.815$. The test statistic is

$$\chi^2 = \sum_{i=1}^{k} \frac{(0 - E_i)^2}{E_i} = \frac{(65 - 75)^2}{75} + \frac{(60 - 75)^2}{75} + \frac{(85 - 75)^2}{75}$$
$$+ \frac{(80 - 75)^2}{75} = 13$$

$13 > 7.815$; therefore reject H_0.

7. H_0: The proportion of people who watch the news on each network is the same for each city.

H_1: The proportion is not the same.

At a .025 level of significance and $(3 - 1)(3 - 1) = 4$ degrees of freedom, the critical value of the test statistic is $\chi^2_{.095} = 11.143$. The test statistic is

$$\chi^2 = \sum_{i=1}^{k} \frac{(0 - e_i)^2}{e_i} = 1.84284$$

We accept H_0.

9. H_0: Blonds have more fun.

H_1: Blonds do not have more fun.

At a .01 level of significance and $(3 - 1)(3 - 1) = 4$ degrees of freedom, the critical value of the test statistic is $\chi^2_{.01} = 13.277$. The test statistic is

$$\chi^2 = \sum_{i=1}^{k} \frac{(0 - e_i)^2}{e_i} = 7.78282$$

We accept H_0.

Exercise 7.5

1. $n_1 = 12$, $\tilde{s}_1^2 = 7$, $n_2 = 8$, $\tilde{s}_2^2 = 5$

H_0: $\sigma_1^2 = \sigma_2^2$

H_1: $\sigma_1^2 \neq \sigma_2^2$

$\alpha = .02$

The critical regions are $F < f_{1-.01}(11,7) = .2045$ and $F > f_{.01}(11,7) = 6.47$. The calculated value of the F-ratio is

$$F = \frac{\tilde{s}_1^2}{\tilde{s}_2^2} = \frac{\sigma_1^2}{\sigma_2^2} = 1.4$$

We accept H_0.

3. $n_1 = 15$, $\tilde{s}_1^2 = 64$, $n_2 = 20$, $\tilde{s}_2^2 = 36$

H_0: $\sigma_1^2 = \sigma_2^2$

H_1: $\sigma_1^2 < \sigma_2^2$

$\alpha = .05$

The critical region is $F < f_{.95}(14,19) = .429$. The calculated value of the F-ratio is $F = \dfrac{64}{76} = 1.78$.

We accept H_0.

5. $H_0: \sigma_1{}^2 = \sigma_2{}^2 = \sigma_3{}^2$
  $H_1: \sigma_1{}^2 \neq \sigma_2{}^2 \neq \sigma_3{}^3$
  $\alpha = .05$

The critical region is $F > f_{.05}(2,12) = 3.89$. The mean of the sampling distribution of means is

$$\bar{X} = \frac{194 + 205 + 196}{3} = 198.3.$$

The calculation of σ^2 based on the variation of the sample means is

$$s_{\bar{x}}{}^2 = \frac{(194 - 198.3)^2 + (205 - 198.3)^2 + (196 - 198.3)^2}{3 - 1} = 34.3334$$

and

$$\sigma^2 = 5\,(34.3334) = 171.667 = (s_2{}^2)$$

The estimate of σ^2 based on the variation within the sample is

$$\sigma^2 = \frac{\tilde{s}_1{}^2 + \tilde{s}_2{}^2 + \tilde{s}_2{}^2}{3} = \frac{1}{3}$$

$$\left[\frac{((175 - 194)^2 + (225 - 194)^2 + (200 - 194)_2 + (150 - 194)^2 + (220 - 194)^2)}{5 - 1} \right.$$

$$+ \frac{((190 - 205)^2 + (210 - 205)^2 + (180 - 205)^2 + (230 - 205)^2 + (215 - 205)^2)}{5 - 1}$$

$$+ \left. \frac{(215 - 196)^2 + (185 - 196)^2 + (175 - 196)^2 + (205 - 196)^2 + (200 - 196)^2}{5 - 1} \right]$$

$$= 549.167 = (s_1{}^2)$$

$$F = \frac{549.167}{171.667} = 3.199$$

We accept H_0.

7. $H_0: \sigma_1{}^2 = \sigma_2{}^2 = \sigma_3{}^2$
  $H_1: \sigma_1{}^2 \neq \sigma_2{}^2 = \sigma_3{}^2$
  $\alpha = .01$

The critical region is $F > f_{.01}(2,12) = 5.95$.
The estimate of σ^2 based on the variation of the sample means where

$$X = 79.07 \text{ and } s_{\bar{x}}{}^2 = \frac{(77 - 79.07)^2 + (81.2 - 79.07)^2 + (79 - 79.07)^2}{3 - 1} = 4.413$$

is $\sigma^2 = 5(\bar{s}_{\bar{x}}{}^2) = 22.06$.

The estimate of σ^2 based on the variation within the samples is

$$\sigma^2 = \frac{\tilde{s}_1{}^2 + \tilde{s}_2{}^2 + \tilde{s}_3{}^2}{3}$$

$$= \frac{1}{3} \left[\frac{((75 - 77)^2 + (83 - 77)^2 + (70 - 77)^2 + (92 - 77)^2 + (65 - 77)^2)}{5 - 1} \right.$$

$$+ \frac{((78-81.2)^2 + (72-81.2)^2 + (84-81.2)^2 + (90-81.2)^2 + (82-81.2)^2)}{5-1}$$

$$+ \frac{((70-79)^2 + (68-79)^2 + (78-79)^2 + (84-79)^2 + (95-79)^2)}{5-1} \Bigg]$$

$$= \frac{1}{3}\,280.7 = 93.56$$

$$F = \frac{93.56}{22.06} = 4.24$$

We accept H_0.

CHAPTER 8

Exercise 8.1

1. Question 1 is a subjective question, with no absolute answer.

3. (a)

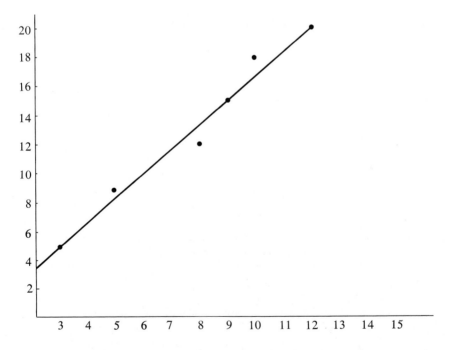

(b) $x = 4$, $\widetilde{y} = 10$; $x = 1$, $\widetilde{y} = 1$; $x = 15$; $\widetilde{y} = 20$

5. $\Sigma x = 417$, $\Sigma y = 413$, $\Sigma x^2 = 29{,}041$, $\Sigma y^2 = 28{,}459$, $\Sigma xy = 28{,}728$

(a)

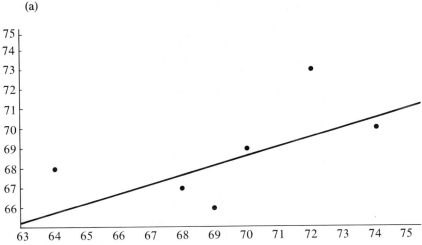

(b) The slope b is

$$b = \frac{n(\Sigma\, xy) - (\Sigma\, y)(\Sigma\, y)}{n(\Sigma\, x^2) - (\Sigma\, x)^2} = \frac{6(28,728) - (417)(413)}{6(29,041) - (417)^2} = .41$$

The y-intercept is

$$a = \frac{\Sigma\, y}{n} - \frac{\Sigma\, x}{n} = \frac{413}{6} - .41\left(\frac{417}{6}\right) = 40.2$$

The least squares regression line is

$$\tilde{y} = 40.2 + .41x$$

(c) The standard error of estimate is

$$SEE = \sqrt{\frac{\Sigma\, y^2 - \dfrac{(\Sigma\, y)^2}{n} - b\left[\Sigma\, xy - \dfrac{(\Sigma\, x)\,(\Sigma\, y)}{n}\right]}{n-2}}$$

$$= \sqrt{\frac{28,459 - \dfrac{(413)^2}{6} - .41\left[28,728 - \dfrac{(417)(413)}{6}\right]}{4}}$$

$$= \sqrt{\frac{31 - 10.25}{4}} = \sqrt{\frac{20.75}{4}} = 2.28$$

(d) $r = \dfrac{\Sigma\, xy - \dfrac{(\Sigma\, x)\,(\Sigma\, y)}{n}}{\sqrt{\left[\Sigma\, x^2 - \dfrac{(\Sigma\, x)^2}{n}\right]\left[\Sigma\, y^2 - \dfrac{(\Sigma\, y)^2}{n}\right]}}$

$$= \frac{28,728 - \dfrac{(417)(413)}{6}}{\sqrt{29,041 - \dfrac{(417)^2}{6}\left[28,459 - \dfrac{(413)^2}{6}\right]}} = \frac{24.5}{\sqrt{(59.5)(3)}}$$

$$= \frac{24.5}{43} = .57$$

7. $\Sigma x = 467, \Sigma y = 1,325, \Sigma x^2 = 22,309, \Sigma y^2 = 176,575, \Sigma xy = 62,235$

(a) The slope is

$$b = \frac{n(\Sigma xy) - (\Sigma x)(\Sigma y)}{n(\Sigma x)^2 - (\Sigma x)^2} = \frac{10(62,235) - (467)(1325)}{10(22,309) - (467)^2}$$

$$= \frac{622,350 - 618,775}{223,090 - 218,089} = \frac{3,575}{5,001} = .715$$

The y-intercept is

$$a = \frac{\Sigma y}{n} - b\frac{\Sigma x}{n} = \frac{1,325}{10} = .715\left(\frac{467}{10}\right) = 99.1$$

The equation of the best fitting line is

$$y = 99.1 + .715x$$

(c)

$$r = \frac{\Sigma xy - \frac{(\Sigma x)(\Sigma y)}{n}}{\sqrt{\left[\Sigma x^2 - \frac{(\Sigma x)^2}{n}\right]\left[\Sigma y^2 - \frac{(\Sigma y)^2}{n}\right]}}$$

$$= \frac{62,235 - 61,877.5}{\sqrt{(22,309 - 21,808.9)(176,575 - 175,562.5)}}$$

$$= \frac{357.5}{\sqrt{(500.1)(1,012.5)}} = \frac{375.5}{711.5} = .53$$

(d) The standard error of estimate is

$$SEE = \sqrt{\frac{\Sigma y^2 - \frac{(\Sigma y)^2}{n} - b\left[\Sigma xy - \frac{(\Sigma x)(\Sigma y)}{n}\right]}{n-2}}$$

$$= \sqrt{\frac{176,575 - \frac{(1,325)^2}{10} - .715\left[62,235 - \frac{(467)(1,325)}{10}\right]}{8}}$$

$$= \sqrt{\frac{1,012.5 - 255.6}{8}} = 9.73$$

(e) The correlation is not significant.

Index

Elementary Probability and Statistics

Statistical Tables

A. William Gray and Otis M. Ulm

St. Petersburg Junior College
St. Petersburg, Florida

GLENCOE PRESS
A division of Benziger Bruce & Glencoe, Inc.
New York • Beverly Hills

Collier-Macmillan, Publishers
London

Table I. Squares and Roots

n	n^2	$\sqrt{n}$	$\sqrt{10n}$	n	n^2	$\sqrt{n}$	$\sqrt{10n}$
1.0	1.00	1.000	3.162	5.5	30.25	2.345	7.416
1.1	1.21	1.049	3.317	5.6	31.36	2.366	7.483
1.2	1.44	1.095	3.464	5.7	32.49	2.387	7.550
1.3	1.69	1.140	3.606	5.8	33.64	2.408	7.616
1.4	1.96	1.183	3.742	5.9	34.81	2.429	7.681
1.5	2.25	1.225	3.873	6.0	36.00	2.449	7.746
1.6	2.56	1.265	4.000	6.1	37.21	2.470	7.810
1.7	2.89	1.304	4.123	6.2	38.44	2.490	7.874
1.8	3.24	1.342	4.243	6.3	39.69	2.510	7.937
1.9	3.61	1.378	4.359	6.4	40.96	2.530	8.000
2.0	4.00	1.414	4.472	6.5	42.25	2.550	8.062
2.1	4.41	1.449	4.583	6.6	43.56	2.569	8.124
2.2	4.84	1.483	4.690	6.7	44.89	2.588	8.185
2.3	5.29	1.517	4.796	6.8	46.24	2.608	8.246
2.4	5.76	1.549	4.899	6.9	47.61	2.627	8.307
2.5	6.25	1.581	5.000	7.0	49.00	2.646	8.367
2.6	6.76	1.612	5.099	7.1	50.41	2.665	8.426
2.7	7.29	1.643	5.196	7.2	51.84	2.683	8.485
2.8	7.84	1.673	5.292	7.3	53.29	2.702	8.544
2.9	8.41	1.703	5.385	7.4	54.76	2.720	8.602
3.0	9.00	1.732	5.477	7.5	56.25	2.739	8.660
3.1	9.61	1.761	5.568	7.6	57.76	2.757	8.718
3.2	10.24	1.789	5.657	7.7	59.29	2.775	8.775
3.3	10.89	1.817	5.745	7.8	60.84	2.793	8.832
3.4	11.56	1.844	5.831	7.9	62.41	2.811	8.888
3.5	12.25	1.871	5.916	8.0	64.00	2.828	8.944
3.6	12.96	1.897	6.000	8.1	65.61	2.846	9.000
3.7	13.69	1.924	6.083	8.2	67.24	2.864	9.055
3.8	14.44	1.949	6.164	8.3	68.89	2.881	9.110
3.9	15.21	1.975	6.245	8.4	70.56	2.898	9.165
4.0	16.00	2.000	6.325	8.5	72.25	2.915	9.220
4.1	16.81	2.025	6.403	8.6	73.96	2.933	9.274
4.2	17.64	2.049	6.481	8.7	75.69	2.950	9.327
4.3	18.49	2.074	6.557	8.8	77.44	2.966	9.381
4.4	19.36	2.098	6.633	8.9	79.21	2.983	9.434
4.5	20.25	2.121	6.708	9.0	81.00	3.000	9.487
4.6	21.16	2.145	6.782	9.1	82.81	3.017	9.539
4.7	22.09	2.168	6.856	9.2	84.64	3.033	9.592
4.8	23.04	2.191	6.928	9.3	86.49	3.050	9.644
4.9	24.01	2.214	7.000	9.4	88.36	3.066	9.695
5.0	25.00	2.236	7.071	9.5	90.25	3.082	9.747
5.1	26.01	2.258	7.141	9.6	92.16	3.098	9.798
5.2	27.04	2.280	7.211	9.7	94.09	3.114	9.849
5.3	28.09	2.302	7.280	9.8	96.04	3.130	9.899
5.4	29.16	2.324	7.348	9.9	98.01	3.146	9.950

Table II. Normal Curve Areas

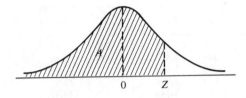

(The proportion of area given is that to the left of the given z score. It should be noted that all area values have been rounded to three decimal places.)

z	AREA	z	AREA	z	AREA
−4.0	.000	−1.3	.097	1.4	.919
−3.9	.000	−1.2	.115	1.5	.933
−3.8	.000	−1.1	.136	1.6	.945
−3.7	.000			1.7	.955
−3.6	.000	−1.0	.159	1.8	.964
		−0.9	.184	1.9	.971
−3.5	.000	−0.8	.212		
−3.4	.000	−0.7	.242	2.0	.977
−3.3	.001	−0.6	.274	2.1	.982
−3.2	.001			2.2	.986
−3.1	.001	−0.5	.308	2.3	.989
		−0.4	.345	2.4	.992
−3.0	.001	−0.3	.382		
−2.9	.002	−0.2	.421	2.5	.994
−2.8	.003	−0.1	.460		
−2.7	.004			2.6	.995
−2.6	.005	0.0	.500	2.7	.996
		0.1	.540	2.8	.997
−2.5	.006	0.2	.579	2.9	.998
−2.4	.008	0.3	.618		
−2.3	.011	0.4	.655	3.0	.999
−2.2	.014			3.1	.999
−2.1	.018	0.5	.692	3.2	.999
		0.6	.726	3.3	.999
−2.0	.023	0.7	.758	3.4	1.000
−1.9	.029	0.8	.788		
−1.8	.036	0.9	.816	3.5	1.000
−1.7	.045			3.6	1.000
−1.6	.055	1.0	.841	3.7	1.000
		1.1	.864	3.8	1.000
−1.5	.067	1.2	.885	3.9	1.000
−1.4	.081	1.3	.903	4.0	1.000

Table III. Normal Curve Areas

z	.00	.01	.02	.03	.04	.05	.06	.07	.08	.09
0.0	.0000	.0040	.0080	.0120	.0160	.0199	.0239	.0279	.0319	.0359
0.1	.0398	.0438	.0478	.0517	.0557	.0596	.0636	.0675	.0714	.0753
0.2	.0793	.0832	.0871	.0910	.0948	.0987	.1026	.1064	.1103	.1141
0.3	.1179	.1217	.1255	.1293	.1331	.1368	.1406	.1443	.1480	.1517
0.4	.1554	.1591	.1628	.1664	.1700	.1736	.1772	.1808	.1844	.1879
0.5	.1915	.1950	.1985	.2019	.2054	.2088	.2123	.2157	.2190	.2224
0.6	.2257	.2291	.2324	.2357	.2389	.2422	.2454	.2486	.2517	.2549
0.7	.2580	.2611	.2642	.2673	.2704	.2734	.2764	.2794	.2823	.2852
0.8	.2881	.2910	.2939	.2967	.2995	.3023	.3051	.3078	.3106	.3133
0.9	.3159	.3186	.3212	.3238	.3264	.3289	.3315	.3340	.3365	.3389
1.0	.3413	.3438	.3461	.3485	.3508	.3531	.3554	.3577	.3599	.3621
1.1	.3643	.3665	.3686	.3708	.3729	.3749	.3770	.3790	.3810	.3830
1.2	.3849	.3869	.3888	.3907	.3925	.3944	.3962	.3980	.3997	.4015
1.3	.4032	.4049	.4066	.4082	.4099	.4115	.4131	.4147	.4162	.4177
1.4	.4192	.4207	.4222	.4236	.4251	.4265	.4279	.4292	.4306	.4319
1.5	.4332	.4345	.4357	.4370	.4382	.4394	.4406	.4418	.4429	.4441
1.6	.4452	.4463	.4474	.4484	.4495	.4505	.4515	.4525	.4535	.4545
1.7	.4554	.4564	.4573	.4582	.4591	.4599	.4608	.4616	.4625	.4633
1.8	.4641	.4649	.4656	.4664	.4671	.4678	.4686	.4693	.4699	.4706
1.9	.4713	.4719	.4726	.4732	.4738	.4744	.4750	.4756	.4761	.4767
2.0	.4772	.4778	.4783	.4788	.4793	.4798	.4803	.4808	.4812	.4817
2.1	.4821	.4826	.4830	.4834	.4838	.4842	.4846	.4850	.4854	.4857
2.2	.4861	.4864	.4868	.4871	.4875	.4878	.4881	.4884	.4887	.4890
2.3	.4893	.4896	.4898	.4901	.4904	.4906	.4909	.4911	.4913	.4916
2.4	.4918	.4920	.4922	.4925	.4927	.4929	.4931	.4932	.4934	.4936
2.5	.4938	.4940	.4941	.4943	.4945	.4946	.4948	.4949	.4951	.4952
2.6	.4953	.4955	.4956	.4957	.4959	.4960	.4961	.4962	.4963	.4964
2.7	.4965	.4966	.4967	.4968	.4969	.4970	.4971	.4972	.4973	.4974
2.8	.4974	.4975	.4976	.4977	.4977	.4978	.4979	.4979	.4980	.4981
2.9	.4981	.4982	.4982	.4983	.4984	.4984	.4985	.4985	.4986	.4986
3.0	.4987	.4987	.4987	.4988	.4988	.4989	.4989	.4989	.4990	.4990
3.1	.49903									
3.2	.49931									
3.3	.49952									
3.4	.49966									
3.5	.49977									
3.6	.49984									
3.7	.49989									
3.8	.49993									
3.9	.49995									
4.0	.50000									

Table IV. Binomonial Probabilities

						p					
n	r	0.10	0.20	0.25	0.30	0.40	0.50	0.60	0.70	0.80	0.90
5	0	0.5905	0.3277	0.2373	0.1681	0.0778	0.0312	0.0102	0.0024	0.0003	0.0000
	1	0.9185	0.7373	0.6328	0.5282	0.3370	0.1875	0.0870	0.0308	0.0067	0.0005
	2	0.9914	0.9421	0.8965	0.8369	0.6826	0.5000	0.3174	0.1631	0.0579	0.0086
	3	0.9995	0.9933	0.9844	0.9692	0.9130	0.8125	0.6630	0.4718	0.2627	0.0815
	4	1.0000	0.9997	0.9990	0.9976	0.9898	0.9688	0.9222	0.8319	0.6723	0.4095
	5	1.0000	1.0000	1.0000	1.0000	1.0000	1.0000	1.0000	1.0000	1.0000	1.0000
10	0	0.3487	0.1074	0.0563	0.0282	0.0060	0.0010	0.0001	0.0000	0.0000	0.0000
	1	0.7361	0.3758	0.2440	0.1493	0.0464	0.0107	0.0017	0.0001	0.0000	0.0000
	2	0.9298	0.6778	0.5256	0.3828	0.1673	0.0547	0.0123	0.0016	0.0001	0.0000
	3	0.9872	0.8791	0.7759	0.6496	0.3823	0.1719	0.0548	0.0106	0.0009	0.0000
	4	0.9984	0.9672	0.9219	0.8497	0.6331	0.3770	0.1662	0.0474	0.0064	0.0002
	5	0.9999	0.9936	0.9803	0.9527	0.8338	0.6230	0.3669	0.1503	0.0328	0.0016
	6	1.0000	0.9991	0.9965	0.9894	0.9452	0.8281	0.6177	0.3504	0.1209	0.0128
	7	1.0000	0.9999	0.9996	0.9984	0.9877	0.9453	0.8327	0.6172	0.3222	0.0702
	8	1.0000	1.0000	1.0000	0.9999	0.9983	0.9893	0.9536	0.8507	0.6242	0.2639
	9	1.0000	1.0000	1.0000	1.0000	0.9999	0.9990	0.9940	0.9718	0.8926	0.6513
	10	1.0000	1.0000	1.0000	1.0000	1.0000	1.0000	1.0000	1.0000	1.0000	1.0000
15	0	0.2059	0.0352	0.0134	0.0047	0.0005	0.0000	0.0000	0.0000	0.0000	0.0000
	1	0.5490	0.1671	0.0802	0.0353	0.0052	0.0005	0.0000	0.0000	0.0000	0.0000
	2	0.8159	0.3980	0.2361	0.1268	0.0271	0.0037	0.0003	0.0000	0.0000	0.0000
	3	0.9444	0.6482	0.4613	0.2969	0.0905	0.0176	0.0019	0.0001	0.0000	0.0000
	4	0.9873	0.8358	0.6865	0.5155	0.2173	0.0592	0.0094	0.0007	0.0001	0.0000
	5	0.9978	0.9389	0.8516	0.7216	0.4032	0.1509	0.0338	0.0037	0.0001	0.0000
	6	0.9997	0.9819	0.9434	0.8689	0.6098	0.3036	0.0951	0.0152	0.0008	0.0000
	7	1.0000	0.9958	0.9827	0.9500	0.7869	0.5000	0.2131	0.0500	0.0042	0.0000
	8	1.0000	0.9992	0.9958	0.9848	0.9050	0.6964	0.3902	0.1311	0.0181	0.0003
	9	1.0000	0.9999	0.9992	0.9963	0.9662	0.8491	0.5968	0.2784	0.0611	0.0023
	10	1.0000	1.0000	0.9999	0.9993	0.9907	0.9408	0.7827	0.4845	0.1642	0.0127
	11	1.0000	1.0000	1.0000	0.9999	0.9981	0.9824	0.9095	0.7031	0.3518	0.0556
	12	1.0000	1.0000	1.0000	1.0000	0.9997	0.9963	0.9729	0.8732	0.6020	0.1841
	13	1.0000	1.0000	1.0000	1.0000	1.0000	0.9995	0.9948	0.9647	0.8329	0.4510
	14	1.0000	1.0000	1.0000	1.0000	1.0000	1.0000	0.9995	0.9953	0.9648	0.7941
	15	1.0000	1.0000	1.0000	1.0000	1.0000	1.0000	1.0000	1.0000	1.0000	1.0000
20	0	0.1216	0.0115	0.0032	0.0008	0.0000	0.0000	0.0000	0.0000	0.0000	0.0000
	1	0.3917	0.0692	0.0243	0.0076	0.0005	0.0000	0.0000	0.0000	0.0000	0.0000
	2	0.6769	0.2061	0.0913	0.0355	0.0036	0.0002	0.0000	0.0000	0.0000	0.0000
	3	0.8670	0.4114	0.2252	0.1071	0.0160	0.0013	0.0001	0.0000	0.0000	0.0000
	4	0.9568	0.6296	0.4148	0.2375	0.0510	0.0059	0.0003	0.0000	0.0000	0.0000
	5	0.9887	0.8042	0.6172	0.4164	0.1256	0.0207	0.0016	0.0000	0.0000	0.0000
	6	0.9976	0.9133	0.7858	0.6080	0.2500	0.0577	0.0065	0.0003	0.0000	0.0000
	7	0.9996	0.9679	0.8982	0.7723	0.4159	0.1316	0.0210	0.0013	0.0000	0.0000
	8	0.9999	0.9900	0.9591	0.8867	0.5956	0.2517	0.0565	0.0051	0.0001	0.0000
	9	1.0000	0.9974	0.9861	0.9520	0.7553	0.4119	0.1275	0.0171	0.0006	0.0000
	10	1.0000	0.9994	0.9961	0.9829	0.8725	0.5881	0.2447	0.0480	0.0026	0.0000
	11	1.0000	0.9999	0.9991	0.9949	0.9435	0.7483	0.4044	0.1133	0.0100	0.0001
	12	1.0000	1.0000	0.9998	0.9987	0.9790	0.8684	0.5841	0.2277	0.0321	0.0004
	13	1.0000	1.0000	1.0000	0.9997	0.9935	0.9423	0.7500	0.3920	0.0867	0.0024
	14	1.0000	1.0000	1.0000	1.0000	0.9984	0.9793	0.8744	0.5836	0.1958	0.0113
	15	1.0000	1.0000	1.0000	1.0000	0.9997	0.9941	0.9490	0.7625	0.3704	0.0432
	16	1.0000	1.0000	1.0000	1.0000	1.0000	0.9987	0.9840	0.8929	0.5886	0.1330
	17	1.0000	1.0000	1.0000	1.0000	1.0000	0.9998	0.9964	0.9645	0.7939	0.3231
	18	1.0000	1.0000	1.0000	1.0000	1.0000	1.0000	0.9995	0.9924	0.9308	0.6083
	19	1.0000	1.0000	1.0000	1.0000	1.0000	1.0000	1.0000	0.9992	0.9885	0.8784
	20	1.0000	1.0000	1.0000	1.0000	1.0000	1.0000	1.0000	1.0000	1.0000	1.0000

Table V. Critical Values of t

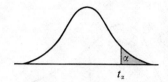

n	$t_{.100}$	$t_{.050}$	$t_{.025}$	$t_{.010}$	$t_{.005}$	$d.f.$
2	3.078	6.314	12.706	31.821	63.657	1
3	1.886	2.920	4.303	6.965	9.925	2
4	1.638	2.353	3.182	4.541	5.841	3
5	1.533	2.132	2.776	3.747	4.604	4
6	1.476	2.015	2.571	3.365	4.032	5
7	1.440	1.943	2.447	3.143	3.707	6
8	1.415	1.895	2.365	2.998	3.499	7
9	1.397	1.860	2.306	2.896	3.355	8
10	1.383	1.833	2.262	2.821	3.250	9
11	1.372	1.812	2.228	2.764	3.169	10
12	1.363	1.796	2.201	2.718	3.106	11
13	1.356	1.782	2.179	2.681	3.055	12
14	1.350	1.771	2.160	2.650	3.012	13
15	1.345	1.761	2.145	2.624	2.977	14
16	1.341	1.753	2.131	2.602	2.947	15
17	1.337	1.746	2.120	2.583	2.921	16
18	1.333	1.740	2.110	2.567	2.898	17
19	1.330	1.734	2.101	2.552	2.878	18
20	1.328	1.729	2.093	2.539	2.861	19
21	1.325	1.725	2.086	2.528	2.845	20
22	1.323	1.721	2.080	2.518	2.831	21
23	1.321	1.717	2.074	2.508	2.819	22
24	1.319	1.714	2.069	2.500	2.807	23
25	1.318	1.711	2.064	2.492	2.797	24
26	1.316	1.708	2.060	2.485	2.787	25
27	1.315	1.706	2.056	2.479	2.779	26
28	1.314	1.703	2.052	2.473	2.771	27
29	1.313	1.701	2.048	2.467	2.763	28
30	1.311	1.699	2.045	2.462	2.756	29
inf.	1.282	1.645	1.960	2.326	2.576	inf.

Table VI. Chi-square Distribution

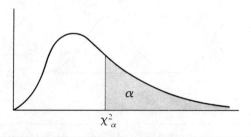

$$\chi^2_\alpha$$

ν	α							
	0.995	0.99	0.975	0.95	0.05	0.025	0.01	0.005
1	0.0^4393	0.0^3157	0.0^3982	0.0^2393	3.841	5.024	6.635	7.879
2	0.0100	0.0201	0.0506	0.103	5.991	7.378	9.210	10.597
3	0.0717	0.115	0.216	0.352	7.815	9.348	11.345	12.838
4	0.207	0.297	0.484	0.711	9.488	11.143	13.277	14.860
5	0.412	0.554	0.831	1.145	11.070	12.832	15.086	16.750
6	0.676	0.872	1.237	1.635	12.592	14.449	16.812	18.548
7	0.989	1.239	1.690	2.167	14.067	16.013	18.475	20.278
8	1.344	1.646	2.180	2.733	15.507	17.535	20.090	21.955
9	1.735	2.088	2.700	3.325	16.919	19.023	21.666	23.589
10	2.156	2.558	3.247	3.940	18.307	20.483	23.209	25.188
11	2.603	3.053	3.816	4.575	19.675	21.920	24.725	26.757
12	3.074	3.571	4.404	5.226	21.026	23.337	26.217	28.300
13	3.565	4.107	5.009	5.892	22.362	24.736	27.688	29.819
14	4.075	4.660	5.629	6.571	23.685	26.119	29.141	31.319
15	4.601	5.229	6.262	7.261	24.996	27.488	30.578	32.801
16	5.142	5.812	6.908	7.962	26.296	28.845	32.000	34.267
17	5.697	6.408	7.564	8.672	27.587	30.191	33.409	35.718
18	6.265	7.015	8.231	9.390	28.869	31.526	34.805	37.156
19	6.844	7.633	8.907	10.117	30.144	32.852	36.191	38.582
20	7.434	8.260	9.591	10.851	31.410	34.170	37.566	39.997
21	8.034	8.897	10.283	11.591	32.671	35.479	38.932	41.401
22	8.643	9.542	10.982	12.338	33.924	36.781	40.289	42.796
23	9.260	10.196	11.689	13.091	35.172	38.076	41.638	44.181
24	9.886	10.856	12.401	13.848	36.415	39.364	42.980	45.558
25	10.520	11.524	13.120	14.611	37.652	40.646	44.314	46.928
26	11.160	12.198	13.844	15.379	38.885	41.923	45.642	48.290
27	11.808	12.879	14.573	16.151	40.113	43.194	46.963	49.645
28	12.461	13.565	15.308	16.928	41.337	44.461	48.278	50.993
29	13.121	14.256	16.047	17.708	42.557	45.722	49.588	52.336
30	13.787	14.953	16.791	18.493	43.773	46.979	50.892	53.672

Table VII. Values of r

n	$r_{.025}$	$r_{.005}$	n	$r_{.025}$	$r_{.005}$
3	0.997		18	0.468	0.590
4	0.950	0.999	19	0.456	0.575
5	0.878	0.959	20	0.444	0.561
6	0.811	0.917	21	0.433	0.549
7	0.754	0.875	22	0.423	0.537
8	0.707	0.834	27	0.381	0.487
9	0.666	0.798	32	0.349	0.449
10	0.632	0.765	37	0.325	0.418
11	0.602	0.735	42	0.304	0.393
12	0.576	0.708	47	0.288	0.372
13	0.553	0.684	52	0.273	0.354
14	0.532	0.661	62	0.250	0.325
15	0.514	0.641	72	0.232	0.302
16	0.497	0.623	82	0.217	0.283
17	0.482	0.606	92	0.205	0.267

Table VIII. f Distribution

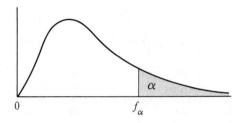

$$f_{0.05}(\nu_1, \nu_2)$$

ν_2	\multicolumn{9}{c}{ν_1}								
	1	2	3	4	5	6	7	8	9
1	161.4	199.5	215.7	224.6	230.2	234.0	236.8	238.9	240.5
2	18.51	19.00	19.16	19.25	19.30	19.33	19.35	19.37	19.38
3	10.13	9.55	9.28	9.12	9.01	8.94	8.89	8.85	8.81
4	7.71	6.94	6.59	6.39	6.26	6.16	6.09	6.04	6.00
5	6.61	5.79	5.41	5.19	5.05	4.95	4.88	4.82	4.77
6	5.99	5.14	4.76	4.53	4.39	4.28	4.21	4.15	4.10
7	5.59	4.74	4.35	4.12	3.97	3.87	3.79	3.73	3.68
8	5.32	4.46	4.07	3.84	3.69	3.58	3.50	3.44	3.39
9	5.12	4.26	3.86	3.63	3.48	3.37	3.29	3.23	3.18
10	4.96	4.10	3.71	3.48	3.33	3.22	3.14	3.07	3.02
11	4.84	3.98	3.59	3.36	3.20	3.09	3.01	2.95	2.90
12	4.75	3.89	3.49	3.26	3.11	3.00	2.91	2.85	2.80
13	4.67	3.81	3.41	3.18	3.03	2.92	2.83	2.77	2.71
14	4.60	3.74	3.34	3.11	2.96	2.85	2.76	2.70	2.65
15	4.54	3.68	3.29	3.06	2.90	2.79	2.71	2.64	2.59
16	4.49	3.63	3.24	3.01	2.85	2.74	2.66	2.59	2.54
17	4.45	3.59	3.20	2.96	2.81	2.70	2.61	2.55	2.49
18	4.41	3.55	3.16	2.93	2.77	2.66	2.58	2.51	2.46
19	4.38	3.52	3.13	2.90	2.74	2.63	2.54	2.48	2.42
20	4.35	3.49	3.10	2.87	2.71	2.60	2.51	2.45	2.39
21	4.32	3.47	3.07	2.84	2.68	2.57	2.49	2.42	2.37
22	4.30	3.44	3.05	2.82	2.66	2.55	2.46	2.40	2.34
23	4.28	3.42	3.03	2.80	2.64	2.53	2.44	2.37	2.32
24	4.26	3.40	3.01	2.78	2.62	2.51	2.42	2.36	2.30
25	4.24	3.39	2.99	2.76	2.60	2.49	2.40	2.34	2.28
26	4.23	3.37	2.98	2.74	2.59	2.47	2.39	2.32	2.27
27	4.21	3.35	2.96	2.73	2.57	2.46	2.37	2.31	2.25
28	4.20	3.34	2.95	2.71	2.56	2.45	2.36	2.29	2.24
29	4.18	3.33	2.93	2.70	2.55	2.43	2.35	2.28	2.22
30	4.17	3.32	2.92	2.69	2.53	2.42	2.33	2.27	2.21
40	4.08	3.23	2.84	2.61	2.45	2.34	2.25	2.18	2.12
60	4.00	3.15	2.76	2.53	2.37	2.25	2.17	2.10	2.04
120	3.92	3.07	2.68	2.45	2.29	2.17	2.09	2.02	1.96
∞	3.84	3.00	2.60	2.37	2.21	2.10	2.01	1.94	1.88

Table VIII. (continued)

$$f_{0.05}(\nu_1, \nu_2)$$

ν_2					ν_1					
	10	12	15	20	24	30	40	60	120	∞
1	241.9	243.9	245.9	248.0	249.1	250.1	251.1	252.2	253.3	254.3
2	19.40	19.41	19.43	19.45	19.45	19.46	19.47	19.48	19.49	19.50
3	8.79	8.74	8.70	8.66	8.64	8.62	8.59	8.57	8.55	8.53
4	5.96	5.91	5.86	5.80	5.77	5.75	5.72	5.69	5.66	5.63
5	4.74	4.68	4.62	4.56	4.53	4.50	4.46	4.43	4.40	4.36
6	4.06	4.00	3.94	3.87	3.84	3.81	3.77	3.74	3.70	3.67
7	3.64	3.57	3.51	3.44	3.41	3.38	3.34	3.30	3.27	3.23
8	3.35	3.28	3.22	3.15	3.12	3.08	3.04	3.01	2.97	2.93
9	3.14	3.07	3.01	2.94	2.90	2.86	2.83	2.79	2.75	2.71
10	2.98	2.91	2.85	2.77	2.74	2.70	2.66	2.62	2.58	2.54
11	2.85	2.79	2.72	2.65	2.61	2.57	2.53	2.49	2.45	2.40
12	2.75	2.69	2.62	2.54	2.51	2.47	2.43	2.38	2.34	2.30
13	2.67	2.60	2.53	2.46	2.42	2.38	2.34	2.30	2.25	2.21
14	2.60	2.53	2.46	2.39	2.35	2.31	2.27	2.22	2.18	2.13
15	2.54	2.48	2.40	2.33	2.29	2.25	2.20	2.16	2.11	2.07
16	2.49	2.42	2.35	2.28	2.24	2.19	2.15	2.11	2.06	2.01
17	2.45	2.38	2.31	2.23	2.19	2.15	2.10	2.06	2.01	1.96
18	2.41	2.34	2.27	2.19	2.15	2.11	2.06	2.02	1.97	1.92
19	2.38	2.31	2.23	2.16	2.11	2.07	2.03	1.98	1.93	1.88
20	2.35	2.28	2.20	2.12	2.08	2.04	1.99	1.95	1.90	1.84
21	2.32	2.25	2.18	2.10	2.05	2.01	1.96	1.92	1.87	1.81
22	2.30	2.23	2.15	2.07	2.03	1.98	1.94	1.89	1.84	1.78
23	2.27	2.20	2.13	2.05	2.01	1.96	1.91	1.86	1.81	1.76
24	2.25	2.18	2.11	2.03	1.98	1.94	1.89	1.84	1.79	1.73
25	2.24	2.16	2.09	2.01	1.96	1.92	1.87	1.82	1.77	1.71
26	2.22	2.15	2.07	1.99	1.95	1.90	1.85	1.80	1.75	1.69
27	2.20	2.13	2.06	1.97	1.93	1.88	1.84	1.79	1.73	1.67
28	2.19	2.12	2.04	1.96	1.91	1.87	1.82	1.77	1.71	1.65
29	2.18	2.10	2.03	1.94	1.90	1.85	1.81	1.75	1.70	1.64
30	2.16	2.09	2.01	1.93	1.89	1.84	1.79	1.74	1.68	1.62
40	2.08	2.00	1.92	1.84	1.79	1.74	1.69	1.64	1.58	1.51
60	1.99	1.92	1.84	1.75	1.70	1.65	1.59	1.53	1.47	1.39
120	1.91	1.83	1.75	1.66	1.61	1.55	1.50	1.43	1.35	1.25
∞	1.83	1.75	1.67	1.57	1.52	1.46	1.39	1.32	1.22	1.00

Table VIII. (continued)

$$f_{0.01}(v_1, v_2)$$

v_2	v_1								
	1	2	3	4	5	6	7	8	9
1	4052	4999.5	5403	5625	5764	5859	5928	5981	6022
2	98.50	99.00	99.17	99.25	99.30	99.33	99.36	99.37	99.39
3	34.12	30.82	29.46	28.71	28.24	27.91	27.67	27.49	27.35
4	21.20	18.00	16.69	15.98	15.52	15.21	14.98	14.80	14.66
5	16.26	13.27	12.06	11.39	10.97	10.67	10.46	10.29	10.16
6	13.75	10.92	9.78	9.15	8.75	8.47	8.26	8.10	7.98
7	12.25	9.55	8.45	7.85	7.46	7.19	6.99	6.84	6.72
8	11.26	8.65	7.59	7.01	6.63	6.37	6.18	6.03	5.91
9	10.56	8.02	6.99	6.42	6.06	5.80	5.61	5.47	5.35
10	10.04	7.56	6.55	5.99	5.64	5.39	5.20	5.06	4.94
11	9.65	7.21	6.22	5.67	5.32	5.07	4.89	4.74	4.63
12	9.33	6.93	5.95	5.41	5.06	4.82	4.64	4.50	4.39
13	9.07	6.70	5.74	5.21	4.86	4.62	4.44	4.30	4.19
14	8.86	6.51	5.56	5.04	4.69	4.46	4.28	4.14	4.03
15	8.68	6.36	5.42	4.89	4.56	4.32	4.14	4.00	3.89
16	8.53	6.23	5.29	4.77	4.44	4.20	4.03	3.89	3.78
17	8.40	6.11	5.18	4.67	4.34	4.10	3.93	3.79	3.68
18	8.29	6.01	5.09	4.58	4.25	4.01	3.84	3.71	3.60
19	8.18	5.93	5.01	4.50	4.17	3.94	3.77	3.63	3.52
20	8.10	5.85	4.94	4.43	4.10	3.87	3.70	3.56	3.46
21	8.02	5.78	4.87	4.37	4.04	3.81	3.64	3.51	3.40
22	7.95	5.72	4.82	4.31	3.99	3.76	3.59	3.45	3.35
23	7.88	5.66	4.76	4.26	3.94	3.71	3.54	3.41	3.30
24	7.82	5.61	4.72	4.22	3.90	3.67	3.50	3.36	3.26
25	7.77	5.57	4.68	4.18	3.85	3.63	3.46	3.32	3.22
26	7.72	5.53	4.64	4.14	3.82	3.59	3.42	3.29	3.18
27	7.68	5.49	4.60	4.11	3.78	3.56	3.39	3.26	3.15
28	7.64	5.45	4.57	4.07	3.75	3.53	3.36	3.23	3.12
29	7.60	5.42	4.54	4.04	3.73	3.50	3.33	3.20	3.09
30	7.56	5.39	4.51	4.02	3.70	3.47	3.30	3.17	3.07
40	7.31	5.18	4.31	3.83	3.51	3.29	3.12	2.99	2.89
60	7.08	4.98	4.13	3.65	3.34	3.12	2.95	2.82	2.72
120	6.85	4.79	3.95	3.48	3.17	2.96	2.79	2.66	2.56
∞	6.63	4.61	3.78	3.32	3.02	2.80	2.64	2.51	2.41

Table VIII. (continued)

$$f_{0.01}(\nu_1, \nu_2)$$

ν_2					ν_1					
	10	12	15	20	24	30	40	60	120	∞
1	6056	6106	6157	6209	6235	6261	6287	6313	6339	6366
2	99.40	99.42	99.43	99.45	99.46	99.47	99.47	99.48	99.49	99.50
3	27.23	27.05	26.87	26.69	26.60	26.50	26.41	26.32	26.22	26.13
4	14.55	14.37	14.20	14.02	13.93	13.84	13.75	13.65	13.56	13.46
5	10.05	9.89	9.72	9.55	9.47	9.38	9.29	9.20	9.11	9.02
6	7.87	7.72	7.56	7.40	7.31	7.23	7.14	7.06	6.97	6.88
7	6.62	6.47	6.31	6.16	6.07	5.99	5.91	5.82	5.74	5.65
8	5.81	5.67	5.52	5.36	5.28	5.20	5.12	5.03	4.95	4.86
9	5.26	5.11	4.96	4.81	4.73	4.65	4.57	4.48	4.40	4.31
10	4.85	4.71	4.56	4.41	4.33	4.25	4.17	4.08	4.00	3.91
11	4.54	4.40	4.25	4.10	4.02	3.94	3.86	3.78	3.69	3.60
12	4.30	4.16	4.01	3.86	3.78	3.70	3.62	3.54	3.45	3.36
13	4.10	3.96	3.82	3.66	3.59	3.51	3.43	3.34	3.25	3.17
14	3.94	3.80	3.66	3.51	3.43	3.35	3.27	3.18	3.09	3.00
15	3.80	3.67	3.52	3.37	3.29	3.21	3.13	3.05	2.96	2.87
16	3.69	3.55	3.41	3.26	3.18	3.10	3.02	2.93	2.84	2.75
17	3.59	3.46	3.31	3.16	3.08	3.00	2.92	2.83	2.75	2.65
18	3.51	3.37	3.23	3.08	3.00	2.92	2.84	2.75	2.66	2.57
19	3.43	3.30	3.15	3.00	2.92	2.84	2.76	2.67	2.58	2.49
20	3.37	3.23	3.09	2.94	2.86	2.78	2.69	2.61	2.52	2.42
21	3.31	3.17	3.03	2.88	2.80	2.72	2.64	2.55	2.46	2.36
22	3.26	3.12	2.98	2.83	2.75	2.67	2.58	2.50	2.40	2.31
23	3.21	3.07	2.93	2.78	2.70	2.62	2.54	2.45	2.35	2.26
24	3.17	3.03	2.89	2.74	2.66	2.58	2.49	2.40	2.31	2.21
25	3.13	2.99	2.85	2.70	2.62	2.54	2.45	2.36	2.27	2.17
26	3.09	2.96	2.81	2.66	2.58	2.50	2.42	2.33	2.23	2.13
27	3.06	2.93	2.78	2.63	2.55	2.47	2.38	2.29	2.20	2.10
28	3.03	2.90	2.75	2.60	2.52	2.44	2.35	2.26	2.17	2.06
29	3.00	2.87	2.73	2.57	2.49	2.41	2.33	2.23	2.14	2.03
30	2.98	2.84	2.70	2.55	2.47	2.39	2.30	2.21	2.11	2.01
40	2.80	2.66	2.52	2.37	2.29	2.20	2.11	2.02	1.92	1.80
60	2.63	2.50	2.35	2.20	2.12	2.03	1.94	1.84	1.73	1.60
120	2.47	2.34	2.19	2.03	1.95	1.86	1.76	1.66	1.53	1.38
∞	2.32	2.18	2.04	1.88	1.79	1.70	1.59	1.47	1.32	1.00